INTERPRETIVE SPECTROSCOPY

EDITED BY

Stanley K. Freeman

International Flavors & Fragrances, Inc.

Union Beach, New Jersey

New York
REINHOLD PUBLISHING CORPORATION
Chapman & Hall, Ltd., London

PREFACE

The plethora of publications concerning structure confirmation and elucidation is testimony to the tremendous impact of instrumental techniques upon organic chemistry. The physical methods now available to the organic chemist frequently enable him to circumvent the complicated, laborious, and sometimes uncertain, classical procedures of chemical degradation followed by synthesis. It is not unusual to perform a reaction, or series of reactions, employing milligram quantities of reagents, to separate and isolate the resulting components by gas liquid chromatography (GLC) or thin layer chromatography (TLC), and finally, to ascertain the nature of the products formed by interpretation of their ultraviolet, infrared, mass, and nuclear magnetic resonance spectra. These total spectral data can be obtained on less than 0.1 mg material. Since it is necessary to use wider slits when recording far infrared spectra, and low-frequency absorption bands are generally weaker, a considerably larger sample is required than for the $2-25\mu$ region.

Unless the mate of a particular spectrum of an unknown material is available, it is generally not a simple matter to arrive at an identification. However, the fusion of information derived from the several spectral disciplines is obviously of great value in characterizing a substance. For example, determination of the presence or absence of carbonyl, alcohol, substituted benzene, etc., moieties via infrared often immeasurably aids a mass spectral interpretation. The empirical formula and molecular weight of a compound, obtained from its mass spectrum, significantly ease the task of interpreting nuclear magnetic resonance, infrared, and ultraviolet spectra. Demonstrating the presence of a tetra-substituted double bond, usually most readily accomplished by means of ultraviolet spectrometry, sometimes can supply the last bit of information required to ascertain the structure of a material under examination.

A knowledge of the limitations of a particular instrumental technique is a *sine qua non* for the chemist concerned with wresting information from spectral data. It is for this reason that our contributors have described in no little detail the limitations as well as the advantages of the spectral fields they have discussed. It should be realized at the outset that a reasonable degree of proficiency in spectral diagnosis cannot be acquired simply by understanding the basic concepts and facts described in this book. Continual exposure to the profusion of literature data pertaining to structure-spectra correlations will prove extremely helpful in developing interpretive competence. Some of the more fortunate readers may have access to laboratory spectral files and can sharpen their wits by studying them.

With regard to the authors of the various chapters of this book, we were indeed fortunate to enlist the aid of investigators who are actually engaged in the related fields of organic chemistry and spectrometry.

Union Beach, N. J.   S. K. Freeman
November 1965

CONTENTS

1 ULTRAVIOLET ABSORPTION SPECTROSCOPY

W. F. Forbes
*University of Waterloo, Ontario, Canada and
University of Rochester, Rochester, New York*

1. Introduction

1.1. Types of Spectra Involved. Electronic absorption spectroscopy is the study of absorption of ultraviolet or visible light. This process is associated with changes in the electronic energy of the molecule. Since electronic energy is quantized, one might expect the electronic spectrum of a molecule, like that of an atom, to consist of discrete lines. However, each electronic energy level has a number of vibrational and rotational sublevels ($\Delta E_{\text{electronic}} > \Delta E_{\text{vibrational}} > \Delta E_{\text{rotational}}$) so that a large number of transitions of similar energies are allowed which, being closely spaced together, cannot generally be resolved instrumentally; hence, absorption bands are observed. For simple molecules, these bands can be resolved using spectrophotometers of high resolution, and the resulting fine structure can be analyzed. Each fine structure line can be assigned, in principle at least, to its appropriate transition. However, organic molecules are usually too complex for such an analysis to be of value to the organic chemist or biochemist.

The absorption bands obtained in this way are generally *specific* for an organic molecule and correspond to transitions from a ground state to an electronic excited state. This is illustrated in Figure 1. The molecule, when raised to the electronic excited state, remains there for a short time (of the order of 10^{-8} sec), and the excess energy is then released in a number of ways. Either the molecule dissociates or is ionized, or the excess energy is converted into heat, or the absorbed light is reemitted, generally at longer wavelength (see Figure 1). This reemission is called fluorescence if irradiation and reemission terminate at the same instant; if there is a time lag between the termination of irradiation and the reemission, the phenomenon is called phosphorescence.

The nature of the excited state is determined partly by the Franck-Condon principle which implies that, since the time for electronic excitation is only of the order of 10^{-15} sec (frequency *ca.* 10^{15} sec^{-1}), the nuclei of the molecule have no time to rearrange appreciably during this period (vibrational frequency of nuclei *ca.* 10^{12} sec^{-1}, rotational frequency of nuclei *ca.* 10^{10} sec^{-1}). This similarity in nuclear configuration justifies the vertical nature of the arrows in Figure 1. Electronic distribution in the excited state can sometimes be deduced by considering that during electronic excitation an electron is raised from a filled molecular orbital (usually from a non-bonding p or a π-bonding orbital) to the next higher empty molecular orbital (usually a π^*-orbital; see Figure 2), and the relevant calculations can afford some insight into the appropriate transition energies (see Section 1.3 for appropriate references).

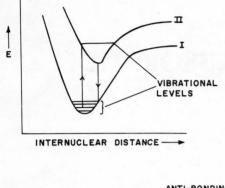

FIGURE 1. Potential energy curves (schematic) of a diatomic molecule showing transitions from a ground state (I) to an electronic excited state (II). The upward arrow illustrates absorption and the downward arrow illustrates subsequent fluorescence.

ANTI-BONDING	σ	(σ*)
ANTI-BONDING	π	(π*)
NON-BONDING	p	(n)
BONDING	π	
BONDING	σ	

FIGURE 2. Schematic representation of electronic transitions between molecular orbitals in organic molecules.

Semiquantitatively, but more simply, the relevant ground and excited states can sometimes be visualized by assuming that the most appropriate dipolar resonance form contributes to both ground and excited states, but it contributes to a greater extent to the excited state. Hence, as resonance forms become more stabilized (for example, on substitution, especially in the para position), the energy of the excited state relative to that of the ground state will be preferentially lowered, and this leads to increased absorption at longer wavelength, corresponding to transitions of lower energy. This is illustrated in Figure 3, which shows how ultraviolet spectra reflect increased conjugation.

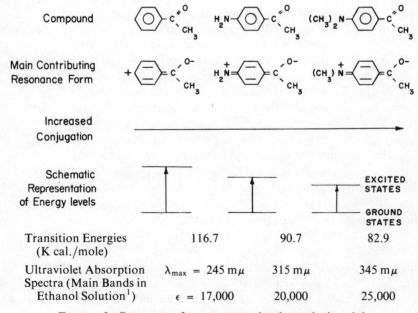

FIGURE 3. Resonance forms, energy levels, and ultraviolet absorption spectra of substituted acetophenones.

It is, in fact, the empirical use of ultraviolet and visible light absorption properties, rather than precise mathematical calculations, which have been most useful to the organic chemist. Such properties were used in this way as early as 1910 to distinguish between geometrical isomers, and a large number of additional correlations between spectra have been recorded during the last 25 years. It is mainly these correlations which will be covered in this Chapter.

1.2. Comparison with Other Spectroscopic Methods. When seeking to elucidate the structure of a molecule, ultraviolet spectroscopy is but one of a number of spectroscopic methods available to the organic chemist. Generally, ultraviolet spectroscopy tends only to confirm conclusions previously deduced by other methods. Nevertheless, ultraviolet spectroscopy has been one of the spectroscopic methods most frequently used in structural studies since it is only recently that such methods as Nuclear Magnetic Resonance (NMR) have attained their present-day importance.

The reasons for this are outlined in Table 1 which attempts to compare the usefulness of the major related spectroscopic techniques. It may be noted that other methods of major importance, such as X-ray diffraction spectra, are not considered. This is because a different type of problem, involving a different type of research effort, is usually investigated by such methods. For example, X-ray methods afford very *precise* structural information but are incomparably more time-consuming; also, no organic molecule without an element of symmetry can have its structure determined by X-ray methods without partial knowledge of its structure. Hence, such studies will generally be undertaken at a different stage of investigation, usually after an approximate structure has been suggested by the methods listed in Table 1. Raman spectral studies have been excluded from Table 1 because data thus obtained are similar to those obtained by infrared spectroscopy and the latter method, if applicable, is normally the method of choice.

Considerations (1) and (2) in Table 1 underline the difficulties of ultraviolet spectroscopy. First, the physical nature of the electronic excited states involved is generally understood in what is at best only a semiquantitative way. Moreover, molecules in excited states interact in various ways with solvent molecules; hence, it is normally impossible to calculate a complete ultraviolet spectrum from a theoretical model. This contrasts with, for example, ESR spectroscopy, where it is frequently possible to compute the hyperfine structure of an unpaired electron in a certain environment, and the calculated spectrum obtained in this way is almost identical with the experimentally obtained ESR spectrum. Hence, ultraviolet spectra have the disadvantage of representing merely empirical correlations without giving a precise understanding of the corresponding electronic transition.

Further, ultraviolet spectra are normally obtained conveniently *only for conjugated systems* (but see also p. 8). Hence, other spectroscopic methods are frequently employed for the majority of organic systems.

These major disadvantages are partly redeemed by important advantages as shown by considerations (3), (4), (5), and (7) of Table 1. That is, absorptivity units can be determined accurately and readily, thus permitting a large number of quantitative analytical applications. Next, there is no difficulty of working in aqueous solutions; and, since generally only low concentrations of material are required, lack of solubility is a less formidable problem than in other spectroscopic methods. Finally, ultraviolet spectroscopy is the least expensive of all spectroscopic methods. Not only are the basic instrument and accessories lower priced, but also the instrument can be operated by less experienced assistants than are required for other spectrometers.

Recently, the advent of more sophisticated theoretical treatments and the greater accessibility of the region below 200mμ has, to some extent, overcome the above-men-

TABLE 1.   Comparison of Some Spectral Techniques Useful in the Elucidation of Structural Problems in Organic Chemistry or Biochemistry

Spectroscopic Method	Ultraviolet	Infrared	NMR	Mass	Electron Spin Resonance (ESR)
(1) Understanding of underlying theory	mainly empirical	⟵———— reasonably precise ————⟶			
(2) Applicability	limited to a few, mostly conjugated, systems	applicable to a large number of systems, limited only by special considerations such as solubility			limited to systems containing unpaired electrons
(3) Suitability for quantitative work	good	fair	good	good	good
(4) Determination of spectra in aqueous solution	satisfactory	only with difficulty	satisfactory	usually satisfactory	partly satisfactory
(5) Determination of spectra in non-aqueous solution	satisfactory	satisfactory, but "appreciable" amounts must be soluble	satisfactory	not normally applicable	partly satisfactory
(6) Determination of spectra in solid state	relatively difficult	satisfactory	a different technique (wide-line NMR) of as yet limited usefulness	satisfactory, if compound can be volatilized	satisfactory
(7) Cost (including cost of accessories and operation)	relatively inexpensive	fairly expensive	expensive	expensive	expensive

tioned disadvantages of ultraviolet spectroscopy. However, it would seem that ultraviolet spectroscopy will be used most successfully in the future, as at present, in conjunction with other spectroscopic methods.

1.3. Bibliography. A number of collections of spectral data are available, the most useful one from the point of view of the organic chemist being the series entitled "Organic Electronic Spectral Data." These books have been compiled by a comprehensive search of over seventy chemical journals. They are published by Interscience Publishers, New York and London. Volume I (Editor, M. J. Kamlet) covers the period 1946–1952, Volume II (Editor, H. E. Ungnade) the period 1953-1955, Volume IV (Editor, J. P. Phillips and F. C. Nachod) the period 1958–1959, and further volumes are in preparation. O.E.S.D. lists all ultraviolet and visible spectra which can be considered as adequately described in the literature, the data being presented in a consistent manner by compound name (following Chemical Abstract formula index), absorption maxima (in mμ and log ϵ units), solvent or phase, and literature reference. O.E.S.D. does not list actual spectral curves.

A less comprehensive work is the collection entitled "Ultraviolet and Visible Absorption Spectra; Index for 1930–1954" and "Index for 1955–1959" compiled by H. M. Hershenson (published by Academic Press, New York and London). This index covers fewer journals and does not list any spectral data but merely refers the reader to the appropriate literature reference where an actual spectral trace is located.

A number of other collections reproduce actual spectral curves, but do not attempt to be comprehensive. The most useful of these is the "Catalog of Ultraviolet Spectral Data," which represents the American Petroleum Institute Research Project 44; it is distributed by the Chemical and Petroleum Research Laboratory, Carnegie Institute of Technology, Pittsburgh 13, Pa.

Two other fairly extensive collections are:

(1) "Absorption Spectra in the Ultraviolet and Visible Region" (Editor, L. Lang, published by Academic Press, New York) Volume I (1961) and Volume II (1961).

(2) "Ultraviolet Spectra of Aromatic Compounds," R. A. Friedel and M. Orchin (published by Wiley, New York, and Chapman & Hall, London, 1951). Both volumes include short discussions on spectroscopic theory.

There is also the A.S.T.M. collection, devised for machine sorting, which uses IBM punched cards and records absorption data within the wavelength range 200 to 420mμ; absorption maxima being indexed to the nearest 2mμ.

Apart from collections of spectral data, a number of articles and books deal in a general way with absorption spectroscopy as applicable to organic chemistry and biochemistry. The following may be singled out, having been found particularly useful by the author:

(1) "An Introduction to Electronic Absorption Spectroscopy in Organic Chemistry," A. E. Gillam and E. S. Stern (published by Edward Arnold, London, 1957).

(2) "Ultraviolet and Visible Light Absorption," E. A. Braude in "Determination of Organic Structures by Physical Methods," E. A. Braude and F. C. Nachod (published by Academic Press, New York, 1957).

(3) "Ultraviolet and Visible Spectroscopy; Chemical Applications," C. N. R. Rao (published by Butterworths, London, 1961).

(4) "Visible and Ultraviolet Spectrophotometry," G. H. Beavan and E. A. Johnson in "Molecular Spectroscopy" (published by the MacMillan Company, New York, 1961).

(5) "Theory and Applications of Ultraviolet Spectroscopy," H. H. Jaffé and M. Orchin (published by John Wiley & Sons, Inc., New York, 1962).

More specialized references will be cited in the text. It may be noted that references dealing with the theory of electronic spectra, for example the article by A. B. F. Duncan in "Chemical Applications of Spectroscopy" (published by Interscience), are not specifically mentioned, mainly because the theoretical approach to electronic spectroscopy has been found to be of less value to the organic chemist or biochemist.

2. Qualitative Investigation of a Selection of Functional Groups Using Ultraviolet Spectroscopy

2.1. Terminology.

This section is mainly concerned with the application of ultraviolet spectroscopy to a limited number of structural problems in organic chemistry. First, however, the subject of appropriate terminology should be discussed briefly.

Wavelength displacements may be bathochromic or hypsochromic. *Bathochromic* wavelength displacement refers to the wavelength of maximal absorption moving to longer wavelength (lower frequency). It is also called a *red shift*, since the absorption band is displaced towards the red and infrared part of the spectrum. In physical terms it corresponds to a drawing together of the energy levels of the ground and electronically excited states (see Figure 1). This can be brought about by the energy of the excited state being lowered more than that of the ground state, or by the energy of the ground state being raised more than that of the excited state.

The opposite of a bathochromic shift is a *hypsochromic* wavelength shift when the wavelength of maximal absorption is displaced to shorter wavelength (higher frequency). It is also referred to as a *blue shift*. Either of these changes is frequently produced by structural changes, for example, on introducing a substituent or on altering the environment.

The molar absorptivity, ϵ, or molecular extinction coefficient, of a compound is defined by the relation $I = I_0 \times 10^{-\epsilon cl}$, or $\log_{10}(I_0/I) = \epsilon cl$, where I_0 and I are the intensities of the incident and emerging light beams, l = thickness of absorbing layer and c = concentration in gram moles per litre. Spectrophotometers are usually designed to measure $\log_{10}(I_0/I)$ directly and this value is referred to as the absorbance, or optical density, of a solution.

Structural or environmental changes also often result in changes in molar absorptivities. An increase in molar absorptivity is known as a *hyperchromic effect,* whereas a decrease is called a *hypochromic effect*. Hyperchromic effects usually accompany an increase in conjugation in a system, while hypochromic effects generally indicate a decrease in conjugation, for example, because of steric interactions.

Organic compounds generally afford a number of absorption bands in the more readily accessible ultraviolet region. The most important of these is the band associated with the whole of the conjugated system. Bands can correspond to π-π^* or n-π^* transitions (see Figure 2), and these usually undergo characteristic solvent and other changes (see Section 3.4). Bands are designated in the literature in different ways. Systems of band nomenclature used by organic chemists are shown in Table 2. For reasons discussed elsewhere,[2] the Moser and Kohlenberg nomenclature will be used in the present discussion.

The term *B*-band, used to describe the main conjugation band, indicates that other bands, i.e. *A*-bands, occur at shorter wavelength. *A*-bands are ascribed mainly to Rydberg transitions for which a change in principal quantum number takes place. Conversely, bands at longer wavelength sometimes are described conveniently as *C*- and *D*-bands to indicate that they have different properties and should be discussed separately.

It is useful, but not essential, to attempt to describe the ground and excited states of a molecule. For *B*-bands, this can sometimes be done very simply using resonance

TABLE 2. Correspondence Between Various Systems of Band Nomenclature

System	Absorption Bands			
Doub and Vandenbelt	Second primary band	First primary band	Secondary band	
Burawoy and Braude		$\begin{cases} K\text{-band} \\ E\text{-band} \end{cases}$	B-band	R-band
Klevens and Platt	$\begin{cases} A\text{-band} \\ B\text{-band} \end{cases}$	C-band	D-band	
Moser and Kohlenberg	A-band	B-band	C-band	D-band

language, and this can assist in the rationalization of a number of observed spectral changes. For example, the transitions leading to the B-band of p-nitroaniline, which is displaced bathochromically with respect to the B-band of either nitrobenzene or aniline, may be assumed to involve the energetically more favorable resonance forms of type I (cf. also Figure 3).

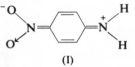

(I)

It is unfortunate that band assignment is frequently difficult (cf. Ref. 2). For example, a compound may afford a number of B-bands, some corresponding to locally excited states or "partial-chromophore" bands. Thus, in the spectrum of stilbene two main maxima are observed; one near 290mμ, the other near 225mμ.[3] Since the absorption band at 225mμ has a higher molar absorptivity in the more sterically hindered *cis*-stilbene than in *trans*-stilbene, one is tempted to assume that this band is also a B-band, corresponding to a locally excited state *not* involving the whole of the conjugated molecule. In practice, it is frequently difficult to distinguish between a B-band corresponding to a locally excited state and an A-band.

Finally, the terms *chromophore* and *auxochrome* should be defined. Chromophores have characteristic ultraviolet or visible absorption characteristics, and some well-known chromophoric structures will be discussed in the following sections. Auxochromes, on the other hand, are substituents such as —OH, —OCH₃, and —NH₂ which themselves do not afford characteristic absorption bands in the ultraviolet region but which give rise to pronounced spectral effects when introduced into a chromophoric system.

2.2. Conjugated Dienes. Most simple functional groups absorb weakly or not at all in the ultraviolet or visible part of the spectrum. However, certain combinations of functional groups afford chromophoric systems which give rise to characteristic absorption bands in the ultraviolet region. One of the best known of these is the butadiene system. Figure 4 illustrates how the π-electrons of two conjugated double bonds, each of which contains a pair of electrons, interact to determine the appropriate energy levels in buta-diene. That is, a double bond corresponds to two π-energy levels (one bonding and one anti-bonding), but when two double bonds are in conjugation there are four possible π-orbitals. Since each of the four π-orbitals thus formed has a different energy level, and since it may be shown that only the two lower π-orbitals are occupied in the ground state, four transitions are theoretically possible, of which the lowest in transition energy will be those from the second filled π-orbital to the third and fourth unfilled π-orbitals.

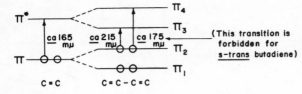

FIGURE 4. Energy levels and electronic transitions for ethylene and butadiene.

This explains the observed absorption properties of conjugated dienes. An unconjugated double bond does not normally absorb in the accessible ultraviolet region although substitution moves the absorption band toward 200 mμ. A tetrasubstituted double-bond chromophore actually absorbs maximally near 205 mμ, and this provides a convenient method of investigating this type of system. Also, measurement of the absorption above 200 mμ, so-called "end-absorption," has been used to determine the number of alkyl substituents attached to the C=C group.[4,5] Conjugated dienes, however, because of the energy level splitting, afford absorption at longer wavelength. Excited states can be visualized as involving dipolar resonance forms of type II.

$$\overset{\oplus}{C}H_2—CH=CH—\overset{\ominus}{C}H_2$$

(II)

The absorption properties of a number of conjugated dienes are listed in Table 3.

TABLE 3.   Main Absorption Maxima (B-Bands) of Some Conjugated Dienes

Compound	Solvent	λ_{max}*	ϵ_{max}	Ref.
CH_2=CH·CH=CH_2	Hexane	217	20,900	6
CH_2=C(CH_3)·CH=CH_2	Hexane	220	23,900	6
CH_3CH=CH·CH=CH_2(trans)	Ethanol	223.5	23,000	6
CH_2=C(CH_3)·C(CH_3)=CH_2	Hexane	225	20,400	6
CH_3CH=CH·CH=CHCH_3	Ethanol	227	22,500	6
$(CH_3)_2$C=CH·C(CH_3)=CH_2	Ethanol	232	8,500	8
$(CH_3)_2$C=CH·CH=C$(CH_3)_2$	Ethanol	241	22,500	9
$(CH_3)_2$C=CH·C(CH_3)=CH·CO_2CH_3	Ethanol	270	6,500	10
⬡—CH=CH·CH(CH_3)OH	Ethanol	235	23,000	11
⬡—CH=CH·CH(CH_3)OH	Ethanol	236	11,000	11
Et_2N·CH=CH·CH=CH_2	Hexane	281	23,500	12
⬡	Hexane	256	7,940	6
⬡	Isooctane	248	7,400	6
⬡	Cyclohexane	228	5,600	13

*Wavelengths are expressed in millimicron (mμ) units in this and subsequent tables.

Certain generalizations have been deduced from this type of datum as follows:[6,7]
(1) An unsubstituted conjugated diene may generally be assumed to absorb maximally

near 214mμ unless both double bonds are contained within the same ring. In that case, absorption occurs near 253mμ.

(2) A simple substituent showing no absorption itself (e.g., an alkyl group) attached to the chromophoric system displaces these absorption bands bathochromically by *ca.* 5mμ.

(3) An exocyclic double bond accounts for an additional displacement of 5mμ.

(4) A further wavelength displacement of 30mμ is brought about by another double bond in conjugation.

This is illustrated by the following examples:[14]

Compound				
Observed absorption	λ_{max}	243	283	319
	ϵ_{max}	14,500	33,000	16,200
Calculated absorption	Parent system	214	214	253
	Substituents	4 × 5 = 20	5 × 5 = 25	5 × 5 = 25
	Exocyclic >C=	2 × 5 = 10	3 × 5 = 15	3 × 5 = 15
	C=C extending conjugation	—	30	30
Total (calc)		244	284	323

It may be noted that the above correlations, known as the Woodward rules, are useful for a large number of systems of type $(C=C)_x$ where x = 2, 3, or 4. As x gets larger, these rules are no longer satisfactory, but other empirical expressions can be formulated.[15] An extension of the Woodward rules has also been recommended for simple systems to obtain more precise agreement between calculated and observed values.[16]

Molar absorptivities range from *ca.* 3,000 to 30,000. Hyperchromic effects usually accompany red shifts, absorptivities being approximately proportional to the square of the distance between the ends of the chromophoric system.[17] Some of the hypochromic effects are believed to be caused by steric interactions or changes in conformation. For example, the relatively low absorptivity of $(CH_3)_2C=CH \cdot C(CH_3)=CH_2$ (see Table 3) may be a consequence of a change from an *s-trans* (III) to a (nonplanar) *s-cis* (IV) conformation. *s-Trans* forms usually have ϵ_{max} values of *ca.* 14,000 to 30,000 while *s-cis* forms usually have ϵ_{max} values of *ca.* 3,000 to 12,000. This generalization only holds for simple butadienes; for compounds like conjugated trienes, the effective over-all length of the chromophore will be an additional factor determining absorptivity.

(III)   (IV)

Table 3 also indicates that, for cyclic dienes, the energy levels π_2 and π_3 are closer together since absorption occurs at longer wavelength. Auxochromic substituents also affect all energy levels, but they lower the excited state levels more than the ground state levels. For example, substituted butadienes may have absorption maxima from *ca.* 217 to longer than 270 *mμ*. This illustrates the difficulty of assigning a particular wavelength range to a chromophoric system such as the diene system. However, there are certain properties which permit identification of most chromophoric systems. For example, the *B*-bands of butadienes do not undergo appreciable solvent changes, and this property can assist in their band identification (see Table 4.)

TABLE 4. Absorption Maxima of 2,5-Dimethyl-2,4-Hexadiene[18]

Solvent	λ_{max}
Cyclohexane	244
Ethanol	242.5
Ether	242.5
Chloroform	245.5
Water	245

2.3. α,β-Unsaturated Carbonyl Compounds. α,β-Unsaturated carbonyl compounds absorb in a similar spectral range to conjugated dienes, that is, between *ca.* 215 and 280 *mμ*. Conjugation of the carbonyl with the vinyl group again affords four π-electron energy levels (cf. Figure 4), and the highest occupied and the lowest unoccupied energy levels are closer together than the corresponding orbitals of the carbonyl group.

Empirical rules again apply which permit the location of maximal absorption (π-π* transition) of a compound to be predicted reasonably accurately for many compounds of this type.[19] Thus, in the system

$$\overset{\displaystyle O}{\overset{\displaystyle \|}{-C}}-\underset{\alpha}{C}=\underset{\beta}{C}-\underset{\gamma}{C}=\underset{\delta}{C}$$

a basic value of 215*mμ* is calculated for the α,β-unsaturated carbonyl parent compound and the following are added:

(1) 5*mμ* for each exocyclic double bond.
(2) 30*mμ* for another double bond in conjugation.
(3) 10*mμ* for an α-alkyl substituent.
(4) 12*mμ* for a β-alkyl substituent.
(5) 18*mμ* for a γ- or δ-alkyl substituent, and
(6) 39*mμ* if a homoannular diene system is present.
An illustration is provided by the examples listed below.[20]

Compound					
Observed absorption	λ_{max}	230	241	315	241
	ϵ_{max}	10,700	16,600	7000	5200
Calculated absorption	Parent system	215	215	215	215
	Substituents α	—	—	1 × 10 = 10	1 × 10 = 10
	β	1 × 12 = 12	2 × 12 = 24	—	1 × 12 = 12
	γ, δ	—	—	1 × 18 = 18	—
	Exocyclic C=C	—	1 × 5 = 5	1 × 5 = 5	1 × 5 = 5
	C=C extending conjugation	—	—	1 × 30 = 30	—
	Homoannular diene	—	—	39	—
	Total (calc.)	227	244	317	242

TABLE 5. Main Absorption Maxima of some Dienones[21]

Compound	"Dienone Band"		"Enone Band" (corresponding to transitions involving locally excited states)		Steric Inter-actions
	λ_{max}	ϵ_{max}	λ_{max}	ϵ_{max}	
(cyclohexenyl)—CH=CHCOCH$_3$	281	20,800	—	—	
CH$_3$ CH$_3$ (gem-dimethyl cyclohexenyl)—CH=CHCOCH$_3$	281	13,000	228	4100	
CH$_3$ CH$_3$ (gem-dimethyl cyclohexenyl, CH$_3$)—CH=CHCOCH$_3$	296	10,700	223	6500	INCREASE
CH$_3$ CH$_3$ (gem-dimethyl cyclohexenyl, CH$_3$)—CH=CHCOCH$_2$CH$_3$	295	9,400	220	6500	
CH$_3$ CH$_3$ (gem-dimethyl cyclohexenyl, CH$_3$)—CH=C(CH$_3$)COCH$_3$	278	4,500	228	11,600	

There are a number of minor exceptions to these generalizations (see, for example, Ref. 16 and subsequent discussion in this section). One major exception is that if the α,β-unsaturated ketone is contained in a five-membered ring system, absorption occurs at wavelengths up to 15 mμ shorter than predicted. For example, cyclopent-2-enone absorbs maximally at 218mμ.

α,β-Unsaturated aldehydes generally absorb at about 5mμ shorter wavelength than the corresponding ketones. Apart from generalizations concerning wavelengths, generalizations concerning absorptivities also have been noted. For example, in the series of polyenes $CH_3(CH=CH)_n CHO$ the oscillator strength $f = \int_{v_1}^{v_2} \epsilon dv$ is reported to be directly proportional to the number of double bonds.[22]

Normally, molar absorptivities are determined by similar considerations as discussed for conjugated dienes. *s-Trans* compounds of type V have ϵ_{max} values between *ca.* 7500 and 20,000, whereas *s-cis* compounds (VI) have ϵ_{max} values of *ca.* 3000 to 12,500. The actual conformation may sometimes be deduced by infrared spectroscopy.[23]

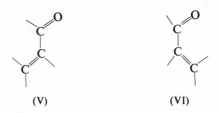

(V)   (VI)

Absorptivity changes again provide a sensitive indication of steric interactions (cf. Refs. 23 and 24). Steric interactions may also account for *s-trans—s-cis* conformational changes (for example, on introducing a second β-methyl substituent into an α,β-unsaturated ketone) and for transitions occurring predominantly to locally excited states as illustrated by the data in Table 5. It may be noted that for some of the latter examples the location of the *main* absorption band will not be predictable by the above-mentioned empirical rules.

Although the absorption characteristics of conjugated dienes and α,β-unsaturated carbonyl compounds are similar, the two groups can be distinguished since only the carbonyl compounds display significant solvent effects. This solvent effect, which occurs generally for α,β-unsaturated carbonyl compounds, is illustrated in Table 6 by the data for mesityl oxide (VII; cf. Table 4)

$$CH_3 \!\!\!\diagdown C=CHCOCH_3$$
$$CH_3 \!\!\!\diagup$$

(VII)

TABLE 6.   Main Absorption Maxima of Mesityl Oxide in Different Solvents.

Solvent	B-Band (π-π^* transition)		D-Band[†] (n-π^* transition)		Ref.
	λ_{max}	ϵ_{max}	λ_{max}	ϵ_{max}	
Cyclohexane	231	8,000	335	25	25
Ethanol	237	12,000	320	63	26
Methanol	237.5	12,300	312	63	Ref. 27 Spectrum 184
Water	245	11,200	ca. 300	112	Ref. 27 Spectrum 182

[†] The term "*C*-band" is reserved for an important π-π^* transition characteristic of aromatic systems occurring at wavelengths between the *B*- and *D*-band locations (see Section 2.4.)

These solvent changes can be rationalized by assuming that the π-π^* transitions involve excited states of type $\overset{+}{C}$—C=C—$\overset{-}{O}$, implying that an electron undergoes a transition from a predominantly ethylenic π-orbital to a predominantly carbonyl π^*-orbital. The band is said to possess charge-transfer character and *B*-bands are assumed to correspond to intramolecular charge transfer spectra. A polar solvent, because of dipole-dipole interactions and because of hydrogen bonding (see Section 3.4) will tend to lower the energy of the excited state and cause a red shift of the π-π^* band.

Table 6 also shows that α,β-unsaturated carbonyl compounds afford an additional band of low absorptivity ($\epsilon < 100$) in the region above 300mμ. These bands are associated with n-π^* transitions (see Figure 2) and undergo different spectral changes on altering the solvent. The lone pair orbital of the carbonyl group in α,β-unsaturated carbonyl compounds remains approximately unchanged compared with this same orbital in unconjugated carbonyl compounds. However, polar solvents usually possess hydrogen-bonding properties and the effect of this hydrogen bonding normally is to lower the energy of the oxygen lone pair electrons more than the energy of the π^*-orbitals of the excited state, thus causing an overall blue shift of the n-π^* band. Essentially, n-π^* excitation weakens or ruptures the hydrogen bond (see also Section 3.4). For a discussion of the effect of substitution on this band, see Ref. 28.

2.4. Aromatic Hydrocarbons. The generalizations discussed in the two previous sections, or similar generalizations, cannot immediately be applied to aromatic systems, since the absorption patterns tend to be more complex. For example, the absorption of the parent compound benzene, in an inert solvent, shows four groups of absorption bands: A-bands at *ca.* 180 to 185mμ (ϵ *ca.* 40,000), B-bands at *ca.* 193 to 204mμ (ϵ *ca.* 5000), C-bands at *ca.* 230 to 270mμ (ϵ *ca.* 250), and D-bands of very low intensity near 330mμ ($\epsilon \ll 1$). Each of these bands shows pronounced "fine structure" associated with vibrational transitions.

All these bands are ascribed mainly to π-π^* band transitions. The transition moments of the first two bands, which provide a measure of the directions of motion of the π-electrons, are believed to lie almost entirely in the plane of the benzene ring. C-bands correspond to "forbidden" transitions and are, therefore, generally much less intense than A- or B-band transitions. However, when the symmetry group of the molecule is modified by substitution, the transition may no longer be forbidden, and the band tends to become intensified (see also Ref. 28a and Refs. cited there).

In polynuclear aromatic systems all the bands are displaced to longer wavelength (see Table 7). Using simple valence bond terminology, the B-band can again be visualized as involving dipolar excited states of types VIII to X. The B-band is displaced bathochromically with increased charge separation of these dipolar excited states, and this indicates that

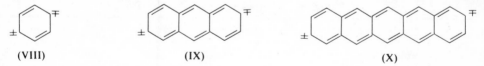

(VIII)   (IX)   (X)

the relevant transitions are polarized longitudinally, that is, along the longest axis of the molecular structure. Wave-mechanical considerations confirm this. Similarly, the B-band of biphenyl can be imagined to involve dipolar excited states of type XI,

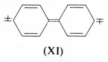

(XI)

with transitions again becoming more favorable as the number of benzene rings is increased. For m-substituted polyphenyls, no conjugated resonance form involving the whole of the molecule can be written for the dipolar excited state and, consequently, transitions occur to locally excited states. For example, the location of maximal absorption of m-terphenyl occurs at the same wavelength as that of biphenyl (see Table 7).

The C-band cannot adequately be represented by valence bond structures. It is of lower molar absorptivity and is frequently hidden by the more intense B-bands. However,

TABLE 7.   Main Maxima of Aromatic Hydrocarbons

Compound	Solvent	A-Band		B-Band		C-Band		Ref.
		λ_{max}	ϵ_{max}	λ_{max}	ϵ_{max}	λ_{max}	ϵ_{max}	
Benzene	n-Heptane	184	60,000	204.5	8,000	255	200	Ref. 27 Spectrum 11, and Ref. 29
Naphthalene	Isooctane	221	110,000	275	5,600	311	245	Ref. 27 Spectrum 383
Anthracene	Isooctane	251.5	195,000	376	4,900	—	—	Ref. 27 Spectrum 91
Naphthacene	n-Heptane	272	180,000	473	12,500	—	—	30
Pentacene	n-Heptane	310	300,000	585	12,000	417	600	30
Phenanthrene	Isooctane	250.5	66,000	292	14,000	330	260	Ref. 27 Spectrum 92
Biphenyl	Chloroform	—	—	251.5	18,300	—	—	31
p-Terphenyl	Chloroform	—	—	280	25,000	—	—	31
p-Tetraphenyl	Chloroform	—	—	300	39,000	—	—	31
m-Terphenyl	Chloroform	—	—	251.5	44,000	—	—	31
o-Terphenyl	Ethanol	—	—	231.5	26,300	—	—	32

certain features of the *C*-band are sometimes characteristic of a compound; for example, the fine structure peak at 320 mμ for naphthalene. Concerning general usefulness, the *B*- and *C*-bands are of greater interest for the simpler aromatic hydrocarbons, since they usually occur in a region which is readily accessible with most spectrophotometers. For the larger aromatic systems the *A*-band is sometimes of interest, since its very large molar absorptivity values permit very small amounts of compounds to be determined quantitatively. This can be important for the angular polycyclic hydrocarbons, such as substituted phenanthrenes, many of which are carcinogenic.

The considerations concerning *B*-band location suggest that these bands may provide a guide to the length of a conjugated aromatic system. However, aromatic systems are

TABLE 8.   B-bands of 1-Phenylnaphthalenes

Compound	Solvent	λ_{max}	ϵ_{max}	Ref.
1-Phenylnaphthalene	Cyclohexane	288	11,500	33
2-Methyl-1-phenylnaphthalene	Cyclohexane	280	8,000	33
Benzanthrene	Ethanol	329	16,500	34

sensitive to steric interactions which can affect the wavelength of maximal absorption. This is illustrated by the data in Table 8 which shows the absorption characteristics of 1-phenylnapththalene, which is believed to be nonplanar. A blue shift occurs if the non-planarity of the compound is increased by additional substituents, and a red shift occurs if the non-planarity is decreased by bridging. Normally, the more planar an aromatic system, the longer the wavelength at which it absorbs. Consequently, an aromatic system may absorb over a wide wavelength range, depending on the planarity of the system. The general effects of substituents will be discussed in subsequent sections.

The main maxima of aromatic hydrocarbons are not affected appreciably by solvents (see Table 9 and Table 4). Moreover, band locations and fine structure tend to be characteristic for many aromatic systems and are frequently used for purposes of identification (see, for example, Ref. 34a).

TABLE 9.   Main Maxima of Naphthalene in Various Solvents * ' [18]
(ϵ_{max} values in brackets)

Solvent	A	B						C							
Cyclo-hexane	221 (120,000)	257 (3500)	266 (5150)	273 (5200)	276 (5600)	283 (3700)	286 (3800)	297 (330)	299 (270)	301 (280)	304 (210)	305 (200)	311 (250)	ca. 315 (46)	320 (17)
Ethanol	220.5 (110,000)	258 (3550)	265.5 (5010)	ca. 273 (5280)	275 (5560)	283 (3740)	285 (3760)	297 (325)		300.5 (285)	304 (215)	306 (190)	311 (235)	315 (65)	320 (17)
Water	219.5 (83,000)	258.5 (3000)	266 (4150)	273.5 (4270)	276.5 (4440)	284 (2980)	ca. 285.5 (2800)	296		300		ca. 305	310	ca. 314	319
								(insufficiently soluble for ϵ determination in this region)							
CHCl₃		260 (3540)	268 (5000)	ca. 275 (5190)	277.5 (5560)	286 (3740)	288 (3670)	ca. 297 (465)		301 (310)		ca. 306 (230)	311 (233)	ca. 315 (95)	ca. 320 (22)
CCl₄		259 (4300)	268.5 (4990)	ca. 275.5 (5100)	278.5 (5450)	287.5 (3830)		ca. 298 (569)		ca. 302 (370)		ca. 307 (228)	312 (245)	ca. 317 (90)	ca. 320.5 (26)

*Values in italics represent inflections in this and subsequent tables.

2.5   Alkyl Substitution.   It has already been noted that the spectral changes brought about on alkyl substitution in some non-aromatic systems can be correlated by simple empirical rules (see Sections 2.2 and 2.3). In aromatic systems also, alkyl substitution usually causes small but appreciable red shifts. Table 10 illustrates that a single alkyl substituent usually affords this displacement in both bands. This spectral change is, approximately, independent of the nature of the alkyl substituent. Additional alkyl substituents cause further wavelength displacements in both bands, each substituent normally causing a displacement of *ca.* 5 mμ (see Table 10).

Table 10 also illustrates the fact that the displacements brought about by alkyl substitution are normally in the order: para-isomer (most intense band) > meta-isomer > ortho-isomer (least intense band). Simple theoretical considerations indicate that a para-substituent causes the largest displacement and affords the relatively simplest spectrum because of the greater degree of symmetry. The changes brought about on ortho- and meta- substitution, in the absence of steric interactions, would be anticipated to be similar.[43] However, in *o*-disubstituted aromatic compounds various steric interactions affect the transitions, most frequently giving rise to a blue shift and a hypochromic effect (see also section 3.1). This accounts for the fact that usually the absorption of the *o*-isomer occurs at the shortest wavelength and with the lowest absorption intensity. Since steric effects may alter the absorption of *o*- disubstituted benzene derivatives, prediction of their spectral properties becomes more difficult. These difficulties are increased in polysubstituted aromatic systems since steric interactions will almost invariably contribute to the observed spectra.   These steric effects are well illustrated in the biphenyl series.

TABLE 10.   The Effect of Alkyl Substitution on the *B*- and *C*-Bands of Some Aromatic Hydrocarbons

Compound	Solvent	B-Band		C-Band		Ref.
		λ_{max}	ϵ_{max}	λ_{max}	ϵ_{max}	
Benzene	Hexane	198	8,000	256	250	35
Toluene	Hexane	207	8,000	262	250	36
t-Butylbenzene	Ethanol	207.5	7,800	257	170	37
p-Xylene	Ethanol	216	7,600	268	500	38
m-Xylene	25% Methanol	212	7,200	264.5	300	39
o-Xylene	25% Methanol	210	8,300	266	300	39
Biphenyl	Light petroleum	248	17,000	—	—	40
p-Methylbiphenyl	" "	251.5	19,000	—	—	40
m-Methylbiphenyl	" "	249	16,300	—	—	40
o-Methylbiphenyl	" "	236.5	10,250	*ca. 270*	900	40
o-t-Butylbiphenyl	Ethanol	233	10,500	—	—	41
2,6-Dimethylbiphenyl	Light petroleum	*231*	*5,600*	$\begin{cases} 257.5 \\ 263.5 \end{cases}$	$\begin{matrix} 660 \\ 520 \end{matrix}$	40
4,5-Dimethyl-9,10--dihydrophenanthrene	Ethanol	260	16,000	—	—	42

Substitution in the ortho-position causes blue shifts and hypochromic effects, and these spectral changes are more pronounced as the size of the substituent increases (see Table 10 for the spectrum of *o-t*-butylbiphenyl) or as the number of substituents increases (see the spectrum of 2,6-dimethylbiphenyl).

The *B*-band may be associated with excited states of type XI (see previous section). As steric interactions increase, the molecule becomes non-planar which increases the energy level of its excited states. Nonplanarity leads to a decreased transition probability, so that the molar absorptivity of the *B*-band decreases. This means that in *o*-substituted biphenyls the submerged *C*-band sometimes appears. With more highly substituted biphenyls, in which conjugation between the two rings is negligible, such as the fully substituted decamethylbiphenyl, the spectrum in fact approximates to a superposition of the spectra of the two parent compounds corresponding to locally excited states—in this example, to the spectra of two molecules of hexamethylbenzene. This is illustrated in Figure 3 of Ref. 40 which shows that there is no evidence of interaction between the two phenyl rings. This is interpreted to mean that the rings are twisted out of a uniplanar configuration and that, therefore, they absorb independently. As judged from the spectrum of 4,5-dimethyl-9,10-dihydrophenanthrene, bridging of the two halves of the biphenyl system presumably partially restores coplanarity since the spectrum again resembles that of biphenyl (see Table 10).

Comparing the spectral changes occuring on alkyl substitution which increase steric interactions in aromatic and non-aromatic systems, it may be noted that hypochromic effects are obtained in both systems. Appreciable blue shifts, however, are observed only in the biphenyl system (see Table 10 and compare Table 3). This difference is explained by assuming that compounds such as mesityl oxide can exist in another configuration (*s-cis*) in which conjugation is still possible, whereas in compounds like *o*-methylbiphenyl the alternative configuration is equally strained. Alkyl-substituted aromatic systems, like alkyl-substituted non-aromatic systems (see Table 4), normally do not undergo any appreciable spectral changes on altering the solvent. However, a significant blue shift sometimes occurs if the spectrum is determined at elevated temperatures in the vapour phase. For example, biphenyl in the vapour phase at 170° absorbs at 238 mμ; ϵ = 12,050.[44]

2.6. Acetyl and Formyl Substitution. α,β-Unsaturated carbonyl compounds have previously been considered in Section 2.3. The present section provides an extension of this, discussing the effect of acetyl and formyl substitution particularly in aromatic systems. Such systems lend themselves to ultraviolet studies partly because a wealth of data concerning the carbonyl group is available from infrared spectroscopy, and the ultraviolet absorption spectrum frequently confirms conclusions deduced from the infrared spectrum.

Generally, if a carbonyl group is in conjugation with a π-electron system, the effect is to displace the B-band to longer wavelength. Using resonance terminology, the *excited state* may be considered to involve resonance forms of type $=C-O^-$. This concept immediately rationalizes a number of observations. For example, in p-substituted acetophenones or benzaldehydes, substituents which favour resonance forms of type XII facilitate transitions, in this way leading to red shifts and hyperchromic effects. This is illustrated in Table 11, which also shows that these effects in the carbonyl compounds are usually slightly greater than for the unsubstituted parent compounds. Table 11 further shows that formyl-substituted compounds can absorb over a wide wavelength range.

TABLE 11. The Effect of Electron-Donating Substituents on the B-Band of Benzaldehyde and on the B-Band of Benzene
(Hexane or Cyclohexane solutions)

Para-Substituent	Benzaldehyde[45]		Benzene		Ref.
	λ_{max}	ϵ_{max}	λ_{max}	ϵ_{max}	
H—	241	14,000	204	8,000	36
	247	*12,000*			
CH$_3$—	251	15,000	208	8,000	36
	257	12,500			
Cl—	253	19,000	211	7,500	
	259	*15,500*	215	7,500	46
			ca. 219	6,000	
OH—	265.5	19,000	210	6,000	47
	*ca.*274	*15,500*			
NH$_2$—	291	16,300	233.5	9,000	48
	296	16,100			

$$\overset{+}{X}=\!\!\!\raisebox{-2pt}{\text{⬡}}\!\!\!=C\overset{O^-}{\underset{R}{}}$$

(XII)

Resonance terminology also rationalizes the observation that the B-bands of m-isomers occur at shorter wavelength than those of the p-isomers (see Table 12), since no completely conjugated resonance form analogous to structure XII can be written for compounds like *m*-hydroxybenzaldehyde. The concept of locally excited states is employed to explain the spectra of the *m*-isomers; that is, the main *B*-band of a compound like *m*-methoxyacetophenone is assumed to correspond to the *B*-band of acetophenone with the *m*-methoxy substituent exerting only a secondary effect.

Resonance terminology is less satisfactory to explain the *B*-bands of *o*-isomers since resonance forms of type XII can be written, but *o*-isomers do *not* generally absorb at longer wavelength than *m*-isomers. The treatment of Förster[43] suggests that the absorption characteristics of *m*- and *o*-isomers are similar. Actually, the absorption properties of *o*-disubstituted benzene derivatives are not completely understood; it is possible that steric interactions caused by the proximity of the two substituents prevent the uniplanarity which is required for resonance forms of type XII. In any case, *o*-isomers normally absorb with lower absorptivity than *m*-isomers, particularly if the two substituents are large. Such hypochromic effects are generally assumed to indicate the operation of steric interactions (see section 3.1). The study of steric interactions in *o*-disubstituted benzene derivatives and related compounds is of considerable interest, especially if conducted in conjunction with infrared measurements. For example, high resolution infrared spectra of the carbonyl band provide information concerning the existence of possible conformational isomers and of intramolecular hydrogen bonding; ultraviolet spectra can provide additional information concerning these interactions.

TABLE 12.   B-bands (Main Maxima) of Substituted Acetophenones in Cyclohexane Solution

Substituent	Para-Isomer		Meta-Isomer*		Ortho-Isomer*	
	λ_{max}	ϵ_{max}	λ_{max}	ϵ_{max}	λ_{max}	ϵ_{max}
F—[49]	240	12,000	235	10,500	233	9,500
Cl—[49]	249	17,000	239	10,000	235	5,700
Br—[49]	253	19,500	240	10,000	235	4,900
CH_3O—[50]	261.5	18,000	244	8,500	241	8,350
NH_2—[49]	285	19,000	*246*	*9,000*	252	5,500

*In *m*- and *o*-isomers a second *B*-band sometimes occurs which is associated with locally excited states involving the second substituent. For example, *m*-aminoacetophenone affords a *B*-band at 226 mμ, ϵ = 26,500[49] which is associated with the *B*-band absorption of aniline.

The contribution of resonance forms of type XII to the excited states involved in the *B*-band absorption of *p*-substituted aromatic carbonyl compounds would be expected to give rise to relatively large solvent effects in polar solvents. Larger solvent effects are in fact observed in the *p*-isomer as is illustrated in Table 13.

TABLE 13.   Main Absorption Maxima (B-Bands) of p- and m-Aminoacetophenone in Cyclohexane and Ethanol[48]

Solvent	Para-Isomer		Meta-Isomer*	
	λ_{max}	ϵ_{max}	λ_{max}	ϵ_{max}
Cyclohexane	285	19,000	226	26,500
			246	*9,000*
Ethanol	316	20,000	231	23,000
			ca. 255	7,000

*See footnote of Table 12.

Apart from B-bands, A-, C-, and D-bands also occur, but their study is generally less fruitful than the investigation of B-bands. Normally, the B-band is readily identified by its location and the characteristic changes observed on altering the solvent or on introducing steric interactions. For an interesting investigation of solvent effects on benzophenone and other molecules, see Ref. 51.

2.7. Nitro Substitution. The effect of nitro substitution provides a suitable field of investigation for ultraviolet spectroscopy. In many ways, acetyl and nitro substituents produce similar spectral effects. For example, both give rise to appreciable red shifts if attached to conjugated systems, and their B-bands afford large solvent effects. Also, if neighbouring substituents are large, steric interactions cause blue shifts and hyperchromic effects in the B-band which increase with the size of the substituent. This similarity between carbonyl-substituted and nitro-substituted conjugated systems is not surprising, since both groups are electron-withdrawing, are fairly large, and are able to extend the conjugated system.

In the previous section, the effect of electron-donating substituents on compounds like acetophenone and benzaldehyde has been discussed. The effect of such substituents on nitrobenzene and related compounds is analogous and may be associated with resonance forms of type I. However, the effect of electron-withdrawing substituents on the spectra of compounds like acetophenone or nitrobenzene has not yet been considered. Appropriate examples are the spectra of the nitrobenzaldehydes which are listed in Table 14.

TABLE 14. Main Absorption Maxima (B-Bands) of Nitrobenzaldehydes

Solvent	Para-Isomer[52]		Meta-Isomer[53]		Ortho-Isomer[53]	
	λ_{max}	ϵ_{max}	λ_{max}	ϵ_{max}	λ_{max}	ϵ_{max}
Hexane or cyclohexane	259	13,800	227	30,000	222	18,000
			ca. 245	10,500	248	6,500
			ca. 260	6,000		
Ethanol	265	11,400	227	11,000	219.5	9,500
			258.5	7,500	252	5,000
Water	266	14,500	233	22,000	225	12,000
			ca. 266	7,000	259	5,000

Table 14 first shows that in the m- and o-isomers two B-bands are observed (cf footnote to Table 12). These are again associated with locally excited states corresponding to the nitrobenzene and benzaldehyde partial chromophoric systems. This can be rationalized in terms of resonance theory since no extended resonance form can be written for m-nitrobenzaldehyde. Interactions occur in the p-isomer, but not in the o-isomer because of steric interactions between the two vicinal substituents. Steric interactions, which are well established from other physical data, are also indicated by the lower absorptivity values in the o-isomers. Absorptivities are further reduced in compounds like o-dinitrobenzene, where both substituents are large, and which shows no maximal absorption above $220\,m\mu$.[54] It may next be noted that the nitro substituent causes a blue shift in the benzaldehyde absorption, presumably by withdrawing electrons from the benzaldehyde partial chromophoric system and, thus, raising the energy level of the electronic excited state involving resonance forms of type XII (R = H; XIII). A similar effect is observed in 5 percent aqueous ethanol in the spectrum of m-dinitrobenzene which absorbs maximally at $242\,m\mu$, whereas nitrobenzene absorbs maximally at $269\,m\mu$.

Nitro groups also give rise to characteristic absorption bands in aliphatic nitro compounds. Such compounds afford strong and weak absorption maxima near 200mμ (ϵ ca. 5000) and near 280mμ (ϵ ca. 15–35), corresponding to B- and D-bands, respectively (Refs. 55, 56 and Refs. cited there). The weaker band, associated with n-π*-transitions is, unlike the D-band of compounds such as acetophenone, *not* displaced to longer wavelength if the nitro group is in conjugation with another π-electron system. Since the band at 210mμ (B-band) is displaced toward the red under these conditions, the weaker band near 280mμ is covered by the more intense band and is no longer discerned in compounds like nitrobenzene.

2.8. Amino, Hydroxy, Methoxy and Halogen Substitution. All these substituents, if attached to a conjugated system such as a benzene ring, afford red shifts and hyperchromic effects in the B- and C-bands. The band maxima for benzene derivatives are listed in Table 15. These substituents, which are sometimes referred to as auxochromes, possess unshared electron pair(s) but no π-electrons; the resulting conjugation is, therefore, sometimes referred to as π-p conjugation. The spectral changes can be associated with resonance forms of type XIV; hence, substituents possessing a large mesomeric (+M) effect normally give rise to a large spectral change.

(XIV)

TABLE 15. Main Absorption Maxima (B- and C-Bands) of Monosubstituted Benzenes in Cyclohexane Solution

Compound	B-Band		C-Band	
	λ_{max}	ϵ_{max}	λ_{max}	ϵ_{max}
Phenol[47]	211	6,000	263	1,400
			269	2,200
			276	1,100
Anisole[50]	220	8,100	265	1,400
	224	6,400	271	2,100
			277.5	2,100
Aniline[48]	233–234	9,000	286	1,900
Fluorobenzene[57]	204	ca. 8,000	248	450
			254	850
			259	1,300
			266	1,150
Chlorobenzene[46]	211	7,500	257	180
	215	7,500	261	170
			264	250
			271	190
Bromobenzene[58]	213	9,000	259	180
	215	8,500	262	180
			265	200
			272	130
Iodobenzene[59]	228.5	15,000	253.5	750
	233.5	14,000	258	800

Table 15 shows the fine structure which is pronounced for benzene tends to disappear as the bands are displaced to longer wavelength. Fine structure also tends to be reduced if spectra are determined in more polar solvents. Some of the systems considered afford characteristic solvent changes. For example, while most of the spectra of the compounds listed show no appreciable wavelength displacements, or undergo only small blue shifts on changing the solvent from cyclohexane to water, very useful solvent changes are observed in the spectra of phenols between neutral and alkaline media or in the aniline spectra between neutral and acidic media. Under these conditions the absorbing species are altered, and the species in the latter solvents absorb at different wavelengths from those of the original compounds. Hence, appreciable solvent changes are observed. The presence of two species may also be confirmed by the appearance of an isosbestic point.* The actual changes for phenol and aniline are shown in Table 16. In aniline the nitrogen atom loses its unshared electron pair because of salt formation and the spectrum reverts essentially to that of benzene. This, incidentally, illustrates the importance of resonance interactions in determining B- and C-band spectra, since the inductive effect of the NH_3^+ group does not appreciably affect these bands. The spectra of halogen substituted benzene derivatives are also of interest in this connection, since they provide information concerning the mesomeric effects of the halogen substituents (see Ref. 60 and Refs. cited there).

TABLE 16. Main Absorption Maxima of Phenol[47] and Aniline[48] in Different Solvents

Compound	Solvent	B-Band		C-Band	
		λ_{max}	ϵ_{max}	λ_{max}	ϵ_{max}
Phenol	Water	211	6,000	268	1,500
Phenol	N Aqueous NaOH	234	10,500	285	2,700
Aniline	Water	230	8,000	278	1,400
Aniline	0.1N Aqueous HCl	202	7,500	$ca.$ 252	170

If one of the above substituents is introduced into a more complicated system, for example, into a benzenoid system which is already substituted, the relevant spectra can again frequently be rationalized in terms of resonance theory. For example, B-bands of p-disubstituted benzene derivatives absorb at considerably longer wavelength if one of the substituents is electron withdrawing. This follows because resonance forms of type XII then assume importance, thus facilitating the intramolecular charge transfer. On the other hand, if both substituents are electron-donating or if they are meta to each other, absorption bands predominate which involve locally excited states corresponding to monosubstituted benzene chromophores.

In o-disubstituted benzene derivatives, relatively low molar absorptivities, indicative of steric interactions, are frequently observed. Some conjugated systems, such as aniline, are not very sensitive to steric interactions, but such interactions can usually be detected as the size of the substituent increases. For example, o-substituted acetophenones afford greater hypochromic effects than o-substituted benzaldehydes because of the relatively

*If only two species, each of which obeys Beer's law, are present in a solution, the optical density-wavelength curves of all equilibrium mixtures (at constant temperature and constant total molar concentration) intersect at a fixed wavelength. At this point, called the isosbestic point, the absorbances of the two species are equal. For example, the yellow and red forms of methyl orange afford an isosbestic point showing that two, and only two, species participate in the equilibrium.

larger size of the acetyl group; similarly, *o*-substituted N,N-dimethylanilines afford larger hypochromic effects than *o*-substituted anilines.[61] Sometimes hypochromic effects are also observed in the *C*-bands. For example, in the phenyl alkyl ethers in hexane solution, phenyl methyl ether affords a *C*-band absorptivity of 1580 while phenyl *t*-butyl ether has an absorptivity of 455.[62]

2.9. Heterocyclic Compounds. In previous sections, the spectral properties of a number of substituted conjugated systems were considered. Some of the more important substituents were discussed, but the effects of other substituents, such as —COOH, —CONH$_2$, —C≡CH, were not specifically mentioned. However, this is not essential because the approach is similar. That is, the spectral properties of an appropriately substituted model system are investigated under a variety of conditions and from these data certain characteristic properties of the substituent can generally be discerned. For example, a band involving the —COOH substituent attached to an aromatic system frequently affords a concentration dependence in inert solvents because of dimerisation.[63] Hence, this property may be used to identify an unknown band suspected of being associated with a conjugated carboxylic acid system.

Also, the chosen conjugated system, to which the substituent was attached, was usually the benzene ring because of the importance and frequent occurrence of systems of this type. However, it is not necessary to confine discussion to substituted benzenes since many heterocyclic compounds possess comparable spectral properties. For example, benzene and pyridine (XV) afford similar spectra (see Table 17). This is as anticipated since both compounds possess six π-electrons, the main difference between the two compounds being the greater electronegativity of nitrogen compared with carbon. One difference between the two compounds is that pyridine affords an additional band, associated with an *n-π**-transition involving the relatively loosely held non-bonded electron pair of the N-atom (see Figure 2), which can readily be identified by the characteristic spectral changes shown by this band on changing the solvent.[64]

TABLE 17.   Comparison of Absorption Maxima for Benzene and Pyridine[64]

	Benzene		Pyridine	
	λ_{max}	*f*-value[†]	λ_{max}	*f*-value[†]
A-Band	184	0.69	176	1.36
B-Band	202	0.10	195	0.20
C-Band	255	0.0014	250	0.03
D-Band	—	—	~285	~0.004
($n \rightarrow \pi$*-transition)				

[†]Instead of using ϵ values as a measure of absorption intensities, i.e. of transition-probabilities, a more satisfactory but more troublesome, measure can be provided by using values of *f*, the oscillator strength. An approximate estimate of *f* can be obtained from the equation

$$f = 2.2 \times 10^{-9} \epsilon_{max} \Delta \nu'_{1/2}$$

where $\Delta \nu'_{1/2}$ is the band width at half maximum extinction expressed in cm^{-1}. *f*-Values are proportional to A(A = $\int \epsilon d\nu'$) and A provides a measure of the transition probability.

If the aromatic ring contains more than one nitrogen atom, as in pyrazine (XVI), spectral changes with respect to benzene become more pronounced. For example, the intensities of the *C*- and *D*-bands are progressively enhanced in the series benzene < pyridine (see Table 17; ϵ_{max} of *C*-band *ca.* 2,000 in cyclohexane solution[65]) < pyrazine (λ_{max} (*C*-band) 260 mμ, ϵ = 6,200; λ_{max} (*D*-band) *ca.* 316 mμ, ϵ = 840 in cyclohexane solution[65]).

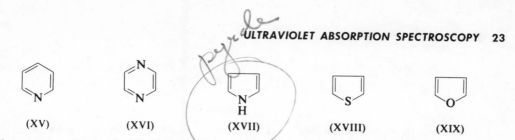

(XV)   (XVI)   (XVII)   (XVIII)   (XIX)

The spectra of pyrrole (XVII) and thiophene (XVIII) show some displacement of their main absorption bands compared with this band in furan (XIX) see Table 18. Since the former two compounds, and particularly thiophene, are known to possess some aromatic character, as judged by their chemical properties, the corresponding spectral shifts have been associated with this aromaticity. The spectrum of furan (XIX) itself resembles that of its acyclic analogue.

Auxochromic or chromophoric substitution of the unsaturated heterocyclic systems usually causes spectral effects similar to those described in previous sections; that is, red shifts and hyperchromic effects are generally observed. The position of the substituent in the aromatic nucleus frequently affects the main band of the heterocyclic compound differently from the B-band of benzene derivatives. For example, substitution in the 2- or 3-position in pyridine causes a greater spectral change than in the 4-position, whereas for disubstituted benzene derivatives the opposite effect is observed. The reason for this is that the "main" band in pyridine is a benzenoid or C-band and not a B-band associated with three conjugated bonds.

TABLE 18.   Main Absorption Maxima of Some Heterocyclic Compounds and of Appropriate Reference Compounds

Compound	Solvent	λ_{max}	ϵ_{max}	Ref.
Pyrrole (XVII)	n-Hexane	210	15,000	66
Thiophene (XVIII)	Ethanol	230	7,000	67
Divinyl sulfide	Ethanol	255	5,600	68
Furan (XIX)	Vapor	204	6,450	69
Divinyl ether	Vapor	203.5	16,000	70

Steric effects in heterocyclic compounds also afford the expected spectral changes, since the introduction of the hetero-atom will not appreciably affect the effective size of a group. For example, in phenyl-substituted pyridines, pyrroles, furans, triazoles, etc., further substitution in the position adjacent to the phenyl group generally tends to give rise to hypso- and hypochromic effects. For example, in ethanolic solution 2,5-biphenyl-pyrrole has a band at 330mμ, $\epsilon = 26,700$, while the same band in the spectrum of 2,5-biphenyl-1-methylpyrrole occurs at λ_{max} 307mμ, $\epsilon = 20,500$.[71]

2.10. Azo Compounds. In previous sections a number of simple organic systems were considered, and their absorbing properties were summarized. Frequently, more complex organic systems can also be investigated through the study of a simple conjugated chromophoric system contained in the more complicated system. For example, steroids can frequently be investigated via their conjugated diene systems, or nucleic acids by the pyrimidine structure (XX) contained in them (see also Section 3.6).

For other relatively complex systems, however, it is necessary to consider the whole of the molecule and not just a part of it as the appropriate chromophoric system. An example of one such moderately complex system is the azobenzene system which also illustrates the method of approach. Azobenzenes were selected because they provide interesting spectra and because certain substituted azobenzenes are important carcinogenic compounds and dyes.

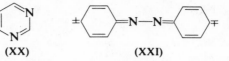

(XX)   (XXI)

TABLE 19. Main Absorption Maxima (Long Wavelength B-Bands) of Some Azobenzenes and of Suitable Reference Compounds

Compound	Solvent	λ_{max}	ϵ_{max}	Ref.
Styrene	Ethanol	248	14,600	72
trans-Stilbene	Ethanol	295	28,000	73
Benzalaniline	95% Aqueous ethanol	312	10,000	74
trans-Azobenzene	50% Aqueous ethanol	320	21,000	75
N,N-Dimethyl-*p*-aminoazobenzene	50% Aqueous ethanol	420	24,000	75
N,N-Dimethyl-*p*-aminoazobenzene	50% Aqueous ethanolic 2N sulfuric acid	{320 / 520	10,000 / 34,000	75
N,N-Dimethyl-*p*-amino-*o'*-methylazobenzene	50% Aqueous ethanol	410	27,000	75
N,N-Dimethyl-*p*-amino-*o'*-methylazobenzene	50% Aqueous ethanolic 2N sulfuric acid	{326 / 520	16,000 / 10,000	75

Simple azobenzenes normally afford two main groups of bands in the region above 300 mμ; an intense band in the 320 to 360 mμ region which may be associated with resonance forms of type XXI, and a weaker band in the 430 to 460 mμ region which may be associated with the azo group (n-π*-transition) and which is mainly responsible for the observed color. On substitution, the B-band is displaced in the expected manner (see Table 19). Compounds like N,N-dimethyl-*p*-aminoazobenzene are of particular interest, since in acid solution two B-bands occur; the band near 320 mμ is associated with the ammonium cation (XXII), mainly because it occurs in the same region as the B-band of azobenzene. (See Section 2.8 for the spectra of aniline in acid media.) The second band near 520 mμ is attributed to the azonium ion which may be represented by structures of type XXIII and XXIV. The occurrence of these two bands in acid media is assumed to arise from a tautomeric equilibrium.[75]

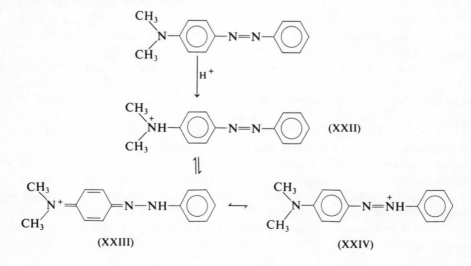

These assignments also receive support from the spectra of N,N-dimethyl-*p*-amino-*o'*-methylazobenzene (see Table 19). Both structures XXIII and XXIV possess an additional hydrogen atom on the nitrogen atom adjoining the *o'*-methyl group; one would, therefore, expect that the steric interactions caused in this way would tend to displace the equilibrium towards structures of type XXII. The data in Table 19, in fact, indicate this, because the band at 326 mμ for the *o'*-methyl compound is relatively much more intense than the band at 320 mμ for N,N-dimethyl-*p*-aminoazobenzene.[75] Tautomeric equilibria have also been observed for more complex azo-compounds, even in neutral solution. For example, 1-phenylazo-2-naphthol (XXV) shows a peak near 490 mμ which has been ascribed to the *o*-quinone hydrazone form (XXVI), while the maximal absorption at shorter wavelength, near 420 mμ, has been convincingly ascribed to the azo-form (XXV).[76] Likewise, the maxima for 4-phenylazo-1-naphthol in solution near 410 and 470 mμ have been ascribed to an equilibrium between the azo-form and the *p*-quinone hydrazone form (XXVII).[77]

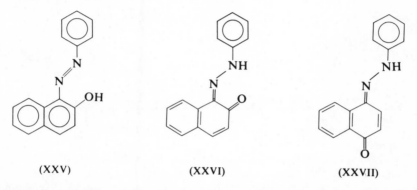

(XXV) (XXVI) (XXVII)

Azobenzenes, like stilbenes, are able to exist in either the *trans* or *cis* configurations. Some azobenzenes, including N,N-dimethyl-*p*-aminoazobenzene in inert solution, are readily converted to the *cis* form unless the solutions are kept in the dark for prolonged periods. The changes in absorbing properties between the two forms can be used to follow such photoisomerisations.[78] *cis*-Azobenzenes generally possess lower molar absorptivities than the *trans* isomers. This is indicative of the shorter chromophoric system and/or of the non-planarity of the *cis* isomer (see Section 3.2).

Although the azobenzene system does not appear to be as readily twisted out of the coplanar conformation as, for example, the biphenyl system, the anticipated steric effects are again observed. For instance, 2,4,6,2',4',6'-hexamethylazobenzene exhibits the usual hypochromic effect (λ_{max} 332 mμ, ϵ = 13,000 in ethanol[79]). However, caution is required in interpreting such spectral changes, particularly in acid media, since steric interactions may alter the equilibrium concentrations if two or more species are present (see previous discussion).

3. A Selection of Topics Which can be Investigated by Ultraviolet Spectroscopy

3.1. Steric Interactions.
The spectral effects brought about by certain steric interactions have previously been mentioned as being characteristic of various chromophoric systems. For example, the data in Table 5 (Section 2.3) and Table 8 (Section 2.4) illustrate that both α,β-unsaturated carbonyl compounds and diaryl compounds afford hypochromic effects when bulky substituents are introduced which tend to prevent the co-planarity of the system; however, the data also indicate that the diaryl compounds more readily give rise to wavelength displacements. In all the examples of steric effects

referred to so far, the steric interactions mainly involve the *twisting of essentially only one single bond.* That is, considering the *o*-methylbiphenyl molecule (XXVIII), it is assumed that the major effect of the steric interactions is to cause a twisting of the 1-1' carbon-carbon bond; bending and other deformations will, of course, also occur but only to a limited extent. In the same way, the main result of steric interactions for compounds like mesityl oxide (XXIX), 2,6-dimethylnitrobenzene (XXX), 2,6,N,N-tetramethylaniline (XXXI), and *o*-bromoacetophenone (XXXII)[80] is assumed to be a twisting of the single bond which, however, may possess double-bond character.

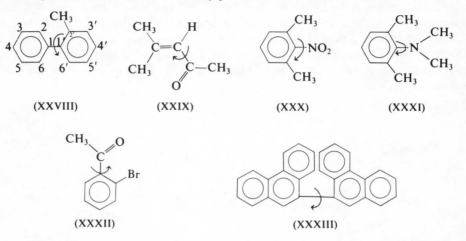

(XXVIII)   (XXIX)   (XXX)   (XXXI)

(XXXII)   (XXXIII)

It was also previously noted, in the discussion of the spectra of isomeric disubstituted benzenes, that the *o*-disubstituted benzene derivative generally possesses the lowest molar absorptivity value (see Section 2.5). This illustrates a general principle which can be formulated as follows: If the introduction of a bulky substituent (such as a methyl group) into a conjugated system produces a marked hypochromic effect in the main conjugation band (*B*-band) of the molecule, this suggests that a single bond has been twisted in such a way as to reduce conjugation between two parts of the molecule. Thus, information can be obtained concerning the conformation of a molecule in solution.

Steric interactions associated with hypochromic effects have frequently been noted, and numerous attempts have been made to provide a satisfactory theoretical explanation of the spectral changes.[81,82,83,84] Empirically, the observed spectral effects can be classified into three types:

(1) Steric interactions which give rise only to hypochromic effects, without causing any unusual change in wavelength.

(2) Steric interactions which cause a change in both wavelength and absorption intensity in the main conjugation band.

(3) Steric interactions when conjugation is almost completely inhibited and the molecule absorbs as two distinct entities.

A variety of mechanisms can be postulated for the first type of effect. For example, it may be merely a special case of a type (2) steric effect in which the wavelength displacement is small or zero; or it may be that the molecule exists in a number of different conformations, but not all of these conformations contribute to the observed absorption maximum of the *B*-band.[24]

In the second type of steric effect, the wavelength displacement depends on the sign and the magnitude of the change in the bond order of the twisted bond during excitation. In molecules like *o*-methylbiphenyl (XXVIII) the more usual hypsochromic effect is observed (see Section 2.5 and Table 10) consistent with the resonance picture of the excited state predominantly involving structures of type XI (see also Figure 5).

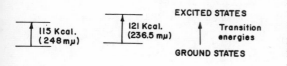

EXCITED STATES

Transition energies

GROUND STATES

115 Kcal. (248 mμ)

121 Kcal. (236.5 mμ)

FIGURE 5. Schematic representation of *B*-band transitions for (i) a planar reference compound, biphenyl; and (ii) a non-planar compound, *o*-methylbiphenyl, in which a greater energy difference between the ground and electronic states results in a hypsochromic (blue) shift.

The interpretation of the third type of effect is unambiguous and corresponds to absorption leading to locally excited states (cf. Section 2.1). Examples are provided by the spectrum of decamethylbiphenyl which absorbs like two molecules of hexamethylbenzene[40]; or by the spectrum of compound XXXIII, which is similar to the spectrum of two molecules of phenanthrene[85] (cf. also Ref. 86).

Apart from the above-mentioned examples, all of which involve as a first approximation the twisting of only one single bond, other types of steric effects are also possible. For example, 1,12-dimethylbenzo(c)phenanthrene (XXXIV) absorbs maximally at 336 mμ, $\epsilon = 7,600$, while the parent compound benzo(c)phenanthrene absorbs maximally at 317 mμ, $\epsilon = 10,000$;[87] or compound XXXV in chloroform solution absorbs maximally at 510 mμ, $\epsilon = 57,000$, while the corresponding non-methylsubstituted cyanine (XXXVI) absorbs maximally at 473 mμ, $\epsilon = 135,000$.[88] In compounds of this type the steric strain is more evenly distributed, and the resultant steric effect is generally a red shift accompanied by a reduced absorption intensity.[82]

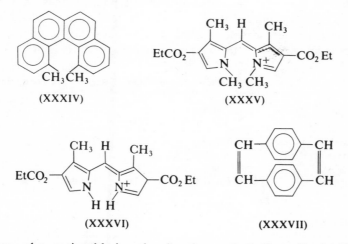

(XXXIV)

(XXXV)

(XXXVI)

(XXXVII)

Steric effects are also noticeable in other bands, particularly in the forbidden transition leading to the *C*-band in benzene. However, these bands do not lend themselves as readily either to generalizations or to theoretical interpretation and have, therefore, been less frequently investigated. One notable exception is the work by Cram and co-workers[89,90] on compounds of type XXXVII and related compounds which give rise to a variety of interactions, generally referred to as transannular effects.

3.2. Cis-Trans Isomerism. *Cis-trans* isomerism is of interest spectroscopically partly because ultraviolet spectroscopy can frequently distinguish between two or more geometrical isomers when other means of determining the configuration are not readily available. For example, in the polyene carotenoid series ultraviolet absorption spectra are indispensable in the elucidation of *cis-trans* isomerism,[91] and two isomers such as XXXVIII and

XXXIX, which can readily be separated by chromatography, can be distinguished by their different molar absorptivities. Further, as previously mentioned, *trans → cis* isomerization can sometimes be effected by exposure to ultraviolet or visible light (see Section 2.10).

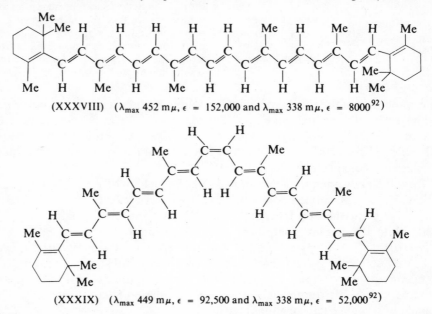

(XXXVIII)   (λ_{max} 452 mμ, ϵ = 152,000 and λ_{max} 338 mμ, ϵ = 8000[92])

(XXXIX)   (λ_{max} 449 mμ, ϵ = 92,500 and λ_{max} 338 mμ, ϵ = 52,000[92])

Generally, the *cis* isomer of a conjugated compound absorbs with lower intensity, apparently as a sterically hindered *trans* isomer. In fact, steric interactions are strongly affected by *cis-trans* isomerism since many of the characteristic effects associated with *cis-trans* isomerism are partly due to steric hindrance in the *cis*-isomer.

TABLE 20.   **Main Long Wavelength Absorption Maxima (B-Bands)* of cis and trans Isomers**

Compound	Solvent	*cis* Isomer		*trans* Isomer		Ref.
		λ_{max}	ϵ_{max}	λ_{max}	ϵ_{max}	
$CH_3CH{=}CH \cdot CH{=}CH_2$ (XL)	Ethanol	223	22,600	223.5	23,000	93
$CH_3CH{=}C(CH_3)CO_2H$	Ethanol	212.5	12,500	215.5	9,360	94
PhCH=CHPh(XLI)	Ethanol	280	10,500	295.5	29,000	3
α,β-Dimethylstilbene	Ethanol	252	8,800	243.5	12,000	95, 96
2-Phenyl-2-butene	Cyclohexane	235	8,200	243	12,000	97
Propenylbenzene	Ethanol	241	13,800	250	17,300	98
PhCH=CH · CH=CH$_2$	Isooctane	268	18,500	280	27,000	99
PhCH=CH · COPh	Hexane	290	9,000	298	23,600	100
PhCH=CH · CO$_2$H	Methanol	261	10,500	272	19,500	101
PhCO · CH—CH · Ph $\diagdown \diagup$ O	Ethanol	248	12,900	250	16,800	102

*B-bands also sometimes occur at lower wavelength, corresponding to transitions involving locally excited states. For example, stilbene (XLI) also affords a band near 225 mμ which is considerably more intense in the *cis*-form (ϵ = 24,400) than in the *trans*-form (ϵ = 16,400).

Table 20 illustrates that for simpler conjugated compounds the absorbing properties of the *cis* and *trans* forms are similar. That is, for systems like piperylene (XL) the over-all length of the conjugated system and, hence, the transition moment (*i.e.* the effective path length of the electronic oscillation) for both *cis* and *trans* forms are similar. If, in addition, both forms are approximately coplanar, the spectral character-istics will be determined by secondary interactions in the ground and excited states, which are not readily predictable. However, as the length of the conjugated system increases, the conjugated system of π-electrons in the *trans*-isomer will be more elongated and, hence, compounds like XXXIX will absorb with lower intensity and at shorter wavelength than compounds like XXXVIII (cf. Ref. 103).

In addition to spectral changes determined by the overall length of the conjugated system, the *cis* isomer will generally more readily be forced into a nonplanar conformation because of various steric interactions between neighbouring atoms. This will normally give rise to a type (2) steric effect (see Section 3.1); and, depending on the bond orders in the ground and excited states, either a blue or, less likely, a red shift will be observed relative to the absorption maximum in the *trans* isomer (see Table 20). Either displace-ment in the *cis* isomer is generally accompanied by the usual hypochromic effect.

Related effects are also sometimes observed when the *cis-trans* isomerism is brought about by cyclic systems such as epoxy, α-ethylenimine, and even by cyclopropyl groups, instead of by double bonds. An example is shown in Table 20. It is, of course, necessary that some electronic interactions can take place between the two substituents which give rise to the *cis-trans* isomerism. Such interaction may, however, occur only in the electronically excited state. *cis-trans* Isomerism frequently also affects *B*-bands associated with locally excited states (see footnote of Table 20) as well as other bands. However, these latter effects have been less thoroughly investigated.

Another phenomenon which often can be investigated advantageously by ultraviolet spectroscopy is *s-cis*, *s-trans* isomerism, when the *cis-trans* isomerism occurs across what is essentially a single bond. For example, a study of compounds such as pulegone (XLII) and carvone (XLIII), which exist in a fixed *s-cis* and *s-trans* conformation respectively,[22] indicate that the *s-cis* form again generally absorbs with lower intensity. In compounds like *o*-chloroacetophenone an equilibrium exists between the two planar or near-planar *s-cis* and *s-trans* conformations (XLIV and XLV), but the two forms are too readily interconverted to permit their separation. However, the presence of the two forms can be detected by infrared spectroscopy,[80] and explanations of the associated ultraviolet spectral changes should take into account the effect of steric and other interactions on both *s-cis* and *s-trans* forms (see Problem No. 22).

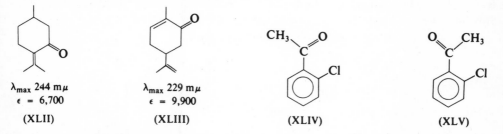

λ_{max} 244 mμ	λ_{max} 229 mμ		
ϵ = 6,700	ϵ = 9,900		
(XLII)	(XLIII)	(XLIV)	(XLV)

Further the ultraviolet spectral properties of *cis* or *s-cis* isomers, frequently representing sterically hindered compounds, might be expected to show a different temperature depend-ence than the corresponding *trans* or *s-trans* isomers (cf, for example, Ref. 3). Some work has, in fact, been reported which suggests that certain *cis* isomers afford unusual temperature dependences, possibly because steric hindrance to coplanarity is decreased on reducing the temperature.[104]

3.3. Tautomerism. The phenomenon of tautomerism (the existence of a substance as an equilibrium mixture of two or more readily interconvertible isomers) in solution or in biological systems frequently lends itself to study by ultraviolet spectroscopy. A well known example is ethylacetoacetate, the two forms of which absorb as shown:

$$CH_3COCH_2CO_2Et \rightleftharpoons CH_3C(OH){=}CHCO_2Et$$

λ_{max} 275 mμ, ϵ = 16 λ_{max} 244 mμ, ϵ = 16,000

(XLVI)   (XLVII)

Since as a first approximation only the enolic form (XLVII) absorbs at 244 mμ, the amount present of this form in a mixture can readily be determined. This method has, in fact, been used as early as 1924, when Grossman,[105] using ultraviolet spectroscopy, investigated the effect of solvent on this equilibrium.

Numerous other examples of keto-enol tautomerism are recorded in the literature. A recent example is benzoylacetanilide which is assumed to exist in two forms, XLVIII and XLIX, and which in cyclohexane solution absorbs maximally at 245 and 308 mμ.[106] Inspection of the two structures suggests that the absorption maximum at 245 mμ corresponds to the keto form XLVIII and that the maximum at 308 mμ corresponds to the enol form, XLIX. These assignments receive support by the determination of the spectra at pH 12, when the absorption maxima occur at 245 and at 323 mμ; as anticipated, in alkaline media the enolic form exists as structure L, and the corresponding absorption is displaced to longer wavelength (cf Section 2.8).

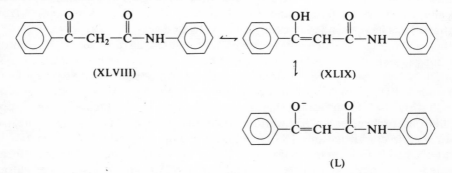

(XLVIII)   (XLIX)

(L)

Examples of ring-chain isomerism involving structures of type LI $\rightleftharpoons$ LII can also be investigated using both infrared and ultraviolet spectroscopy. Incidentally, it is not always the intense conjugation band (*B*-band) which is used to study a tautomeric equilibrium. For example, in the study of the equilibrium LIII $\rightleftharpoons$ LIV, use is made of the low intensity (*D*-band) absorption of the carbonyl group.

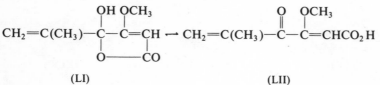

(LI)   (LII)

(LIII)   (LIV)

Other examples of tautomerism are provided by the equilibria involving azo compounds XXV and XXVI and the compounds XXII, XXIII and XXIV (see Section 2.10). Apart from these examples which represent azo-hydrazo equilibria, imino-enamine (CH—C=N ⇌ C=C—NH), and amido-imidol (NH—C=O ⇌ N=C—OH) equilibria have also been investigated. Each of these equilibria represents the migration of a double bond; and these systems, when attached to another unsaturated system, therefore lend themselves to investigation using ultraviolet spectroscopy. One example involving a heterocyclic compound is given in Problem No. 17. Another example is provided by the spectra of isonicotinic acid in ethanol-water mixtures where appreciable spectral changes are observed. These changes are associated with the tautomeric equilibrium LV ⇌ LVI. Since the curves, moreover, almost meet in an isosbestic point[107] this suggests that only two species contribute to the equilibrium. (At the isosbestic point, the absorbances of the two species are equal, see footnote on p. 21 and cf also Refs. 108 and 106.)

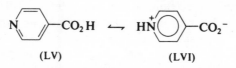

(LV)   (LVI)

As long as the two or more tautomeric forms possess distinct absorption spectra, changes brought about by environmental effects or on substitution often can conveniently be investigated as outlined above. It may also be noted that the related phenomena of acid-base equilibria and complex formation can be studied in a similar manner.

3.4. Hydrogen Bonding and Related Phenomena. The study of keto-enol equilibria shows that frequently these tautomeric systems are affected by solvents, sometimes very markedly. (See, for example, Problem 25.) These solvent changes can often be explained by assuming an interplay of intra- and inter-molecular hydrogen bonding, so that one form or another is favored in a particular solvent system. For example, the enolic form of ethylacetoacetate (XLVII) can be assumed to be stabilized by an intramolecular hydrogen bond in inert solvents. In aqueous solution however, because of the proton-donating tendency of water molecules, there is a tendency for intermolecular hydrogen bonding to occur at the expense of intramolecularly bonded structures. Consequently, ethylaceto-acetate in aqueous solution, schematically represented by the equilibrium LVII ⇌ LVIII, tends to contain a relatively greater proportion of the keto form than ethylacetoacetate in an inert medium.

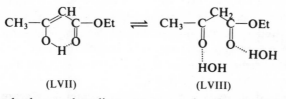

(LVII)   (LVIII)

This illustrates that hydrogen bonding can cause drastic spectral changes by altering the equilibria involving two or more chemical species in tautomeric or acid-base equilibria. Spectral changes caused by hydrogen bonding and related phenomena are also important in distinguishing between different types of bands. Thus, B-bands normally afford red shifts whereas D-bands afford blue shifts on changing from an inert to a polar solvent. (See Table 6.) The accepted explanation for transitions leading to B-band absorption is that the relevant excited state involves dipolar forms of type I and that the existence of such forms is favored in a more polar medium. This preferentially lowers the energy of the excited state, in this way causing the red shift. Exceptions may occur for molecules which are highly dipolar or zwitterionic in the ground state and which for this or other reasons have a reduced and reorientated dipole moment in the excited state; these molecules will afford a blue shift.

On the other hand, for an $n \rightarrow \pi^*$ (*D*-band) transition in aqueous solution, the two non-bonding (*n*)-electrons are normally stabilized by hydrogen bonding with polar molecules. This lowers the energy of the ground state. In the excited state there is only one *n*-electron (see Figure 2), and the solvation energy, therefore, tends to be smaller or negligible in that state. Thus, the energy of the excited state is not lowered as much as that of the ground state. Consequently, the transition energy is increased in polar solvents, resulting in a blue shift.

The above discussion is, however, rather over-simplified. Actually, a variety of interactions occur, apart from those normally described as hydrogen bonding, since almost all spectra are influenced by solvents and both energy levels are likely to be affected. The difficulty is illustrated by the observation that appreciable spectral changes frequently occur even on determining a spectrum in the vapor phase and in an inert solvent. For example, the *B*-band of nitrobenzene occurs at 239.1 mμ in the vapor phase but at 252.9 mμ in cyclohexane solution.[109] This spectral change occurs partly because the absorbing molecule, containing the oscillating electron, polarizes the surrounding solvent; this provides a favorable electrostatic field and, consequently less energy is required to displace the electron from its equilibrium position. This effect is sometimes called a "solvent orientation effect."

Generally, since most spectral changes are caused by a number of interactions, such as van der Waals interactions, dipole orientations, and induced dipole orientations, which operate in both ground and excited states, it is difficult to estimate such interactions better than semi-quantitatively. A hydrogen bond is essentially a particular combination of such interactions which give rise to characteristic effects, especially in the infrared region. In solution, solvent molecules arrange themselves around the solute molecules in a manner determined by these interactions. During excitation the molecule normally has no time to rearrange (Franck-Condon principle; see Section 1.1); hence, depending whether the surrounding solvent molecules raise or lower the energy of the excited state relative to the energy of the ground state, either a blue or a red shift will be observed.

The spectrum of a compound showing most fine structure is usually obtained in the vapor state, and with sufficient resolution the vibrational and rotational fine structure can be resolved. Lowering the temperature of a solution in an inert solvent likewise sharpens the spectrum in a similar way as the number of solute-solvent collisions is reduced. For this reason inert solvents, such as cyclohexane, hexane, pentane, or 2,2,4-trimethylpentane (isooctane), can be used to reveal fine structural details. Also, information concerning interactions between solute and inert solvents can be obtained by studying the spectral changes which occur on reducing the temperature. Most frequently, lowering the solution temperature causes a red shift in the *B*-band.

Other commonly used solvents are ethanol and water which are readily purified and which have the advantage of being better solvents, particularly for polar compounds. Moreover, since aqueous solutions cannot be studied easily by infrared spectroscopy, investigation by ultraviolet spectroscopy may be the best method of attack (cf. Table 1). However, these solvents have the disadvantage that a large number of solvent-solute interactions are possible. Thus, in addition to the interactions occuring in an inert solvent, there will be hydrogen-bond type interactions involving the H and the O atoms of the OH groups, both of which are known to give rise to appreciable spectral changes.

In theory, it might be possible to deduce from an observed solvent effect the nature of the contributing interactions and the parts of the molecules involved in the interaction. In practice, this is usually too difficult except for simple examples. However, a number of observed spectral changes can be rationalized in a reasonably satisfactory manner. For example, in the monomer-dimer equilibrium LIX-LX, for a number of benzoic acids, the two species absorb in a slightly different way and consequently the effect of the substituent on the strength of the dimeric hydrogen bond can be estimated. Further, on addition of ether to the monomer-dimer equilibrium there is evidence of competitive intermolecular hydrogen bonding between the structures LIX, LX and LXI.[63] The data also indicate that hydrogen bonding involves the constant forming, breaking, and reforming of the "bonds." (See also Problem 29 at the end of this Chapter.) Related studies have been carried out for phenol.[110,111] However, it should be mentioned that infrared and NMR spectroscopy are the methods of choice, and ultraviolet spectroscopy usually provides only supporting information in the study of hydrogen bonding.

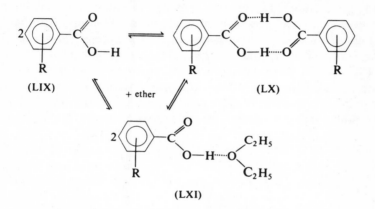

The phenomenon of intramolecular hydrogen bonding frequently also gives rise to characteristic spectral changes. For example α-hydroxy-α,β-unsaturated ketones, such as LXIII or LXIV, in which intramolecular hydrogen bonding is believed to occur, absorb at longer wavelength than β-hydroxy-α,β-unsaturated ketones such as LXV, whereas in the absence of such bonding the β-substituted-α,β-unsaturated carbonyl compounds absorb at longer wavelength (see Section 2.3 and absorption maxima of compounds LXII and LXV).

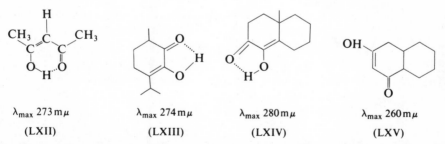

λ_{max} 273 mμ	λ_{max} 274 mμ	λ_{max} 280 mμ	λ_{max} 260 mμ
(LXII)	(LXIII)	(LXIV)	(LXV)

Apart from wavelength displacements, intramolecular hydrogen bonding may often be detected by the absence of solvent changes which are otherwise observed in non-bonded reference compounds. For example, the main absorption bands of salicylaldehyde are only slightly affected on changing the solvent from hexane to ether, whereas more appreciable solvent changes are observed if the spectrum of *m*-hydroxybenzaldehyde is determined in hexane and in ether solution.[112] This difference can be explained by assuming that *m*-hydroxybenzaldehyde gives rise to intermolecularly hydrogen-bonded structures of type LXVI which are less probable in salicylaldehyde because intramolecular hydrogen bonding is favored instead.

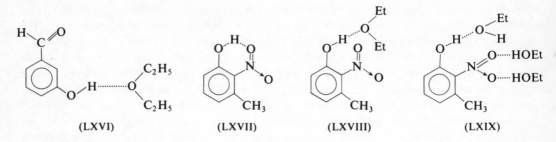

(LXVI)   (LXVII)   (LXVIII)   (LXIX)

In the above interpretations, steric considerations involved in solvent-solute interactions have been neglected, but these may be important. For example, the solvent molecule may not be able to approach the chromophoric center in the solute molecule because of steric interactions; hence, the anticipated spectral effect does not occur. Another possibility is illustrated in Figure 6 which shows the spectrum of 3-methyl-2-nitrophenol in different solvents.[113] The drastic spectral changes observed are ascribed to the different species of types LXVII, LXVIII and LXIX which probably predominate in cyclohexane, ether, and ethanol respectively. Structures LXVII to LXIX are progressively more hindered because of the increase in the effective size of the substituents, thus giving rise to the hypochromic effects characteristic of increased steric interactions (see Section 3.1).

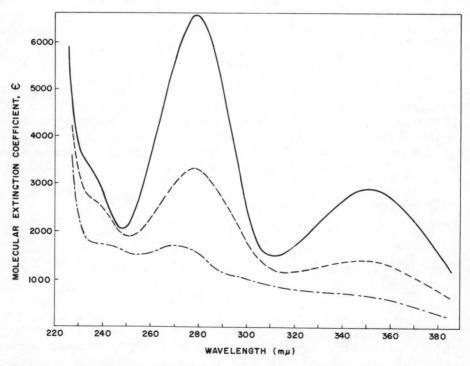

FIGURE 6. The spectrum of 3-methyl-2-nitrophenol in cyclohexane (———), ether (----), and ethanol (- ·· ·).

3.5. Protein Structure.   The development of theories of protein structure is intimately connected with the development of the associated theories of hydrogen bonding. For example, it is well known that the α-helix configuration contains —C=O...H—N— hydrogen bonds; also, changes in protein structure brought about by external agents, particularly the denaturation of proteins, are assumed to involve changes in some of the hydrogen bonding. In fact, concepts of hydrogen bonding and of protein structure developed at the same time and theories of hydrogen bonding are frequently judged by their usefulness in explaining problems of protein structure.

From the point of view of ultraviolet spectroscopy proteins present a special problem since, unlike many steroids, alkaloids, and other natural products, proteins do not afford an intense absorption band in the readily accessible parts of the ultraviolet spectrum. This partly explains why most of the spectral work on protein structure has been done using X-ray and, to a lesser extent, infrared spectroscopy. The main ultraviolet absorption band of proteins occurs in the 210mμ region, and is associated with the —CONH—chromophore. Unfortunately, until recently it has been difficult to obtain accurate spectral data near 210mμ, mainly because of stray light effects. Stray light effects may give rise to apparent failures of Beer's law and even to fictitious short-wave bands.[114] However, considerable efforts are now being made to improve techniques suitable for this region.[115,116,117] It, therefore, seems probable that, using these techniques, significant advances may be made in the near future in understanding problems such as how and why the absorption associated with the —CONH— group is affected by its environment.

Because of the experimental difficulties involved in carrying out measurements in the 210mμ region, most, though not all, of the ultraviolet work on proteins has been carried out in the 280mμ region, where most proteins give rise to low intensity (C-band) absorption. This is due mainly to the tyrosine (LXX), tryptophan (LXXI), and to a lesser degree, to the phenylalanine (LXXII) residues. Thus, proteins like human albumin, bovine albumin, insulin, pepsin, trypsin, etc., all afford E_1^1 values* of about 10 in the 280mμ region. Such protein concentration is frequently followed in a quantitative way, for example, in column chromatography, using this absorption near 280mμ.

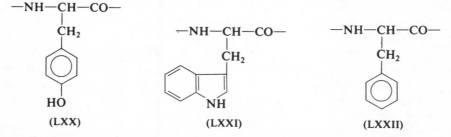

(LXX) (LXXI) (LXXII)

Moreover, the absorption characteristics of these amino acid residues may undergo characteristic solvent changes (cf. Section 2.8.), and these assist in the identification. For example, tyrosine at pH values greater than 8 affords a pronounced red shift because of the ionization of the phenolic OH group. Hence, if the E_1^1 value at 280mμ of a protein does not change appreciably on altering the pH of the solution from below 8 to above 8, this indicates that no tyrosine residues are contained in the molecule. Sometimes, however, a protein molecule containing tyrosine may fail to exhibit the typical displaced absorption on raising the pH of the solution; this is explained by assuming that the phenolic OH group is not free to ionize, possibly because of inaccessibility due to intramolecular hydrogen bonding.[118]

Generally, the absorption associated with any one of the chromophoric systems mentioned is different in a simple amino acid or peptide from that in the protein; usually in

---

*$E_1^1 = E_{1\,cm}^{1\%} = \dfrac{\log_{10}(I_0/I)}{c \times l}$ where c represents the concentration in grams per 100 ml and l is the thickness of the absorbing layer (1 cm.). Values of E_1^1 are used if the absorbing substance is not known. E_1^1 and ϵ are related by the equation $E_1^1 = \dfrac{\epsilon \times 10}{\text{Molecular weight}}$.

the protein the absorption is displaced slightly to longer wavelength. This is as expected since hydrogen bonding and related phenomena will affect the characteristic protein absorption (particularly that due to tyrosine and tryptophan residues) depending on the environment of the absorbing groups. For example, on denaturation or on altering the pH value of a protein solution, small but characteristic spectral changes are frequently observed. Occasionally these changes are not due to ionization but can be rationalized in terms of hydrogen bonding. For a full discussion, see Ref. 119 and refs. cited there.

These spectral differences are frequently quite small and a special technique, that of differential spectrophotometry, is sometimes employed. (See Refs. 119, 120, and refs. cited there.) In this method, a protein solution is placed in the solvent cell, and a slightly modified protein solution in the solution cell. Under favorable circumstances, the spectral change can, thus, be obtained more precisely. The method is frequently used to study spectral changes resulting from exposure of protein solutions to low pH, hydrogen-bond-breaking reagents, limited enzymatic degradation, and so on.

Another special technique used is the measurement of the spectral changes occurring in colored ninhydrin or other colored complexes or compounds, such as dye-protein complexes or dinitrophenylated amino acids. In this way, it is sometimes possible to estimate quantitatively the amount of protein present or to follow conformational changes using a more accessible region of the spectrum.

One inherent difficulty in determining the ultraviolet spectra of proteins is their frequent lack of solubility. Methods are, however, available by which the spectrum of a solid protein can be determined (see, for example, Ref. 121 and refs. cited there. The use of polarized ultraviolet microspectrography[122] may also be mentioned at this stage). Unfortunately, light scattering effects are usually large under these conditions. Occasionally, it is advantageous to immerse the insoluble protein in a liquid with refractive index similar to that of the protein, as long as the liquid itself does not absorb within the investigated wavelength range.

However, the best approach to the study of protein structure using ultraviolet spectroscopy probably lies in the investigation of the hydrogen bonding and other electronic interactions in suitable model compounds. For example, a number of reagents such as $8N$ aqueous urea or perfluorooctanoic acid have striking effects on the conformation of proteins. The interaction of these reagents with simple model compounds containing the —CONH—group or with amino acids, such as tyrosine, would seem to lend itself to investigation by ultraviolet spectroscopy.

3.6. Applications to Natural Products Chemistry. In the previous section, methods were outlined which can be used in the understanding of protein structure using ultraviolet spectroscopy. It was noted that the use of model compounds was of great importance in understanding spectral changes occurring in proteins. Generally, one of the purposes of considering simple systems, as has been done in Sections 2.1 to 2.9, was that these systems are frequently contained in complex organic molecules which can be investigated in this way. Sometimes it is necessary to consider some relatively more complex model compound; for example, the use of the azobenzene spectra in the elucidation of spectral changes occuring in azo-dyes (see Section 2.10).

This section is intended to outline briefly how ultraviolet spectroscopy assists in providing information concerning structural problems in various groups of natural products, other than proteins (Section 3.5) and azo-dyes (Section 2.10) which have previously been considered. The first group which may be discussed are *steroids*. An excellent survey is provided in reference 20 which illustrates how the absorbing properties of various steroids correspond to the absorbing properties of the conjugated system contained in the steroid. The relevant conjugated system is usually either a diene, a polyene, a conjugated enone, or a dienone. The absorption characteristics of these chromophores have been discussed in sections 2.2 and 2.3. The same conjugated systems also account for the ultraviolet absorption spectra of many terpenes. Sometimes even in the absence of a conjugated system, a steroid or terpene may be investigated via an isolated ethylenic or carbonyl linkage, by determining the spectrum of the colored complexes or compounds obtained on treatment with tetranitromethane and 2,4-dinitrophenylhydrazine respectively.

Alkaloids, which contain conjugated chromophores, also can be investigated by considering the absorbing properties of the conjugated systems contained in them. For example, thebaine (LXXIII) would be expected to and does afford an absorption curve arising from *B*-band absorption of a substituted 1,3-cyclohexadiene absorption superimposed on *C*-band absorption of a substituted phenyl group. On opening the ether linkage two products, LXXIV and LXXV, are obtained, which can be identified by their spectral properties mainly because isomer LXXV absorbs with much lower intensity near 283 mμ; infrared data confirm the assignments.[123] Generally, ultraviolet spectroscopy is widely used in alkaloid chemistry. However, in this field, as in many other natural product studies, it is used most frequently in conjunction with other physical techniques, particularly in conjunction with infrared spectroscopy.

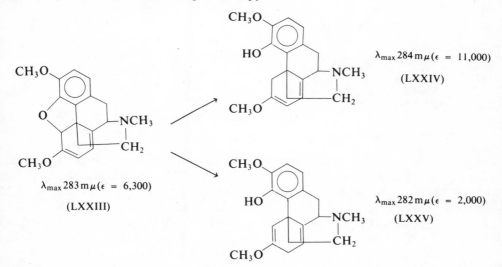

λ_{max} 284 mμ(ϵ = 11,000)

(LXXIV)

λ_{max} 283 mμ(ϵ = 6,300)

(LXXIII)

λ_{max} 282 mμ(ϵ = 2,000)

(LXXV)

Nucleic acids, which occur in living cells combined with proteins (nucleoproteins), on alkaline hydrolysis afford substituted purines (LXXVI; cf. structure XX),

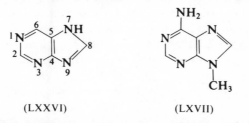

(LXXVI)   (LXVII)

and these compounds again lend themselves to investigation by ultraviolet spectroscopy. Purines are also obtained from a number of other biologically active compounds. By investigating the absorption spectra of substituted purines, it is sometimes possible to deduce how the purine is substituted in a naturally occurring compound. For example, it was shown in this way that the light-absorbing properties of a purine obtained from certain nucleic acids resemble more closely the spectrum of 9-methyladenine (LXXVII) than that of 7-methyladenine. From this it has been concluded that the corresponding sugar residue is, in fact, attached to the 9-position.[124]   (See also Ref. 124a for a general discussion of the ultraviolet spectra of purine and pyrimidine bases.)

Next, mention may be made of various pigments which all contain extended conjugated systems and which consequently afford characteristic ultraviolet spectra, for example, polyenes such as carotenoids which have previously been discussed in connection with *cis-trans* isomerism (see Section 3.2).   Also anthocyanins, the 3-glucosides or 3,5-digluco-sides of anthocyanidines (LXXVIII; see, for example, Ref. 125) and systems containing the porphyrin ring system, such as chlorophyll (LXXIX),[126] all afford characteristic high intensity ultraviolet absorption.   For many compounds of this type, visible absorption

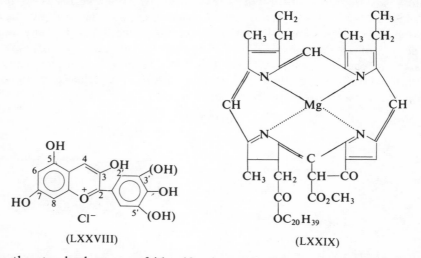

(LXXVIII)   (LXXIX)

spectra are the standard means of identification; this follows since the usual means of identifying organic compounds by melting points is less suitable and moreover does not give a *quantitative* indication of the purity of the substance.

Finally, carbohydrates, like proteins, may sometimes be investigated by their low intensity bands near 280 mμ.   For example, spectral data have been interpreted to show that in *D*-glucose (LIII) less than *ca.* 0.01 per cent of the carbonyl form (LIV) is present in neutral solution, but that up to *ca.* 0.1 per cent of this form is formed reversibly in strong acid solution.[127]

3.7. Ions and Free Radicals.   The formation of organic ions leading to characteristic spectral changes has been mentioned previously as a method of identifying a particular chromophoric system. For example, both aniline and phenol afford quite different spectra with suitable change of solvent because of the formation of ions LXXX and LXXXI (Section 2.8; see also Section 2.10 for the spectra of protonated azo dyes and Section 3.5 for the spectra of ionized tyrosine residues). Generally, ion formation will take place in suitable solvents, and a characteristic spectrum may be obtained. One of the most useful solvents is concentrated sulfuric acid which has been used to obtain a variety of cationic species such as Ph_2CH^+ (λ_{max} 440 mμ, ϵ = 44,000)[128] Ph_3C^+ (λ_{max} 404 mμ, ϵ = 40,000),[128] $Ph_2C^+CH_3$ (λ_{max} 429 mμ, ϵ = 30,000),[129] and various meta-stable allylic carbonium ions of type $R_1CH{=}CR_2C^+HR_3$ ($CH_2{=}CH{\cdot}CH_2^+$; λ_{max} 273 mμ, ϵ = 4700).[130]

(LXXX)   (LXXXI)

Apart from relatively stable ionic species, ultraviolet spectroscopy can also be used in the investigation of unstable ionic or free radical intermediates which are of importance, since their presence is frequently postulated in organic reaction mechanisms. This is a fairly new development because, until recently, it has been difficult to establish unequivocally the existence of unstable intermediates. However, the advent of flash photolysis and electron spin resonance (ESR) spectroscopy have considerably facilitated such studies.

In flash photolysis, light pulses of short duration but of very high intensity are used, which afford appreciable photochemical dissociation. Sometimes over 80 per cent of a gas is dissociated, and frequently the spectral properties of the various transient species formed can be determined by this method. A recent application is the photo-conversion of triphenylamines to carbazoles in which an intermediate is detected which has a life-time of about 0.5 msec at room temperature and which absorbs maximally at 610mμ. Since the lowest triplet state of triphenylamine absorbs at 530mμ and the positive ion of triphenylamine absorbs maximally at 650mμ, it has been suggested that the intermediate is a cyclic species of type LXXXII.[131]

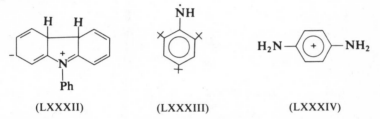

(LXXXII)   (LXXXIII)   (LXXXIV)

In free radical reactions also, for example in radiolysis, ultraviolet spectral changes can provide information concerning the reaction mechanism. A straight-forward application is the observation that aqueous solutions of phenylalanine (cf. LXXII) and tryptophan (cf. LXXI), when irradiated with γ-rays, afford marked ultraviolet spectral changes.[132] Free radical intermediates are sometimes more effectively examined using *both* ultraviolet and ESR spectroscopic methods. For example, the metastable anilino-radical LXXXIII, prepared from a solution of 2,4,6-tri-*t*-butylaniline in hexane using flash photolysis, has in this way been identified by means of both the above spectroscopic techniques.[133] Another example is provided by the spectra of phenylenediamine adsorbed on SiO_2—Al_2O_3. The ultraviolet maxima occur at 324 and 470mμ, and the ESR spectrum afforded a single peak without hyperfine structure. The chemisorbed species is believed to be a semi-quinonoid cation radical of type LXXXIV.[134] For other examples, see Refs. 135 and 136.

Ultraviolet spectra of unstable free radical intermediates can also sometimes be obtained after irradiation of the relevant compound at liquid air temperatures. For example, the absorption spectra of dialkylbenzene radicals have been obtained in this way by the photolysis of dialkylbenzenes in a rigid medium at −196°K.[137] ESR spectra also can be determined very conveniently at liquid air temperatures by irradiating the appropriate compound at that temperature. Again, the use of both techniques provides a powerful method of attack. For example, amino acids photolyzed at liquid air temperatures afford characteristic ESR spectra because of free radicals being trapped in the crystal lattice; ultraviolet spectra of these radicals may be obtained by determining the spectra of the irradiated crystals in a KBr pellet.

For a number of radical ions the ultraviolet absorption spectra are similar to the parent compound spectra except that additional bands appear at longer wavelength. This may be rationalized by assuming that the radical ion possesses one of its electrons in a higher energy level. Hence, the transition energy for this electron to a low-lying excited state will be decreased, thus accounting for the additional absorption bands at longer wavelength.[138]

Spectra of ions and free radicals will also be affected by steric and other electronic interactions. The spectral changes brought about in this way can be rationalized as outlined previously (see also Problem 37).

PROBLEMS

1. Explain how the ultraviolet spectrum can be used to decide between the following isomeric systems:

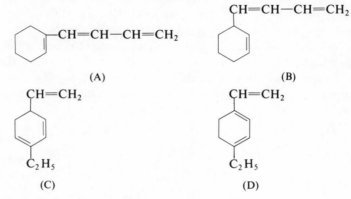

(A)

(B)

(C)

(D)

2. Two isomeric ketones A and B have structures

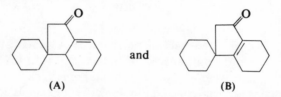

(A)

and

(B)

Their maxima are 241 mμ (ϵ = 12,000) and 247 mμ (ϵ = 9,000). Which absorption maximum corresponds to each compound?

3. Explain how ultraviolet spectroscopy can be used to distinguish between the possible isomers of a carbonyl compound possessing the formula $C_{10}H_{14}O$.

4. Explain how the ultraviolet spectra can assist in deciding between the following isomers:

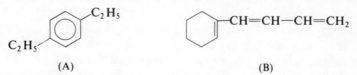

(A)

(B)

5. The main ultraviolet absorption bands in light petroleum for the three biphenyls, A, B, and C, occur as follows:

λ_{max} 259.5 mμ (ϵ = 740), inflection at 228 mμ(ϵ = 6,000)

λ_{max} 250.5 mμ (ϵ = 16,100) and

λ_{max} 254.5 mμ (ϵ = 21,000)

Assign these bands to compounds A, B, and C.

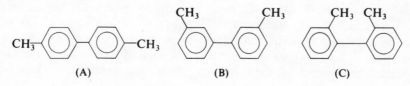

(A)

(B)

(C)

6. The methoxy-substituted benzoyl chlorides absorb as follows above 225 mμ (Main maxima in cyclohexane solution):

A; λ_{max} 272 mμ, ϵ = 19,500; λ_{max} 280 mμ, ϵ = 19,200

B; λ_{max} 253 mμ, ϵ = 10,000; λ_{max} 312 mμ, ϵ = 3,100

C; λ_{max} 251 mμ, ϵ = 9,000; λ_{max} 308 mμ, ϵ = 4,200

Attempt band assignments showing which of the compounds, A, B, and C are the o-, m- and p-isomers.

7. Compound A in hexane solution affords an intense absorption maximum at 248 mμ (at 252 mμ in ethanol solution) and a shoulder near 255 mμ together with a secondary absorption maximum near 290 mμ. What conclusions can be deduced concerning the structure of the molecule?

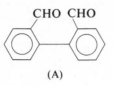

(A)

8. The molar absorptivity value of compound A, $n = 3$ (in 95 percent ethanol near 272 mμ) is 1450, which is *greater* than the value for compound A, $n = 5$ ($\epsilon = 292$). On the other hand, the ϵ value of compound B, $n = 3$ (in 95 percent ethanol near 270 mμ) is 18,100, somewhat less than the value for compound B, $n = 5$ ($\epsilon = 20,600$).[139] Suggest an explanation.

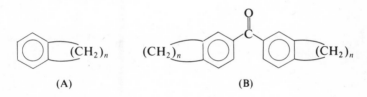

(A)   (B)

9. It is sometimes considered that the nitrobenzene band at 252 mμ (in isooctane solution) corresponds to the band in benzene at 255 mμ. How could the correctness of this hypothesis be tested?

10. p-Nitro-N,N-dimethylaniline absorbs maximally in ethanol at 386.5 mμ ($\epsilon = 21,500$) and in water at 422 mμ. m-Nitro-N,N-dimethylaniline absorbs maximally in ethanol at 400.3 mμ ($\epsilon = 1,350$) and in water at 385 mμ. Suggest an explanation for the different behavior on changing the solvent.

11. 3-Nitro-4'-methoxybenzophenone in cyclohexane solution affords the following absorption maxima: λ_{max} 225 mμ ($\epsilon = 30,000$), $\lambda_{infl.}$ ca. 255 mμ ($\epsilon = 11,500$), λ_{max} 286 mμ ($\epsilon = 16,000$) and $\lambda_{infl.}$ ca. 292 mμ ($\epsilon = 15,000$). Suggest possible band assignments.

12. Suggest a reason why aniline is less sensitive to steric interactions than benzaldehyde.

13. The most intense absorption maxima (above 220 mμ) of the three isomeric iodobenzoyl chlorides in cyclohexane solution are: Para-isomer, λ_{max} 275 mμ ($\epsilon = 18,000$); meta-isomer, λ_{max} 230 mμ ($\epsilon = 29,500$) and ortho-isomer, λ_{max} 228 mμ ($\epsilon = 15,000$). Comment on these absorptivity data.

14. p-Aminobenzoic acid absorbs as follows above 250 mμ: In ether, λ_{max} 277 mμ ($\epsilon = 20,600$); in ethanol, λ_{max} 288 mμ ($\epsilon = 19,000$); in aqueous 2N HCl, λ_{max} 270 mμ ($\epsilon = 970$). Suggest appropriate band assignments.

15. *m*-Nitroaniline absorbs as follows above 220mμ: In water, λ_{max} 224mμ (ϵ = 13,500), λ_{max} 278.5mμ (ϵ = 4,500), λ_{max} 354mμ (ϵ = 1400); in aqueous 0.1N HCl, λ_{max} 256mμ (ϵ = 7,500). Suggest appropriate band assignments.

16. In the nitration of PhN̄Me$_3$, ultraviolet examination of the reaction products does not permit the estimation of the product composition. However, if the mixture is neutralized before the ultraviolet examination, the product composition can be determined (cf. Chem. and Eng. News, Nov. 4, 1963, p. 48). Give reasons for this behaviour.

17. The spectrum of 2-hydroxypyridine does not alter appreciably on changing the solvent from alkaline to acid, whereas the spectrum of 3-hydroxypyridine shows considerable variation under these conditions. Suggest an explanation.

18. N,N-Dimethyl-*p*-aminostilbene in acid solution has an absorption spectrum almost identical with that of stilbene in neutral solution, as expected from proton addition to the dimethylamino group. Explain how this observation supports the band assignments for N,N-dimethyl-*p*-amino-azobenzene in acidic media (see Section 2.10).

19. Comment on the absorption spectra of N,N-dimethyl-*p*-amino-*o*-methylazobenzene which are in ethanol λ_{max} 415mμ, ϵ = 26,000 and in acid solution λ_{max} 327mμ, ϵ = 4,800 and λ_{max} 524 mμ, ϵ = 49,000.

20. Discuss the steric interactions evident in the spectrum of β-methylcrotonaldehyde (λ_{max} 228mμ, ϵ = 11,400 in cyclohexane solution). Crotonaldehyde in cyclohexane solution absorbs maximally at 213mμ, ϵ = 17,300).

21. Discuss the steric interactions illustrated by the compounds in Table 5.

22. Infrared data for *o*-bromoacetophenone indicate that the molecule exists in two conformations, *s-cis* and *s-trans*.[80] The ultraviolet absorption maximum of *o*-bromoacetophenone occurs at 236mμ (ϵ = 4,900) while that of acetophenone occurs at 240mμ (ϵ = 12,500). Discuss the actual conformation of the former compound.

23. Three azoxybenzenes absorb maximally in ethanol at 249, 254 and 292mμ. Their structures are:

(A)   (B)

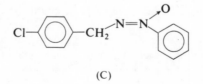

(C)

Which absorption maxima would one expect to correspond to each of the three compounds?

24. Comment on the spectral differences of the two compounds:

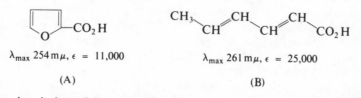

λ_{max} 254mμ, ϵ = 11,000 λ_{max} 261mμ, ϵ = 25,000

(A)   (B)

25. Acetylacetone absorbs in cyclohexane at λ_{max} 269mμ, ϵ = 12,000 and in water at λ_{max} 277mμ, ϵ = 1900. Discuss the structures which contribute to each band.

26. Cyclic 1,3-diketones of type  absorb intensely in the region near 250 mμ. Moreover, the absorption is concentration dependent in ethanolic solution. Suggest an explanation for these phenomena.

27. A compound $C_{16}H_{12}O_3N_2$ may exist in form (A) and/or in form (B). Suggest how ultraviolet and other spectral methods may help to deduce the correct structure.

COPh

CO

COCH₃

(A)

COPh

COCOCH₃

(B)

28. Discuss the spectral changes listed in Table 6. From the D-band data estimate qualitatively the strength of the hydrogen bond between mesityl oxide and ethanol.

29. Benzoic acid within the solute concentration range 10^{-3} to 10^{-5} moles/1: (a) in cyclohexane solution affords a concentration dependence; (b) in ether solution does not afford a concentration dependence, and (c) in a 5 percent ether/cyclohexane solution does afford a concentration dependence. What conclusions can be drawn from these observations?

30. Comment on the following spectral changes:
    (a) Aniline; vapor λ_{max} 230 mμ; cyclohexane solution, λ_{max} 234.5 mμ; ether solution λ_{max} 238 mμ; and aqueous solution λ_{max} 231 mμ.
    (b) Phenol; vapor, λ_{max} 205 mμ; cyclohexane solution λ_{max} 211 mμ; ether solution λ_{max} 218 mμ; ethanol solution λ_{max} 218.5 mμ; and aqueous solution λ_{max} 210 mμ.
    (c) Anisole; vapor, λ_{max} 214.5 mμ; cyclohexane solution, λ_{max} 220 mμ; ether solution λ_{max} 219 mμ; ethanol solution λ_{max} 219 mμ; and aqueous solution, λ_{max} 217.5 mμ.
    (d) 2,6-ditert. butylphenol; cyclohexane solution, λ_{max} 211, 268 and 275 mμ; ethanol solution $\lambda_{infl.}$ 212 mμ, λ_{max} 268 and 274 mμ.

31. When bovine or human serum albumin is added to an aqueous solution of methyl orange (sodium-4-dimethylaminoazobenzene-4'-sulfonate), an absorption maximum occurs at 420 mμ which is also obtained when the dye is dissolved in ethanol. This peak does not occur at this wavelength for the dye alone in aqueous solution. It has been suggested that this absorption at 420 mμ can be associated with strong electrostatic dye-protein interactions represented by $PNH_3^+ \ldots {}^-O_3SR$ which do not take place in aqueous solution because of interaction of the dye with water molecules. However, similar spectral shifts are obtained for 4-dimethylaminoazobenzene when the spectra are determined in ethanol and in water. Show how this disproves the above hypothesis, and suggest another interpretation of the spectral changes.

32. Hyperchromic effects (and red shifts) are observed when human serum albumin is added to solutions of methyl orange buffered at pH 5.7 and pH 9.2. However, solutions of sodium 4-dimethylamino-2',6'-dibromoazobenzene-4'-sulfonate under these conditions afford hypochromic effects. Suggest a possible explanation.

33. Show how the isomeric terpenoid ketones α- and β-ionone can be distinguished by their ultraviolet absorbing properties.

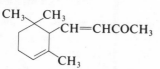

α-ionone

β-ionone

34. The three isomeric diterpenoid acids, abietic acid (A), neoabietic acid (B), and levopimaric acid (C), absorb maximally at $241 m\mu$ (ϵ = 23,000), $250 m\mu$ (ϵ = 24.000) and $272 m\mu$ (ϵ = 6000). Assign each spectrum to the appropriate compound.

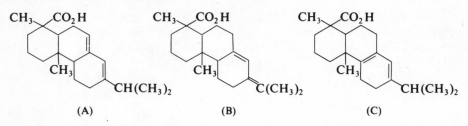

(A)   (B)   (C)

35. One of the formyl groups in a naturally occurring dialdehyde,

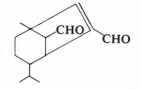

on aerial oxidation is readily converted to a carboxyl group. Show how the ultraviolet spectrum can show which of the formyl groups is affected.

36. The red color of the rose and the blue color of the cornflower are both due to the same pigment, cyanin chloride.

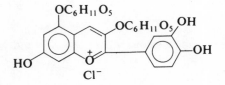

Suggest a reason for this.

37. Comment on the spectral differences between the spectra of Ph_2CH^+ and Ph_3C^+ described in the first paragraph of Section 3.7.

38. The ultraviolet absorption characteristics of anthracene and 1,1-diphenylethylene bear no resemblance in neutral solvents but are similar in sulfuric acid solution. Suggest an explanation for this.

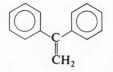

Cyclohexane solution	λ_{max} $252 m\mu$ (ϵ = 200,000)	λ_{max} $250 m\mu$ (ϵ = 11,000)
	λ_{max} $375 m\mu$ (ϵ = 8,000)	
Sulfuric acid solution		
	λ_{max} $315 m\mu$ (ϵ = 12,000)	λ_{max} $315 m\mu$ (ϵ = 8,000)
	λ_{max} $425 m\mu$ (ϵ = 31,000)	λ_{max} $430 m\mu$ (ϵ = 30,000)

39. When a solution of stilbene in tetrahydrofuran is treated with 1 mole of sodium, a dark green color is observed. Addition of another mole of sodium changes this color to deep red. Addition of an excess of stilbene to the red solution reverses the color to deep green. Suggest an explanation for these observations and indicate how these reactions could be investigated further.

ANSWERS

1. The calculated approx. λ_{max} values are as follows:
   (a) $214 + 2 \times 5 + 30 = 254\,m\mu$.
   (b) $214 + 5 = 219\,m\mu$ (third double bond is not conjugated)
   (c) $253 + 3 \times 5 = 268\,m\mu$ (third double bond is not conjugated)
   (d) $253 + 3 \times 5 + 30 = 298\,m\mu$.

   Hence, the λ_{max} values probably permit the identification of these compounds.
2. The conjugated system in structure B is more highly substituted and, therefore, may be associated with the absorption at $247\,m\mu$.
3. A large number of isomers are possible. However, ultraviolet spectroscopy can provide a guide as follows: Saturated compounds of type A will only afford the n-π^* band. α,β-Unsaturated compounds of type B will show characteristic absorption as discussed in Section 2.3. Compounds of type C will not afford intense absorption maxima in the readily accessible ultraviolet region. However, catalytic hydrogenation will reduce the observed absorption near $200\,m\mu$.

   Acyclic systems also can give rise to a variety of spectra depending on the number of conjugated double bonds present and the degree of substitution. Thus, compounds of type D will absorb at the longest wavelength; if the carbonyl group is not conjugated with the remainder of the double bonds, no appreciable solvent effect will be observed; and so on.

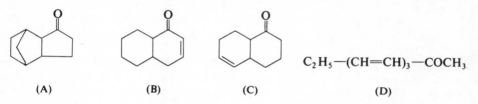

        (A)   (B)   (C)   (D)

4. The benzene derivative would show C-band, i.e. weaker, absorption near $270\,m\mu$, whereas the cyclohexene derivative would show a very intense absorption band in this region. Moreover, the C-band would show fine structure in inert solvents such as in hexane solution.
5. The most intense band at $254.5\,m\mu$ most probably corresponds to the isomer (A). The band at $259.5\,m\mu$ is a forbidden transition and the relatively low intensity of the corresponding main absorption band, and its occurrence at relatively shorter wavelength, suggests that these absorption maxima correspond to isomer (C). The remaining absorption maximum at $250.5\,m\mu$ ($\epsilon = 16,100$) may be associated with isomer (B).
6. "A" is the p-isomer because of the more intense B-bands. "C" is most probably the o-isomer; C-band intensities for o-disubstituted compounds are normally higher than for the m-isomers because of the greater lack of symmetry in the o-isomers.
7. The absorption appears to be like that of benzaldehyde because of the solvent dependence and because of the shoulder at slightly longer wavelength. Consequently, compound A is probably non-planar and in hexane solution absorbs essentially as two molecules of benzaldehyde.
8. Absorption maxima for compounds A represent C-bands but absorption maxima for compounds B represent B-bands.
9. The band at $255\,m\mu$ in benzene is a C-band. In a sterically hindered nitrobenzene, a C-band would tend to be *more* intense but a B-band *less* intense. Further, the intensity of the nitrobenzene band at $252\,m\mu$ should provide a guide; also, whether another band occurs at longer wavelength, particularly in o-substituted nitrobenzenes.
10. The absorption maxima of the p-isomer correspond to B-band absorption, the maxima of the m-isomer do not.
11. The latter two absorption bands probably correspond to CH_3O—⟨◯⟩—CO—, B-band,

   absorption; i.e. the absorption involves locally excited states. The inflection at $255\,m\mu$ then corresponds to the other part of the molecule, i.e. to nitrobenzene absorption. Since the corresponding locally excited state would be the chromophore

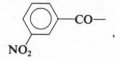

acetophenone-type absorption could account for the maximum at $225\,m\mu$. C-band absorption may contribute to the band at $292\,m\mu$.

12. The nitrogen atom in aniline has tetrahedral symmetry, while the oxygen-bound carbon atom in benzaldehyde has trigonal symmetry.

13. Resonance interaction in the para-isomer; appreciable steric interactions in the ortho-isomer.

14. In acid solution the nitrogen atom loses its unshared electron pair, and the spectrum reverts to that of benzoic acid. This band, unlike the band in neutral solvents, is, therefore, a C-band.

15. In water there are two B-bands corresponding to the aniline and nitrobenzene chromophores and a C-band. In acid solution, only the more intense nitrobenzene B-band can be discerned.

16. Para-nitroaniline absorbs at longer wavelength than the m-isomer, but the anilinium group does not appreciably affect the nitrobenzene absorption.

17. 2-Hydroxypyridine may exist predominantly in the keto-form.

18. Since the spectrum of N,N-dimethyl-p-aminostilbene on acidification reverts to that of stilbene, one could anticipate N,N-dimethyl-p-aminoazobenzene in acidic solution and azobenzene to afford similar absorption maxima. Azobenzene absorbs maximally at $320\,m\mu$; hence the band at $320\,m\mu$ in N,N-dimethyl-p-aminoazobenzene in acidic media is associated with the ammonium cation (XXII).

19. The data are consistent with structures of type XXII, XXIII and XXIV. An o-methyl substitutent will tend to favor structures of type XXIV. The absence of a hypochromic effect, as observed for the o'-isomer, also suggests that the proton resides on the β-azo nitrogen atom as shown in structure XXIV.

20. A β-methyl substituent in the absence of steric interactions would be expected to give rise to a bathochromic wavelength displacement of ca. $12\,m\mu$ (see Section 2.3). Hence, the spectral change *with reference to a hypothetical planar reference compound* is as a first approximation a hypochromic effect with no appreciable wavelength displacement.

21. Apart from the last compound, the dienone band as a first approximation undergoes only a hypochromic effect. Note also the increased absorptivity of the band associated with locally excited states with increased steric interactions.

22. One or both of the s-cis, s-trans isomers must be appreciably non-planar.

23. Compound A absorbs at $292\,m\mu$; other assignments cannot be readily predicted. Actually, compound B absorbs at $254\,m\mu$.

24. Compound A is essentially the s-cis isomer of compound B.

25. The enol form, stabilized by intramolecular hydrogen bonding, accounts for the intense band in cyclohexane solution. In aqueous solution, the intramolecular hydrogen bond tends to be broken and the compound exists predominantly in the keto form.

26. The enolic form absorbs maximally near $250\,m\mu$. The presence of ethanol affects the keto-enol equilibrium.

27. Determine the spectrum of a benziminazole, other than that of compound B, the structure of which is established. Check whether the absorption of the compound $C_{16}H_{12}O_3N_2$ more closely resembles the absorption of this benziminazole or whether it resembles the absorption of a compound like acetanilide. Confirm by determining the high-resolution infrared spectrum. Compound A should show three carbonyl stretching bands, compound B only two.

28. Assuming the solvation energy to be negligible in the electronic excited state, and assuming similar conformations in both solvents, wavelength displacements in the D-band are proportional to the strength of the hydrogen bonding. The displacement between cyclohexane and ethanol is ca. $15\,m\mu$ corresponding to ca. 4 kcals/mole. Wavelengths are converted to energy values by the relation,

$$E = \frac{28.596 \times 10^3}{\lambda(\text{in } m\mu)} \text{ kcal/mole}$$

This follows from $E = h\nu'c$, using

$$h = 6.62491 \times 10^{-27} \quad \text{and} \quad c = 2.99793 \times 10^{10} \text{ cm/sec}$$

Hence,

$$1 \text{ cm}^{-1} = 1.98580 \times 10^{-16} \text{ ergs}.$$

For one gram molecule,

$$1 \text{ cm}^{-1} = 1.98580 \times 10^{-16} \times 6.0250 \times 10^{23} \text{ cal/mole}$$
$$(N = 6.0250 \times 10^{23})$$
$$= 2.8596 \text{ cal/mole}$$

Therefore,

$$E = 2.8596 \times \nu'$$
$$= \frac{2.8596}{\lambda(\text{in cm})} \text{ cal/mole}$$
$$= \frac{2.8596 \times 10^7}{10^3 \lambda(\text{in } m\mu)} \text{ kcal/mole}$$
$$= \frac{28.596 \times 10^3}{\lambda(\text{in } m\mu)} \text{ kcal/mole}$$

29. Observation (a) suggests a monomer-dimer equilibrium. Observation (c) suggests that the dimeric hydrogen bond is stronger than any benzoic acid-ether interaction. Observation (b) suggests that dimeric hydrogen bonding, although stronger, no longer occurs to any appreciable extent. This can be rationalized by assuming a continuous forming, breaking, and re-forming of both types of hydrogen bonds.

30. The data may be interpreted as follows. Cyclohexane gives rise to a solvent orientation effect. In ether, there is interaction with the active hydrogen atom of the solute molecule, if such an atom is available. In ethanol, the solvent molecule may act in the same way but may also act as a proton donor; it may be noted that such interaction is inhibited in a sterically hindered phenol such as (d). Finally, water acts predominantly as a proton donor giving rise to N⋯HOH and O⋯HOH interactions.

31. The displacement cannot be associated with the sulfonate group. Interactions probably involve the azo group activated by the N,N-dimethylamino substituent.

32. Bonding to the azo group causes the dye molecule to assume a non-planar conformation.

33. β-ionone will absorb maximally at much longer wavelength; actually 296 mμ, $\epsilon = 11,000$ (α-ionone; λ_{max} 228 mμ, $\epsilon = 14,000$).

34. A absorbs at 241 mμ, B at 250 mμ, and C at 272 mμ.

35. If the main maximum remains unchanged, the non-conjugated formyl group is oxidized.

36. In the rose the pigment exists as the oxonium salt, but in the cornflower the pigment exists as the alkali-metal salt.

37. The spectral change is due to a steric effect because the three phenyl groups cannot lie in the same plane.

38. The two ions,

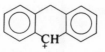

are electronically similar.

39. The dark green color is caused by the formation of $(PhCH{=}CHPh)^-$, and the red color may be caused by the formation of $(PhCHCHPh)^{--}$. ESR spectroscopy could be used to investigate this phenomenon further.

REFERENCES

1. Grammaticakis, P., *Bull. soc. chim. France*, 93 (1953).
2. Forbes, W. F., and Shilton, R., In "Symposium on Spectroscopy," ASTM Special Technical Publication No. 269, p. 176 (1960).
3. Beale, R. N., and Roe, E. M. F., *J. Chem. Soc.*, 2755 (1953).
4. Bladon, P., Henbest, H. B., and Wood, G. W., *J. Chem. Soc.*, 2737 (1952).
5. Ellington, P. S., and Meakins, G. D., *J. Chem. Soc.*, 697 (1960).
6. Booker, H., Evans, L. K., and Gillam, A. E., *J. Chem. Soc.*, 1453 (1940).
7. Woodward, R. B., *J. Am. Chem. Soc.*, **64**, 72, 76, (1942).
8. Lunt, J. C., and Sondheimer, F., *J. Chem. Soc.*, 2957 (1950).
9. Braude, E. A., and Timmons, C. J., *J. Chem. Soc.*, 2000 (1950).
10. Braude, E. A., and Coles, J. A., *J. Chem. Soc.*, 1425 (1952).
11. Braude, E. A., *et al.*, *J. Chem. Soc.*, 1419 (1952).
12. Bowden, K., Braude, E. A., Jones, E. R. H., and Weedon, B. C. L., *J. Chem. Soc.*, 45 (1946).
13. Cope, A. C., and Estes, L. L., Jr., *J. Am. Chem. Soc.*, **72**, 1128 (1950).
14. Dorfman, L., *Chem. Revs.*, **53**, 47 (1953).
15. Fieser, L., *J. Org. Chem.*, **15**, 930 (1950).
16. Forbes, W. F., and Shilton, R., *J. Org. Chem.*, **24**, 436 (1959).
17. Braude, E. A., *J. Chem. Soc.*, 379 (1950).
18. Forbes, W. F., Unpublished information; Forbes, W. F., Shilton, R., and Balasubramanian, A., *J. Org. Chem.*, **29**, 3527 (1964).
19. Woodward, R. B., *J. Am. Chem. Soc.*, **63**, 1123 (1941).
20. Fieser, L. F., and Fieser, M., "Steroids," pp. 15–21, New York, Reinhold, 1959.
21. Braude, E. A., and Jones, E. R. H., *J. Am. Chem. Soc.*, **72**, 1041 (1950).
22. Hausser, K. W., *et al.*, *Z. physik. Chem.*, **29B**, 371 (1935).
23. Mecke, R., and Noack, K., *Spectrochim. Acta*, **12**, 391 (1958); Timmons, C. J., Straughan, B. P., Forbes, W. F., and Shilton, R., In "Advances in Molecular Spectroscopy," p. 933, New York, Pergamon Press, 1962.
24. Forbes, W. F., and Shilton, R., *J. Am. Chem. Soc.*, **81**, 786 (1959).
25. Grammaticakis, P., *Bull soc. chim. France*, 865 (1953).
26. Bonnier, J. M., and Gaudemaris, G. de, *Bull. soc. chim. France*, 997 (1954).
27. American Petroleum Institute Research Project No. 44, "Ultraviolet Spectral Data," Carnegie Institute of Technology, Pittsburgh, Pa.
28. Cookson, R. C. and Dandegaonker, S. H., *J. Chem. Soc.*, 1651 (1955).
28a. Tanaka, J., *Bull. Chem. Soc. Japan*, **36**, 833 (1963); Gorodetsky, M., Amar, D. and Mazur, Y., *J. Am. Chem. Soc.*, **86**, 5218 (1964).
29. Jones, L. C., Jr., and Taylor, L. W., *Anal. Chem.*, **27**, 228 (1955).
30. Platt, J. R., and Klevens, H. B., *J. Chem. Phys.*, **17**, 470 (1949).
31. Gillam, A. E., and Hey, D. H., *J. Chem. Soc.*, 1170 (1939).
32. Derkosch, J., and Langer, F., *Monatsh. Chem.*, **86**, 924 (1955).
33. Friedel, R. A., Orchin, M., and Reggel, L., *J. Am. Chem. Soc.*, **70**, 199 (1948).
34. Stevenson, D. P., and McConnell, H. M., *Spectrochim. Acta*, **12**, 262 (1958).
34a. Pew, J. C., *J. Org. Chem.*, **28**, 1048 (1963).
35. Bowden, K., Braude, E. A., and Jones, E. R. H., *J. Chem. Soc.*, 948 (1946).
36. Bayliss, N. S., and Hulme, L., *Aust. J. Chem.*, **6**, 257 (1953).
37. Bowden, K., and Braude, E. A., *J. Chem. Soc.*, 1068 (1952).
38. Braude, E. A., Jones, E. R. H., and Stern, E. S., *J. Chem. Soc.*, 1087 (1947).
39. Doub, L., and Vandenbelt, J. M., *J. Am. Chem. Soc.*, **71**, 2414 (1949).
40. Beaven, G. H., In "Steric Effects in Conjugated Systems," p. 22, London, Butterworths Scientific Publications, 1958.

41. Braude, E. A., and Forbes, W. F., *J. Chem. Soc.*, 3776 (1955).
42. Wittig, G., and Zimmermann, H., *Chem. Ber.*, **86**, 629 (1953).
43. Förster, T., *Z. Naturforschg.*, **2a**, 149 (1947).
44. Almasy, F., and Laemmel, H., *Helv. Chim. Acta*, **33**, 2092 (1950).
45. Dearden, J. C., and Forbes, W. F., *Can. J. Chem.*, **36**, 1362 (1958).
46. Forbes, W. F., *Can. J. Chem.*, **38**, 1104 (1960).
47. Dearden, J. C., and Forbes, W. F., *Can. J. Chem.*, **37**, 1294 (1959).
48. Forbes, W. F., and Leckie, I. R., *Can. J. Chem.*, **36**, 1371 (1958).
49. Forbes, W. F., Mueller, W. A., Ralph, A. S., and Templeton, J. F., *Can. J. Chem.*, **35**, 1049 (1957).
50. Dearden, J. C., and Forbes, W. F., *Can. J. Chem.*, **37**, 1305 (1959).
51. Leermakers, P. A., Thomas, H. T., *J. Am. Chem. Soc.*, **87**, 1620 (1965).
52. Forbes, W. F., *Can. J. Chem.*, **36**, 1350 (1958).
53. Forbes, W. F., *Can. J. Chem.*, **40**, 1891 (1962).
54. Conduit, C. P., *J. Chem. Soc.*, 3273 (1959).
55. Ungnade, H. E., and Smiley, R. A., *J. Org. Chem.*, **21**, 993 (1956).
56. Ungnade, H. E., Roberts, E. M., and Kissinger, L. W., *J. Phys. Chem.*, **68**, 3225 (1964).
57. Forbes, W. F., *Can. J. Chem.*, **37**, 1977 (1959).
58. Forbes, W. F., *Can. J. Chem.*, **39**, 1131 (1961).
59. Forbes, W. F., *Can. J. Chem.*, **39**, 2295 (1961).
60. Clark, D. T., Murrell, J. N., and Tedder, J. M., *J. Chem. Soc.*, 1250 (1963).
61. Burgers, J., Hoefnagel, M. A., Verkade, P. E., Visser, H., and Wepster, B. M., *Rec. trav. chim.*, **77**, 491 (1958).
62. Baddeley, G., Smith, N. H. P., and Vickars, M. A., *J. Chem. Soc.*, 2455 (1956).
63. Forbes, W. F., Knight, A. R., and Coffen, D. L., *Can. J. Chem.*, **38**, 728 (1960); Forbes, W. F., and Knight, A. R., *Can. J. Chem.*, **37**, 334 (1959).
64. Coulson, C. A., *Photoelect. Spectr. Gr. Bull. No. 13*, 358 (1961).
65. Halverson, F., and Hirt, R. C., *J. Chem. Phys.*, **19**, 711 (1951).
66. Braude, E. A., *Ann. Repts. on Progr. Chem.*, (Chem. Soc. London) **42**, 105 (1945).
67. Campaigne, E., and Diedrich, J. L., *J. Am. Chem. Soc.*, **73**, 5240 (1951).
68. Price, C. C., and Morita, H., *J. Am. Chem. Soc.*, **75**, 4747 (1953).
69. Pickett, L. W., Hoeflich, N. J., and Liu, T., *J. Am. Chem. Soc.*, **73**, 4865 (1951).
70. Harrison, A. J., Gaddis, C. L., and Coffin, E. M., *J. Chem. Phys.*, **18**, 221 (1950).
71. King, S. M., Bauer, C. R., and Lutz, R. E., *J. Am. Chem. Soc.*, **73**, 2253 (1951).
72. Overberger, C. G., and Tanner, D., *J. Am. Chem. Soc.*, **77**, 369 (1955).
73. Beale, R. N., and Roe, E. M. F., *J. Am. Chem. Soc.*, **74**, 2302 (1952).
74. Jaffé, H. H., Yeh, S.-J., and Gardner, R. W., *J. Mol. Spectroscopy*, **2**, 120 (1958).
75. Lewis, G. E., *Tetrahedron*, **10**, 129 (1960).
76. Burawoy, A., Salem, A. G., and Thompson, A. R., *J. Chem. Soc.*, 4793 (1952).
77. Burawoy, A., and Thompson, A. R., *J. Chem. Soc.*, 1443 (1953).
78. Inscoe, M. N., Gould, J. H., and Brode, W. R., *J. Am. Chem. Soc.*, **81**, 5634 (1959); Fischer, E., *J. Am. Chem. Soc.*, **82**, 3249 (1960).
79. Grammaticakis, P., *Bull. soc. chim. France*, 951 (1951).
80. Jones, R. N., Forbes, W. F., and Mueller, W. A., *Can. J. Chem.*, **35**, 504 (1957).
81. Murrell, J. N., *J. Chem. Soc.*, 3779 (1956).
82. Heilbronner, E., and Gerdil, R., *Helv. Chim. Acta*, **39**, 1996 (1956).
83. Dewar, M. J. S., In "Steric Effects in Conjugated Systems," p. 46, London, Butterworths Scientific Publications, 1958.
84. Jaffé, H. H., and Orchin, M., *J. Chem. Soc.*, 1078 (1960).
85. Henri, V., and Bergmann, E., *Nature*, **143**, 278 (1939).
86. Forbes, W. F., In "Steric Effects in Conjugated Systems," p. 62, London, Butterworths Scientific Publications, 1958.
87. Newman, M. S., and Wolf, M., *J. Am. Chem. Soc.*, **74**, 3225 (1952).
88. Brunings, K. J., and Corwin, A. H., *J. Am. Chem. Soc.*, **64**, 593 (1942).
89. Cram, D. J., and Dewhirst, K. C., *J. Am. Chem. Soc.*, **81**, 5963 (1959).

90. Cram, D. J., and Goldstein, M., *J. Am. Chem. Soc.*, **85,** 1063 (1963).
91. Zechmeister, L., *Chem. Rev.*, **34,** 267 (1944).
92. Inhoffen, H. H., Bohlmann, F., Bartram, K., Rummert, G., and Pommer, H., *Ann.*, **570,** 54 (1950); **571,** 75 (1951).
93. Braude, E. A., and Coles, J. A., *J. Chem. Soc.*, 2085 (1951).
94. Dreiding, A. S., and Pratt, R. J., *J. Am. Chem. Soc.*, **76,** 1902 (1954).
95. Braude, E. A., *J. Chem. Soc.*, 1902 (1949).
96. Suzuki, H., *Bull. Chem. Soc. Japan*, **25,** 146 (1952).
97. Cram, D. J., *J. Am. Chem. Soc.*, **71,** 3883 (1949).
98. Mixer, R. Y., Heck, R. F., Winstein, S., and Young, W. G., *J. Am. Chem. Soc.*, **75,** 4094 (1953).
99. Craig, L. E., and Larrabee, C. E., *J. Am. Chem. Soc.*, **73,** 1191 (1951).
100. Lutz, R. E., and Jordan, R. H., *J. Am. Chem. Soc.*, **72,** 4090 (1950).
101. Havinga, E., and Nivard, R. J. F., *Rec. trav. chim.*, **67,** 846 (1948).
102. Cromwell, N. H., Schumacher, F. H., and Adelfang, J. L., *J. Am. Chem. Soc.*, **83,** 974 (1961).
103. Mulliken, R. S., *J. Chem. Phys.*, **7,** 364 (1939).
104. Jurkowitz, L., Loeb, J. N., Brown, P. K., and Wald, G., *Nature*, **184,** 614 (1959).
105. Grossman, P., *Z. physik. Chem.*, **109,** 305 (1924).
106. Bishop, C. A., and Tong, L. K. J., *J. Phys. Chem.*, **66,** 1034 (1962).
107. Stephenson, H. P., and Sponer, H., *J. Am. Chem. Soc.*, **79,** 2050 (1957).
108. Cohen, M. D., and Fischer, E., *J. Chem. Soc.*, 3044 (1962).
109. Schubert, W. M., Steadly, H., and Craven, J. M., *J. Am. Chem. Soc.*, **82,** 1353 (1960).
110. Keussler, V. v., *Z. Elektrochem.*, **58,** 136 (1954).
111. Dearden, J. C., *Can. J. Chem.*, **41,** 2683 (1963).
112. Dearden, J. C., and Forbes, W. F., *Can. J. Chem.*, **38,** 1837 (1960).
113. Dearden, J. C., and Forbes, W. F., *Can. J. Chem.*, **38,** 1852 (1960).
114. *Photoelect. Spectr. Gr. Bull. No. 3*, (Stray Light Number) (1950).
115. Kaye, W., In "Symposium on Spectroscopy," ASTM Special Technical Publications No. 269, p. 63 (1960).
116. Turner, D. W., *J. Chem. Soc.*, 4555 (1957); *Photoelect. Spectr. Gr. Bull. No. 14*, 388 (1962).
117. Goodman, M., and Listowsky, I., *J. Am. Chem. Soc.*, **84,** 3770 (1962).
118. Sizer, I. W., and Peacock, A. C., *J. Biol. Chem.*, **171,** 767 (1947).
119. Beaven, G. H., In "Advances in Spectroscopy," Vol. II, p. 331, New York, Interscience Publishers, Inc., 1961.
120. Glazer, A. N., and Smith, E. L., *J. Biol Chem.*, **236,** 2942 (1961); Kronman, M. J. *et al.*, *Biochem.*, **4,** 518, 526 (1965).
121. Bendit, E. G., *J. Textile Inst.*, **51,** *(No. 12, Part 1)*, T544 (1960).
122. Seeds, W. E., *Progr. in Biophys. and Biophys. Chemistry*, **3,** 27 (1953).
123. Stork, G., *J. Am. Chem. Soc.*, **74,** 768 (1952).
124. Gulland, J. M., and Holiday, E. R., *J. Chem. Soc.*, 765 (1936).
124a. Clark, L. B., and Tinow, I., *J. Am. Chem. Soc.*, **87,** 11 (1965); see also *Advances in Chemical Physics*, **7,** 449 (1964).
125. Robinson, R., and Todd, A. R., *J. Chem. Soc.*, 2488 (1932).
126. Aronoff, S., *Chem. Revs.*, **47,** 175 (1950).
127. Pacsu, E., and Hiller, L. A., *J. Am. Chem. Soc.*, **70,** 523 (1948).
128. Deno, N. C., Jaruzelski, J. J., and Schriesheim, A., *J. Am. Chem. Soc.*, **77,** 3044 (1955).
129. Gold, V., and Tye, F. L., *J. Chem. Soc.*, 2172 (1952).
130. Rosenbaum, J., and Symons, M. C. R., *J. Chem. Soc.*, 1, (1961).
131. Grellman, K. H., Sherman, G. M., and Linschitz, H., *J. Am. Chem. Soc.*, **85,** 1881 (1963).
132. Korgaonkar, K. S., and Donde, R. B., *Intern. J. Radiation Biol.*, **5,** 67 (1962).
133. Land, E. J., and Porter, G., *J. Chem. Soc.*, 3540 (1961).
134. Okuda, M., *Nippon Kagaku Zasshi*, **82,** 1290 (1961).
135. Piette, L. H., and Forrest, I. S., *Biochim. Biophys. Acta.*, **57,** 419 (1962).

136. Stamires, D. N., and Turkevich, J., *J. Am. Chem. Soc.*, **85,** 2557 (1963); Blandamer, M. J., Shields, L., and Symons, M. C. R., *J. Chem. Soc.*, 1127 (1965).
137. Bindley, T. F., Watts, A. T., and Walker, S., *J. Chem. Soc.*, 4327 (1962).
138. Paul, D. E., Lipkin, D., and Weissman, S. I., *J. Am. Chem. Soc.*, **78,** 116 (1956).
139. Moore, W. R., Marcus, E., Fenton, S. E., and Arnold, R. T., *Tetrahedron*, **5,** 179 (1959).

2 | INFRARED ABSORPTION SPECTROSCOPY

Maurizio Gianturco
Head, Fundamental Research Department
The Coca Cola Company
Linden, New Jersey

1. Introduction

The chromatographic methods of separation, especially gas-liquid chromatography, permit the isolation in pure form of minute amounts of substances present in mixtures in very low concentrations. This development, while permitting one to attack many new problems, poses, in turn, the problem of postulating plausible structures for the compounds isolated solely on the basis of spectroscopic data, without the benefit of chemical degradations or transformations. This is one of the reasons why chemists are faced today with the necessity of learning how to extract the maximum amount of information from infrared, ultraviolet, mass spectroscopic, and nuclear magnetic resonance data, since these, in fact, may often be the only data available for the determination of the structure of unknown substances.

Success in such an endeavor will depend upon many factors. Of these, the structural complexity of the compound is generally of prime importance, but when only milligram or submilligram amounts of material are available, the problem of identification may be complex even for relatively simple substances. In any event, it is of paramount importance always to remember that the structural data which can be obtained by means of the various spectroscopic techniques are complementary to each other. The chemist should be well aware not only of the potentialities but also of the limitations of each of the physical methods that he intends to employ and be prepared to exploit their fortunate synergism. For example, while it is generally impossible to determine the structure of an unknown solely on the basis of its infrared spectrum, the problem certainly becomes more tractable if a mass spectrum is also available. In suitable cases, ultraviolet data may permit the clarification of an important structural detail, and finally, NMR may be able to furnish information which could not be obtained by means of the three other common spectroscopic methods. Nuclear magnetic resonance has been mentioned lastly only because, while one hundred micrograms of material, if properly manipulated, are generally sufficient to obtain an IR, a UV, and a mass spectrum, somewhat larger samples are usually necessary for NMR determinations.

The identification of a compound by means of IR spectroscopy alone is a truly simple problem only when the "unknown" is actually a known substance whose IR spectrum has been previously reported in the literature or is otherwise available to the investigator. In this event, the identification may be reduced to a purely mechanical process, and all that really needs to be said on the subject is that the extensive collections of spectra that are commercially available have a very definite place among the "tools" of the research laboratory. However, after having matched the spectrum of the unknown with a published one, it is generally wise to obtain an authentic sample of the substance and record its spectrum in conditions identical with those previously employed for the unknown sample. Furthermore, it is certainly to be recommended that some other physical property be checked, such as chromatographic or mass spectral data. This is important, especially when the molecular weights are relatively high, i.e., the IR spectra of two structurally similar compounds, particularly if they are close members of an homologous series, may be almost identical. On the other hand, if the spectra of the unknown and of a known compound are found to be almost but not completely identical, before considering that the two substances may only be closely related rather than being one and the same compound, it may be wise to perform a purity check. For example, if the spectrum of the unknown shows all the bands present in that of a known compound—and approximately in the proper band intensity relationships—but contains also one or more extra bands, it is always possible that the unknown is an impure sample of the known compound and should then be subjected to further purification. Conversely, in these days of gas chromatography, it may occasionally occur that the published spectrum is that of a sample less pure than the unknown. Finally, it may be worthwhile to call attention to the fact that if the spectrum of an unknown, determined, for example, in solution, does not seem to match any of the spectra contained in a given collection, it does not necessarily follow that the unknown is not one of the compounds whose spectrum is contained in the collection. For instance, if the collection spectrum was determined on a crystalline solid as a KBr pellet, it may be radically different from that of the same sample in solution. Figures 1 and 2 represent the spectra of the same substance determined in chloroform solution and in KBr, respectively.*

When the spectrum of the unknown cannot be matched with any recorded spectrum, the substance must be treated as a true unknown, even if it might ultimately turn out to be a compound reported in the chemical literature. In these cases, the postulation of plausible structures may be possible after the work of an hour or may require the accumulation of many more physical and chemical data, even for relatively simple substances, depending on whether or not the chemist is familiar with the particular type of correlation that is necessary to correctly interpret that particular spectrum. For the chemist making use of spectroscopy, the search for new useful correlations between spectra and specific structural features of interest to him must be, in fact, a continuing project, since familiarity with a good number of such correlations is the key to the successful application of spectroscopy to problems of structural elucidation.

2. Some Examples of Simple Interpretation of Infrared Spectra

While it is certainly not possible to give a set of directions of general validity for the postulation of structures by means of infrared spectroscopy, a few examples can be helpful when trying to illustrate, in a general manner, some ways of approaching the problem.

The first example is typical of the more conventional way of observing an infrared spectrum, that is, by correlating *band positions* with specific structural features.

The routine gas chromatographic analysis of many samples of an essential oil revealed that a few of them were different from the others, inasmuch as they contained a compound that was not present in the great majority of the samples.

*Note that the sharp band near 3.5μ which appears in the lower part of the majority of the spectra presented in this chapter is a calibration mark (polystyrene).

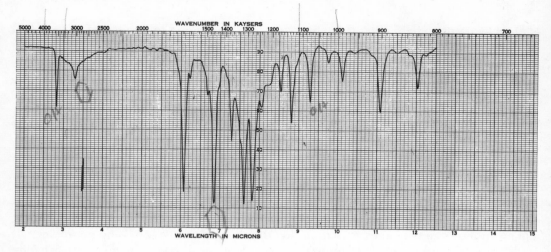

FIGURE 1. Substance of Example 2, p. 58 (CHCl₃).

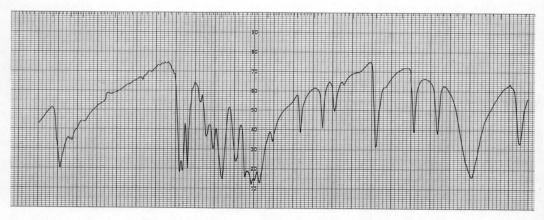

FIGURE 2. Substance of Example 2, p. 58 (KBr).

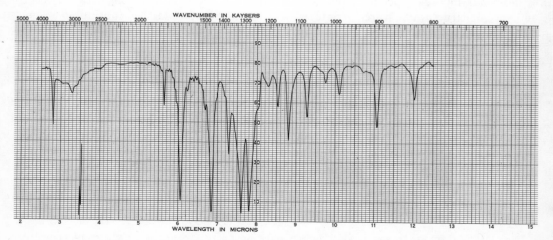

FIGURE 3. Substance of Example 2, impure, p. 58 (CHCl₃).

Employing a polar column, the spurious peak eluted subsequent to the terpenic alcohols, and this fact led to the suspicion that it might be due to a glycol or to a sesquiterpenic alcohol. However, the interpretation of the infrared spectrum (Figure 4) led to quite different conclusions:

(a) The compound is, indeed, an alcohol (bands at approximately 2.75 and 3.0μ and between 9.5 and 10μ), but certainly not of a terpenic nature, considering the low intensity of the aliphatic C—H absorption at 3.4 to 3.5μ.

(b) Aromatic character is, instead, indicated by the absorption at, or below, 3.33μ —which is essentially the dividing line between the wavelengths of paraffinic and aromatic (or olefinic) C—H stretching absorptions (see Table 1)—and by sharp bands near 6.65 and 6.85μ.

The spectra of benzenic derivatives usually exhibit a group of four bands near 6.25, 6.33, 6.66, and 6.90 microns. While the positions of these bands are relatively little affected by the number, orientation, and nature of the substituents, their intensities can vary widely. In weak spectra, only some of these bands may be observed. The relationship between the intensity of these bands and the electronic interactions between substituents and ring have been recently discussed by Katritzky and his collaborators.[55,56,58,61]

(c) If the aromatic ring is benzenic (the simplest possibility), it must be monosubstituted, as indicated by the strong absorptions near 13.6 and 14.4μ and by the weak, but recognizable, pattern between 5 and 6μ.

TABLE 1. Carbon-Hydrogen Stretching Vibrations*

Type	$\lambda < 3.33\mu$ ν_s(C-H) (cm^{-1})	$\approx \lambda$(C-H) (μ)	Type	$\lambda : 3.33-3.53\mu$ ν_s(C-H) (cm^{-1})	$\approx \lambda$(C-H) (μ)
R—C≡C—H	3,310–3,300	3.02–3.03	—CH$_3$ (alkanes)	2,975–2,950 / 2,885–2,860	3.36–3.39 / 3.47–3.50
—CH=C—O / —C=C—O— H	3,150–3,050	3.18–3.28	—CH$_2$— (alkanes)	2,940–2,915 / 2,870–2,845	3.40–3.45 / 3.49–3.52
(cyclopropyl CH$_2$ and epoxide CH$_2$)	3,055–3,040	3.27–3.29	≡CH (alkanes)	2,900–2,880	3.45–3.47
			$\lambda > 3.53\mu$		
=CH— (aromatic)	3,080–3,030	3.25–3.30	—OCH$_3$	2,832–2,815	3.53–3.55
=CH— (heteroaromatic)	3,070–3,020	3.26–3.31	Ar—N—CH$_3$	2,820–2,810	3.54–3.56
CH$_2$=CR$_1$R$_2$	3,095–3,075	3.23–3.25	R—N—CH$_3$	2,805–2,780	3.56–3.60
CHR$_1$=CR$_2$R$_3$			Ar—N(CH$_3$)$_2$	≈2,800	≈3.57
CHR$_1$=CHR$_2$ (cis)	3,040–3,010	3.29–3.32	R—N(CH$_3$)$_2$	2,825–2,810 / 2,775–2,765	3.54–3.56 / 3.60–3.62
CHR$_1$=CHR$_2$ (trans)			O—CH$_2$ (on benzenic ring) O	2,801–2,770	3.57–3.61
CHR$_1$=CH$_2$	3,095–3,075 / 3,040–3,010	3.23–3.25 / 3.29–3.32	H—C=O	2,720–2,695	3.67–3.71

*Some interestingly anomalous values for C-H stretching modes modified by stereoelectronic effects have been recently reported.[19,37] For a study of the C-H absorption of formyl groups, see Ref. 78a. The absorptions of N-methyl groups are discussed in Ref. 49.

The weak patterns between 5 and 6μ (overtone and combination bands) and the strong bands between 10 and 15μ (fundamentals) are of great diagnostic importance and can usually furnish quite reliable information with regard to the type of substitution on an aromatic ring. However, it must be added, as a note of caution, that the presence of certain types of substituents may alter the appearance of the substitution bands between 10 and 15μ and, consequently, also that of the combination patterns between 5 and 6μ.

Thus, the examination of the spectrum led to the conclusion that the compound at hand was aromatic in character, contained a monosubstituted benzenic ring, an alcoholic O—H group, and not many nonaromatic C—H groups. With this information, two compounds, namely, benzyl and phenethyl alcohol, appeared as likely possibilities for the *simplest* structure satisfying the spectral data discussed. Moreover, the distinction between the two types was immediately possible on the basis of the data contained in a study of the C—O stretching absorptions of alcohols, which permits some refinement in the analysis of the IR spectra of these compounds. While the interested reader is referred for details to the original paper,[93] the general classification of alcohols that is now possible is indicated in Table 2. Even an excellent book on infrared spectroscopy (1962) still reports only the old classification of alcohols (primary: 9.62μ; secondary: 9.01μ; tertiary: 8.62μ), which is based on data obtained more than fifty years ago.[90]

TABLE 2.   Classification of Various Types of Alcohols

Group	Position of C—O Bands (μ)*	Type of Alcohol
1	8.30–8.90	a) Saturated tertiary b) Highly symmetrical secondary
2	8.90–9.20	a) Saturated secondary b) α-Unsaturated or cyclic tertiary
3	9.22–9.52	a) α-Unsaturated secondary b) Alicyclic secondary (5- or 6-membered ring) c) Saturated primary
4	> 9.52	a) Highly α-unsaturated tertiary b) Di-α-unsaturated secondary c) α-Unsaturated *and* α-branched secondary d) Alicyclic secondary (7- or 8-membered ring) e) α-Branched and/or α-unsaturated primary

*These limits, valid for pure liquids, must be *slightly* extended for spectra determined in solution. For the differentiation of equatorial and axial hydroxyl groups in the steroid and triterpene series, on the basis of the frequency of the C—O stretching vibrations, see Refs. 3 and 53; for a different approach, based upon the more or less pronounced asymmetry of the free O—H stretching bands, see Ref. 1. An excellent discussion of O—H and C—O vibrations of alicyclic alcohols has been recently given by Cole (Ref. i of General References).**

A useful classification of alcohols via NMR spectroscopy in dimethyl sulfoxide has been reported [Chapman, O. L., and King, R. W., *J. Am. Chem. Soc.*, **86, 1258 (1964)].

Consideration of the data of Table 2 permitted the elimination of phenethyl alcohol (group 3) and left that of benzyl alcohol (group 4) as the *simplest* structure satisfying the spectrum of Figure 4.

One should notice, however, that even in such an elementary case the structure of the unknown did not remain unequivocally established by the detailed examination of its spectrum, since other structures could satisfy all the conditions imposed by the spectral data discussed. For instance, the reader might compare the spectrum of benzyl alcohol (Figure 4) with that of benzhydrol (Figure 5). The spectrum of phenethyl alcohol, a borderline case with respect to the data of Table 2, is presented in Figure 6.

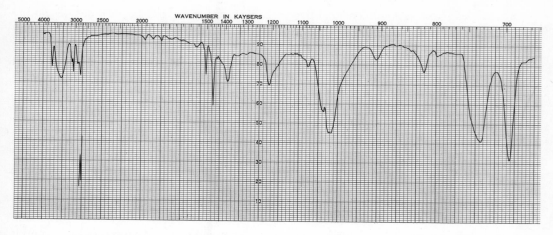

FIGURE 4. Substance of Example 1, p. 53 (12.5–15.0μ: CS₂; 2.5–12.5μ: CCl₄).

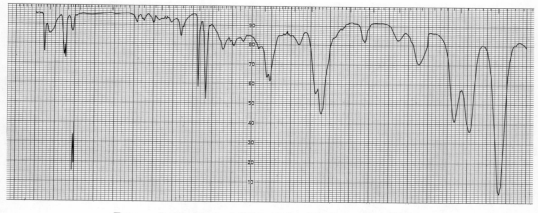

FIGURE 5. Benzhydrol (12.5–15.0μ: CS₂; 2.5–12.5μ: CCl₄).

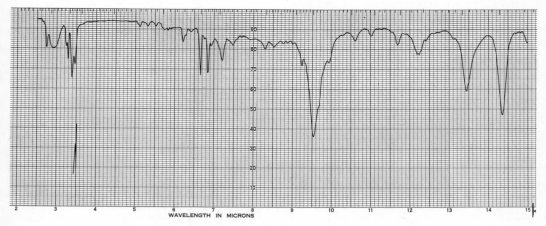

FIGURE 6. Phenylethyl alcohol (12.5–15.0μ: CS₂; 2.5–12.5μ: CCl₄).

57

The next example is included in order to call attention to the importance of taking into consideration not only the position of the bands in the spectrum, but their *shape* as well, since the latter can often convey a very precise message with regard to the structure of the compound under examination. The example will also emphasize the importance of acquiring a certain familiarity with band intensities and of being able to recognize when a band should be attributed to a minor impurity, and, as such, disregarded.

A substance was obtained by thin-layer chromatography of a complex mixture of natural origin and its spectrum recorded in chloroform (Figure 3). The small band at 5.65μ was immediately suspected to be extraneous, since, as a probable carbonyl absorption, it seemed to be far too weak with respect to other bands. Consequently, the sample was recovered from the cell and injected into a gas chromatographic column, without removal of the solvent. In addition to the one due to the solvent, two more peaks were apparent in the chromatogram; the infrared spectrum of the minor component consisted, essentially, of only a very weak band at 5.65μ. The spectrum of the major component (Figure 1) will be discussed directly. [It will be immediately apparent that no major changes resulted from the removal of the impurity, with the exception of the disappearance of the weak band at 5.65μ. This is as expected, considering both the small intensity of the band (Figure 3) and the fact that the C=O stretching bands are intrinsically intense and, quite often, the strongest in the spectra of carbonyl compounds (see Table 3)].

The following were the key observations that led to the postulation of a simple structure:

(a) A *very sharp* band at 2.82μ, not accompanied by a band at 3.0μ, suggested the presence in the molecule of an OH group, possibly engaged in that particular kind of hydrogen bonding which is commonly defined as single-bridge hydrogen-bonding. This should become clearer after inspection of Figures 7a, b, c, and d, where some typical bands corresponding to the stretching of O—H groups in a few different types of hydrogen-bonding situations are reproduced.*

(b) The very weak absorption in the C—H stretching region—and its position (mostly below 3.33μ)—suggested that the compound should have a predominantly aromatic character. This was confirmed by the general sharpness of most bands in the spectrum and by distinct signs of aromaticity at approximately 6.2 and 6.7–6.8μ.

(c) The *broad* absorption observed between 3 and 4μ is characteristic of vibrations involving the O—H of carboxylic acids or of groups that are vinylogous with the carboxyl group (see Figure 7B). However, the band at 6.07μ, probably due to a carbonyl absorption, occurs at too high a wavelength to be due to a carboxylic acid, even if its carbonyl were part of a resonance-stabilized hydrogen bridge.

On the basis of these observations on the position and shape of just a few bands of the spectrum, it was already possible to tentatively consider the following structural features:

From (a):   From (c):   From (a) and (c):   From (a), (b) and (c):

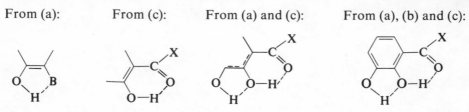

*While the spectra of Figures 7a, b, c, and d will not be discussed in detail, the reader should note that a great deal of information of interpretive significance can be derived by observing not only the band positions but their *shapes* as well. It should be also remarked that for really refined work on O—H stretching bands, such as that discussed by Cole, for instance, in Ref. i of General References, the measurements should be performed on very dilute solutions ($0.005M$) and the instrument should be operated in the single-beam mode, so that the background of atmospheric water vapor can be used as an internal standard for accurate frequency determinations.

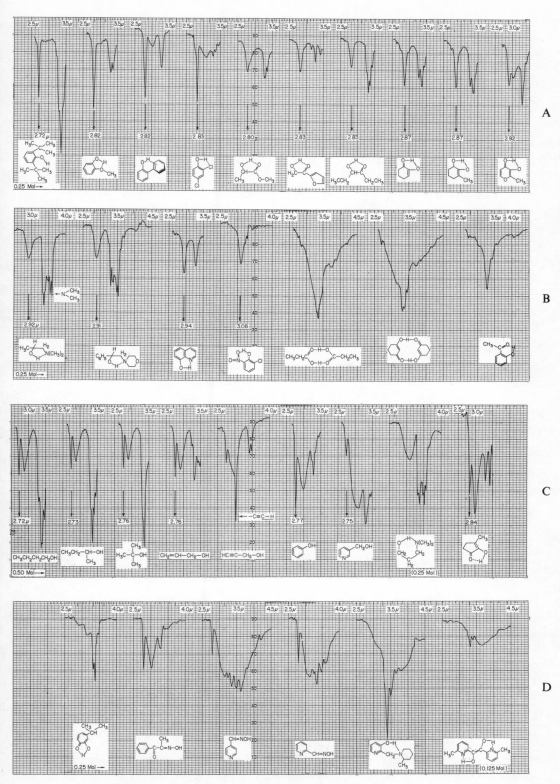

FIGURE 7 (A,B,C,D). O—H (and C—H) stretching region of various types of compounds.

59

TABLE 3. Intensities of Some Group Vibrations. Values of A in Carbon Tetrachloride Solution*
(Units of moles/liter, cm, cm^{-1} and log$_{10}$)

Group	Class of Compound	Approximate Position of Bands cm^{-1}	μ	$A \cdot 10^{-3}$
O—H	Alcohols (1°, 2°)	3630	2.75	*ca.* 2
	Phenols, oximes	3600	2.76	*ca.* 6
	Cyanohydrins	3600	2.76	2–3
N—H	Pyrroles, indoles	3490	2.86	*ca.* 5
	Anilines	{3480 / 3400	{2.87 / 2.94	{1.0–2.5 / 0.8–4.5
	Methylanilines	3450	2.90	1.5–4.3
	Diarylamines	3450	2.90	*ca.* 2
	Dialkylamines	3400	2.94	*ca.* 0.04
—CH$_2$—	Hydrocarbons	{2900 / 1470	{3.45 / 6.80	*ca.* 3.3 / *ca.* 0,2
	—COCH$_2$—	{2900 / 1440–1400	{3.45 / 6.95–7.15	*ca.* 0.6 / *ca.* 1.0
—CH$_3$	Hydrocarbons	{2900 / 1375	{3.45 / 7.27	*ca.* 3.8 / *ca.* 0.35
	—COCH$_3$	{2900 / 1360–1355	{3.45 / 7.36–7.38	*ca.* 0.6 / *ca.* 1.7
—N=C=O	Phenyl isocyanate	2270	4.41	62–74
—C≡N	Aliphatic nitrile	2250	4.44	0.22–0.35
	Aromatic nitrile	2225	4.49	0.25–4.00
—N=C=N	Carbodiimide	2130	4.70	45–50
—N=C=S	Aliphatic isothiocyanate	2100	4.76	17–52
	Aromatic isothiocyanate	2050	4.88	65–90
C=O	Aliphatic esters	1745	5.73	10–14
	Aliphatic aldehydes	1733	5.77	*ca.* 8
	Aliphatic ketones	1724	5.80	*ca.* 8
	Benzoates	1727	5.79	12–16
	Aromatic aldehydes	1718	5.82	8.5–11
	Acetophenones	1691	5.91	7.5–9.5
	Benzophenones	1664	5.99	*ca.* 9
C—O	Esters	~1200	~8.3	*ca.* 13

$*A = \dfrac{1}{cl} \displaystyle\int \log \dfrac{I_o}{I}\, d\nu$—Since these values were taken from various literature sources, they should be viewed only as orientative.

As for the nature of the group X, once established that it was not likely to be an hydroxyl, or, for the same and other reasons, an alkoxyl radical, the spectrum was again searched for some useful clue. The absence of bands due to vibrations of the C—H of a formyl group (see Table 1) could not be taken in this case as positive proof that such group was not present in the molecule, since these often weak bands could be possibly obscured by the broad absorption observed between 3 and 4μ. However, the carbonyl absorption at 6.07μ seemed to occur at too high a wavelength also for an aromatic aldehyde, even if its carbonyl were chelated ($\lambda_{C=O}^{CHCl_3}$ of salicylaldehyde: 5.98μ). Moreover, the presence of a band of good intensity at approximately 7.3μ in the spectrum of a compound that obviously does not contain much nonaromatic C—H (see (b) above) seemed to suggest that the compound might be an aromatic methyl ketone. It is, in fact, known[43] that when a methyl or methylene group is directly attached to a carbonyl, the intensity of the C—H stretching absorption is decreased, while that of the corresponding deformation modes is increased (Table 3). This postulation found tentative support in the presence of an intense band at 7.8μ; many aromatic ketones, but also other types of compounds, show strong absorptions at this wavelength (see spectra in Figures 18 to 22).

Consequently, if the simple assumptions made are well founded, the *simplest* structure satisfying the data discussed would be that of 2,3-dihydroxyacetophenone. Since it was easier in this case to synthesize the compound than to obtain more material for further work, the proof of the correctness of the postulated structure was obtained through a direct comparison of the natural and the synthetic material.

It should be remarked that, in the case of relatively simple compounds which can be easily synthesized and are amenable to isolation and purification by vapor-liquid chromatography, the synthetic approach to a proof of structure can be used with a certain liberality. Vapor-liquid chromatography, in fact, often permits running reactions on the milligram scale, with great economy of time and materials. In fact, when an unknown is available only in very minute amounts, if it is possible to postulate a simple structure that is compatible with its infrared spectrum and with any other physical data that may be available, the synthetic route may be the quickest and most direct to a proof of structure.

The examples given above should not be construed as suggesting that it is usually possible to postulate a structure, at least for simple compounds, on the sole basis of their infrared spectrum; the contrary is more generally true. However, it is also true that, at least in those cases when the "unknown" turns out to be a known substance previously reported in the literature, it is often possible to arrive at its structure on the basis of its *molecular formula* and of a careful study of its infrared spectrum. For instance, in the example described above, merely scanning the names of the 96 compounds listed in Beilstein's formula index under $C_8H_8O_3$ and making a mental note of their expected carbonyl frequencies and of the expected position and shape of their OH bands, the chemist with some experience in IR interpretation would have focused his attention on not more than three or four compounds. With these few possible structures written in front of him, he would have rapidly arrived at the same conclusions that, without knowledge of the molecular formula, could only be reached by a considerably more abstract process.

Unfortunately, while it is certainly very helpful to know the molecular formula of the compound whose structure one is trying to determine by means of its IR spectrum, this datum is not always directly available, since it is often not possible or practical to obtain an amount of material sufficient for a combustion analysis and a determination of molecular weight by classical methods. However, in favorable instances, the same information can be obtained through the determination of the mass spectrum of the substance. This can often give, besides much useful information about the nature of the compound, its molecular formula, or at least its molecular weight.

The third example will show that, in special cases, it is the *relative intensity* of two bands that can furnish clues of distinct diagnostic significance. It will illustrate an approach followed in determining the structure of a simple unknown substance on the basis of its infrared spectrum, with the knowledge of the molecular formula acquired through the mass spectrum and with the help of ultraviolet spectrophotometry for the definition of a structural detail.

The presence of two bands with that particular spacing in that particular section of the C=O stretching region of the infrared spectrum of the substance in question (Figure 8) strongly suggested that this should be an anhydride. However, it was the fact that the absorption at 5.64 microns was so much more intense than that at 5.39 microns that gave a more specific clue to the structure of the compound, by clearly suggesting that it should be a five-membered cyclic anhydride containing a carbon-carbon double bond in the ring, i.e., a maleic anhydride type.*

This deduction was possible on the basis of two recently published studies concerned with the spectra of anhydrides.[14,36] Some of the pertinent data presented by Dauben and Epstein are reported in Table 4, since they permit a considerable refinement in the interpretation of the spectra of anhydrides. One of the important facts shown by these data is that, while it may sometimes be difficult to differentiate on the basis of band positions alone between open chain (or unstrained cyclic) anhydrides and the corresponding strained compounds with a carbon-carbon double bond in the ring, the two types can be easily differentiated on the basis of the relative intensities of the two carbonyl bands. In the spectra of maleic anhydride and its homologues, the band at longer wavelength (lower frequency) is *extremely* more intense than the other (see also Figure 9 and p. 111).

TABLE 4. Infrared Spectral Data for Acid Anhydrides*

Compound	Band Positions	(cm^{-1})	D_H	D_L	D_L/D_H
Acetic anhydride	1825	1754	0.150	0.140	0.93
Propionic anhydride	1818	1745	0.190	0.154	0.81
Glutaric anhydride	1812	1764	0.065	0.174	2.7
Succinic anhydride	1866	1792	0.054	0.367	6.8
Cyclobutane-1,2-dicarboxylic acid anhydride	1859	1786	0.042	0.264	6.3
cis-Endomethylenetetrahydrophthalic anhydride	1855	1783	0.048	0.362	7.6
Cyclopropane-1,2-dicarboxylic acid anhydride	1862	1799	0.049	0.402	8.4
Maleic anhydride	1835	1770	0.030	0.268	9.0
2-Methylmaleic anhydride	1832	1764	0.043	0.342	8.0
2,3-Dimethylmaleic anhydride	1812 (1845)	1757	0.050	0.460	9.2
2-Methyl-3-hexadecylmaleic anhydride	1808	1757	0.034	0.378	11.1

D_H is optical density for the higher frequency band and D_L is optical density for the lower frequency band.

*Data from Ref. 36.

At this point, the mass spectrum of the substance under investigation indicated the molecular weight to be 140 and gave the following values for the intensities of the isotope peaks at mass M + 1 and M + 2 (in per cent of intensity of M, the peak corresponding to the molecular ion):

$$\frac{M + 1}{M} \times 100 = 7.8 \qquad \frac{M + 2}{M} \times 100 = 0.8$$

With these data at hand, consultation of Beynon's tables (see below) led to the molecular formula $C_7H_8O_3$, since the corresponding isotope ratios for the only other formula

*Note that the weak absorption near 2.8μ, which could have been taken as an indication of the presence of an hydroxyl group in the molecule, is probably due to an overtone of the carbonylic bands. The possibility that a band appearing in this region may *not* be due to —OH absorption should always be kept in mind when interpreting spectra of carbonyl compounds.

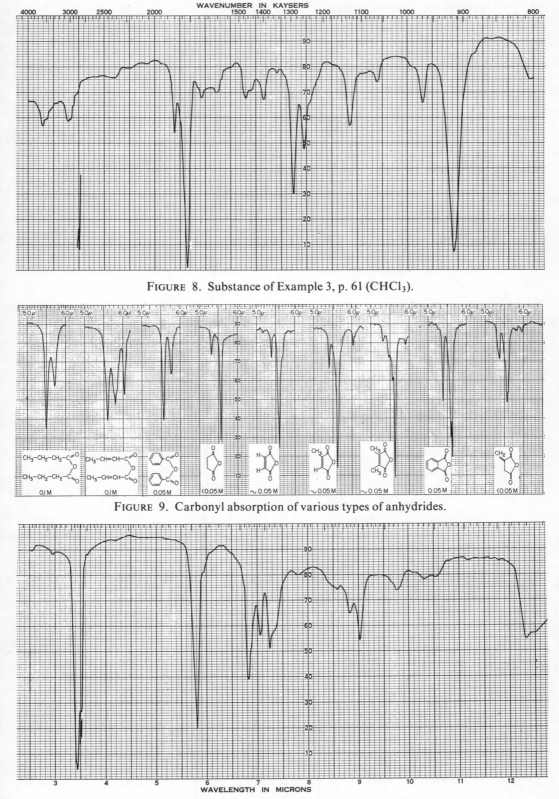

WAVENUMBER IN KAYSERS

FIGURE 8. Substance of Example 3, p. 61 (CHCl₃).

FIGURE 9. Carbonyl absorption of various types of anhydrides.

WAVELENGTH IN MICRONS

FIGURE 10. Substance of Example 4, p. 64 (CS₂).

63

listed which contains sufficient oxygen atoms to accommodate an anhydride structure ($C_5H_4N_2O_3$) are sufficiently at variance to permit differentiation.

The Beynon's tables* list all the most plausible combinations of C, H, N, and O which are possible for any molecular weight from 12 to 250 and also the values of $\frac{M + 1}{M}$ and $\frac{M + 2}{M}$ corresponding to each of the formulas listed. The formulas corresponding to molecular fragments rather than to molecules can be immediately sorted out on the basis of the simple rule that states that all organic molecules with an even molecular weight must either contain no nitrogen or an even number of nitrogen atoms, while an odd molecular weight must correspond to those molecules that contain an odd number of nitrogen atoms. (The rule does not hold for molecules containing bonds other than covalent ones). Furthermore, the sum of all the atoms of elements of odd valence must be even in all organic molecules.

Information gleaned from the infrared spectrum and molecular formula indicated a choice among three structures, those of methylethyl-, i-propyl-, and n-propyl-, maleic anhydrides. While the paucity of the material available did not permit the determination of the NMR spectrum of the unknown, a comparison of the ultraviolet absorption spectra of the unknown and of the commercially available maleic, mono-, and dimethyl maleic anhydrides led to the preparation of methyl ethyl maleic anhydride. This proved to be the substance in question.

The fourth example is included because it shows that, while it is usual to base the interpretation upon the study of the intense bands present in a spectrum, it is sometimes possible for *weak bands* to yield information with regard to important structural details.

In a study of the thermal stability of certain natural fats, it was possible to isolate small amounts of several saturated straight-chain aliphatic ketones. Rough GLC calibration data indicated that one of these ketones (Figure 10) should be in the C_{12}—C_{14} range. However, even considering only the straight-chain aliphatic ketones, the identification would have ordinarily required the examination of as many as seventeen compounds (five C_{12}-, six C_{13}-, and six C_{14}- ketones). Instead, the choice could be limited to only three substances (3-dodecanone, 3-tridecanone and 3-tetradecanone), since the spectrum revealed that the unknown should be an *ethyl* ketone. This simplifying deduction was possible on the basis of the results of a study made in this laboratory which leads to an immediate recognition of whether one is dealing with a methyl ketone or an ethyl ketone or whether the compound at hand does not belong to either one of these two classes. Since the patterns which allow the differentiation might be of use to other investigators, a typical series is reproduced in Figure 11. Inspection of the patterns will promptly reveal that, while ketones of the type CH_3COCH_2R can be recognized by bands of moderate intensity at 7.38μ (see Table 3) and at 8.62μ, those containing the $CH_3CH_2COCH_2R$ ($R \neq H$) grouping can be differentiated from the others of the general type RCH_2CH_2-$COCH_2CH_2R(R \neq H)$ because their spectra show a sharp band of weak to medium intensity (depending on the molecular weight) near 9.03μ.** This is in addition to the

*"Mass Spectrometry and its Applications to Organic Chemistry" by J. H. Beynon, Elsevier. These tables have been recently extended to molecular weights up to 500.
**Acetone, the first member of the series, is anomalous. Methylethyl ketone behaves like a methyl ketone.

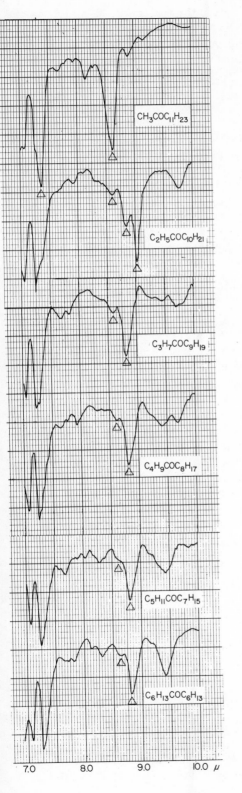

FIGURE 11. 7–10 μ region of isomeric n-tridecanones (CS$_2$).

two weak bands at 8.58 and 8.82μ that are also present in the spectra of the other straight-chain aliphatic ketones.

The fifth example will illustrate an approach followed in determining the structure of an unknown substance on the basis of its infrared spectrum and its molecular weight. It will call attention to the importance of being aware of the existence of *patterns* typical of particular types of compounds and, more specifically, of particular aromatic units. Gas-liquid chromatography of a volatile fraction obtained from roasted coffee furnished a liquid substance whose spectrum is given in Figure 12. Examination of the spectrum did not reveal the presence of any functional group, and the only conclusion which could be immediately reached was that the compound was probably aromatic in nature. It is doubtful, however, that any real progress would have been made in the determination of its structure by infrared if previous experience with furanic compounds had not permitted recognition of a certain pattern, a group of bands, that is typical of furanic compounds carrying a substituent in the α-position (see p. 70). This observation permitted the as-sumption that the grouping $\begin{matrix} C - C \\ \| \quad \| \\ C \quad C-C \\ \diagdown O \diagup \end{matrix}$ was probably present in the molecule. Further study of the spectrum furnished various pieces of information which, taken together, did not allow one to proceed much farther in the interpretation. At this point, a determination of the mass spectrum suggested a molecular weight of 147, but the presence of a small impurity, which masked the intensity of the peak at M + 1, made it impossible to determine a molecular formula on the basis of the isotope ratios. The odd molecular weight indicated, however, the presence in the molecule of an odd number of atoms of nitrogen. Consultation of Beynon's tables, taking into account that the compound should contain, besides nitrogen, at least one atom of oxygen, indicated the following possible formulas: $C_5H_9NO_4$, $C_5H_{13}N_3O$, $C_6H_{13}NO_3$, $C_6H_{17}N_3O$, $C_7H_5N_3O$, $C_7H_{17}NO_2$, $C_8H_5NO_2$ and C_9H_9NO. If the compound contains a furanic ring, it must possess a minimum of three points of unsaturation, and this consideration eliminated directly five of the formulas, leaving only $C_7H_5N_3O$, $C_8H_5NO_2$, and C_9H_9NO, the first two with seven and the last with six points of unsaturation. (The total number, R, of rings and double bonds present in a compound of formula $C_cH_hN_nO_{ox}$ is given by the simple expression

$$R = \left(\frac{2c + 2 + n - h}{2} \right).$$

Substracting from each of the formulas the elements corresponding to the radical of a furanic ring indicated the possible composition of the radical attached to this heterocycle in the molecule of the unknown:

$C_7H_5N_3O-$	$C_8H_5NO_2-$	C_9H_9NO-
C_4H_3O	C_4H_3O	C_4H_3O
$C_3H_2N_3$	C_4H_2NO	C_5H_6N

After the addition of one atom of hydrogen to each of these formulas of radicals, Beilstein was referred to for the compounds that could possibly represent the second moiety of the molecule of the unknown substance. While no compound of interest in this respect was found under $C_3H_3N_3$ or C_4H_3NO, under the formula C_5H_7N were listed, besides some nitriles, the three isomeric methylpyrroles. At this point, a glance at the spectrum indicated that, since no bands corresponding to N—H stretching were

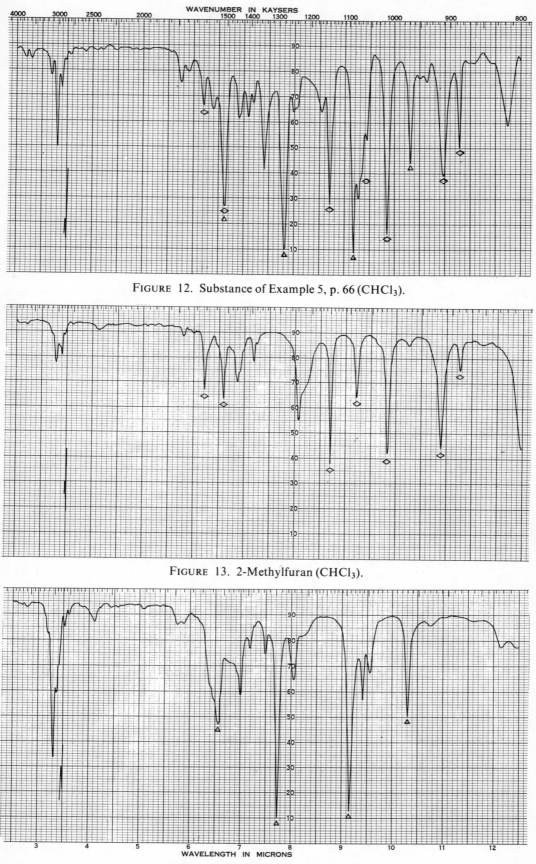

WAVENUMBER IN KAYSERS

FIGURE 12. Substance of Example 5, p. 66 (CHCl₃).

FIGURE 13. 2-Methylfuran (CHCl₃).

WAVELENGTH IN MICRONS

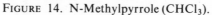

FIGURE 14. N-Methylpyrrole (CHCl₃).

evident, if the unknown actually contained a furanic and a pyrrolic ring, its structure should be the following:

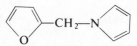

The correctness of this supposition could be immediately put to a test. If the postulated structure actually corresponded to the unknown, it seemed logical to expect that, just as most of the bands of 2-methylfuran were clearly recognizable in its spectrum, many of the bands of N-methylpyrrole should also be evident. Since the results of the comparison of the spectrum of the unknown on one hand and those of 2-methylfuran and N-methyl-pyrrole on the other were most encouraging (see Figures 13 and 14), N-furfuryl-2-pyrrole was synthesized.

It should be noted, however, that the synthesis adopted was not unequivocal (dry distillation of saccaric acid and furfuryl amine) and did, in fact, yield more than one product (VPC). However, the elemental analysis and the NMR spectrum of that compo-nent of the synthetic mixture which had the same retention times (polar and non-polar columns), infrared and mass spectra as the product isolated from coffee were in good agreement with the structure proposed. The NMR spectrum at 60 megacycles of a solution of the synthetic material in deuterochloroform (TMS as internal standard) contained: (a) a quartet for one proton centered at $\delta = 7.38$ ppm (α-hydrogen of the furanic ring); (b) a triplet for two protons centered at $\delta = 6.70$ ppm (α-hydrogens of the pyrrolic ring); (c) complex absorption for four protons between 6.1 and 6.3 ppm, attributed to the β-hydrogens of the furanic and pyrrolic rings; and (d) a singlet for two protons at $\delta = 4.97$ ppm, which can be ascribed to the methylene group.

The next example is also presented with the purpose of stressing the importance of observing and tabulating patterns typical of particular molecular units, since familiarity with these patterns can vastly extend the possibility of postulating plausible structures for simple unknown compounds on the basis of their infrared spectra. The postulation of a structure for the substance whose spectrum is represented in Figure 15 could be, for instance, based on the following observations:

   (a) The sharp bands between 6 and 7μ suggest an aromatic system.

   (b) The band of good intensity near 3.38μ suggests considerable aliphatic character.

   (c) The band of good intensity near 3.58μ indicates the presence of at least one methyl group attached to a nitrogen atom. This deduction is possible on the basis of data shown in Table 1, which have been so arranged as to emphasize the diagnostically important distinction of C—H stretching absorptions as falling below 3.33μ, above 3.53μ, or between these two limiting values.*

At this point, the mass spectrum indicated a possible molecular weight of 162. (This was the peak of the highest mass, but its low intensity did not permit an evaluation of $\dfrac{M + 1}{M}$ and $\dfrac{M + 2}{M}$, which could have been used to obtain a molecular formula.) Cou-pling this information with the knowledge that the molecule must contain at least two atoms of nitrogen (the infrared indicated the presence of one —NCH_3 group, and the even molecular weight dictated the presence of an *even* number of nitrogen atoms) led to the molecular formula $C_{10}H_{14}N_2$. This formula requires five points of unsaturation

---

*Note that methylenedioxy groups on a benzenic ring also show absorption in the range 3.57 to 3.61 microns which, being outside the normal range of C—H stretching frequencies, is of interpretive significance. However, many other strong bands, absent in the spectrum of Figure 15, are present in the spectra of compounds con-taining methylenedioxy groups.[24]

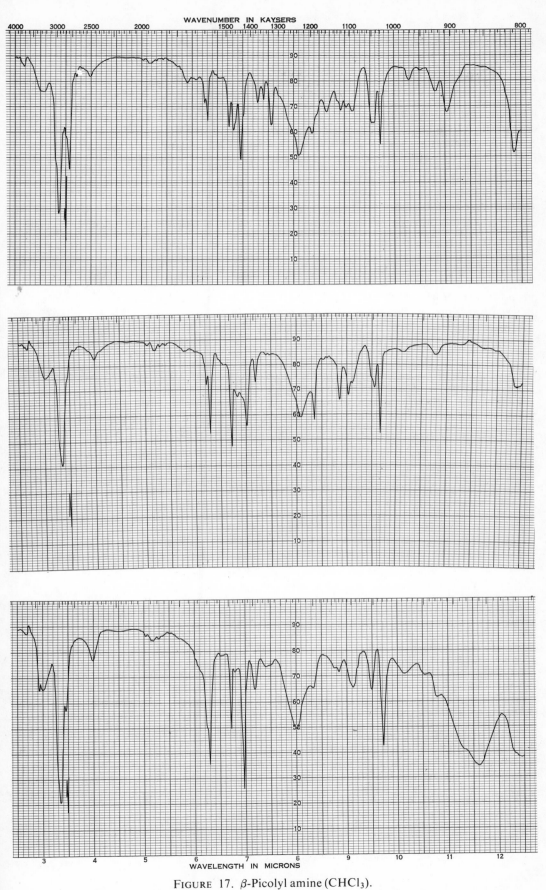

WAVENUMBER IN KAYSERS

WAVELENGTH IN MICRONS

FIGURE 17. β-Picolyl amine (CHCl₃).

69

$\left(\dfrac{20 + 2 + 2 - 14}{2} = 5\right)$, which could be accommodated by a molecule containing either a six-membered aromatic ring and one additional ring or double band, or by a molecule containing a five-membered heteroaromatic system and two other points of unsaturation. A closer examination of the sample's infrared spectrum and of some typical patterns of various types of aromatic systems strongly suggested that the molecule might contain a pyridinic ring substituted in the 3-position, as one may verify by comparing the spectrum in Figure 15 with those in Figures 16 and 17. Moreoever, the band at $3.58\,\mu$ and the absence of bands corresponding to stretching of an NH and of an isolated $C{=}N$ group clearly indicated that the second nitrogen atom of the molecule must occur in a system

such as $CH_3{-}N\Big\langle\begin{smallmatrix}C\\[2pt]C\end{smallmatrix}$

Subtracting the elements of a pyridine radical from the molecular formula of the compound ($C_{10}H_{14}N_2{-}C_5H_4N{=}C_5H_{10}N$) and adding one hydrogen atom to the formula of the resulting radical allowed a search through Beilstein's formula index for compounds that might represent the second moiety of the molecule. These, of course, should satisfy the conditions discussed above; viz., have a molecular formula $C_5H_{11}N$, which requires the presence of either a double bond or a ring, and contain a $CH_3{-}N\Big\langle^{C}$ unit (and, consequently, no primary amino group) but no carbon-nitrogen double bond. Besides N-methylpyrrolidine, only some methyl amines containing a carbon-carbon double bond or a 3- or 4-membered ring satisfy the conditions imposed by the spectral data. While a final choice probably would have been possible if an amount of material sufficient for an NMR determination had been available, the compound was finally identified by a direct comparison of its infrared and mass spectra with those of authentic nicotine.*

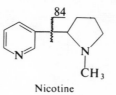

Nicotine

3. The Band-by-band and the Pattern Approach to Postulation of Structures by Infrared

Some of the examples of the preceding section show that, in favorable cases, it may be possible to postulate a few or even a unique structure for a simple compound through the careful study of its infrared spectrum, by what may be called a band-by-band approach. However, this is by no means the rule, since even the spectra of simple compounds may be difficult to analyze in this fashion. Another approach, which has been employed in the last two examples of the previous section, is possible in many instances and is based upon the recognition of a pattern, or a group of bands, that is characteristic of a certain structural feature. The two basic methods certainly do not exclude each other, but rather are complementary. They can, perhaps, be compared to two common systems of teaching

---

* It may be of interest that the base peak of the mass spectrum of the alkaloid falls at $m/e = 84$ and corresponds to the fragmentation indicated above, which would not be considered, a priori, to be the most favorable one.

children to read, namely the syllable-by-syllable approach (the band-by-band method), and the other based upon the instantaneous recognition of whole words (the pattern method). While the former system of interpreting spectra is the more generally useful, and safe, the pattern method deserves more attention and should be recognized as a very powerful tool for structural determination.

The sound foundation of the pattern method will be shown by means of the following brief discussion of the spectra of furanic compounds, which will also serve the purpose of showing that this method is, by its very nature, particularly useful with aromatic or heteroaromatic systems, although not limited to them.

The spectrum of furan exhibits three hands at 6.29, 6.72, and 7.24μ that Thompson and Temple[86] attributed to the normal modes of vibration I to III (ring stretching) and a band at 10.10μ attributed by the same authors to the ring breathing mode IV.

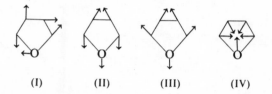

(I)   (II)   (III)   (IV)

It is to be expected that corresponding bands will be present in the spectra of substituted furans and, in fact, Katritsky and Lagowsky[59] found bands at 6.21 to 6.42, 6.61 to 6.80, 7.11 to 7.48, and 9.76 to 9.94μ in the spectra of a large number of 2-substituted furans. The compounds examined by these authors contain a large variety of substituents in the 2-position of the furan nucleus, and this explains the relatively broad ranges indicated above for these vibrations. Actually, in groups of compounds with the same type of substituent, the ranges in which these bands occur are much narrower. For example, statistical treatment of the first three bands indicates the following ranges of wavelengths and intensities (the latter reported as ϵ_A, in parentheses) corresponding to various types of substitution:

Sat. C	6.22–6.24	(20 ± 7)	6.62–6.63	(30 ± 8)	7.20–7.27	†
C=C	6.40–6.41	(65 ± 30)	6.73–6.75	(75 ± 5)	7.17–7.18	(50 + 18)
C=O	6.30–6.35	(100 ± 22)	6.74–6.79	(190 ± 5)	7.11–7.16	(105 + 10)

† Not analyzed statistically because this band is masked by stronger absorption in many of the compounds examined.

In addition to the bands mentioned above, it is reasonable to expect that the spectra of 2-substituted furans will show bands due to in-plane and out-of-plane deformations analogous to those of vicinal trisubstituted benzenes (three adjacent hydrogen atoms on the ring). In fact, Katritzky reports bands at 8.07 to 8.33, 8.52 to 8.73, and 9.22 to 9.36μ, which he attributes to modes V–VII, and at 10.58 to 11.0, 11.2 to 11.3, 12.3 to 12.4 (olefins), or 11.9 to 12.0μ (carbonyl compounds), which are attributed to modes VIII to X.

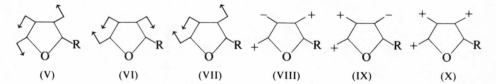

(V)   (VI)   (VII)   (VIII)   (IX)   (X)

It is quite evident that, while the presence in the spectrum of an unknown of only a few of these bands would be of limited diagnostic significance, the presence of all the bands mentioned above (the pattern) would certainly give more than a hint concerning the pres-

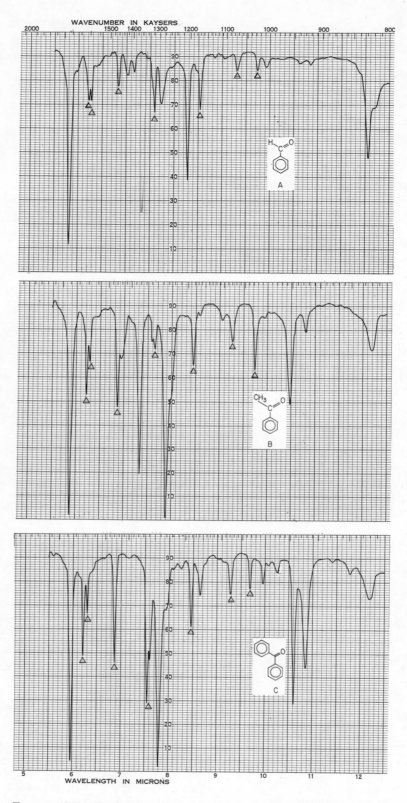

FIGURE 18 (A-F). 5.0–12.5μ region (CCl₄) of C₆H₅COR compounds.
R =: (A) H; (B) CH₃; (C) C₆H₅; (D) OH; (E) OCOC₅H₅; (F) Cl.

72

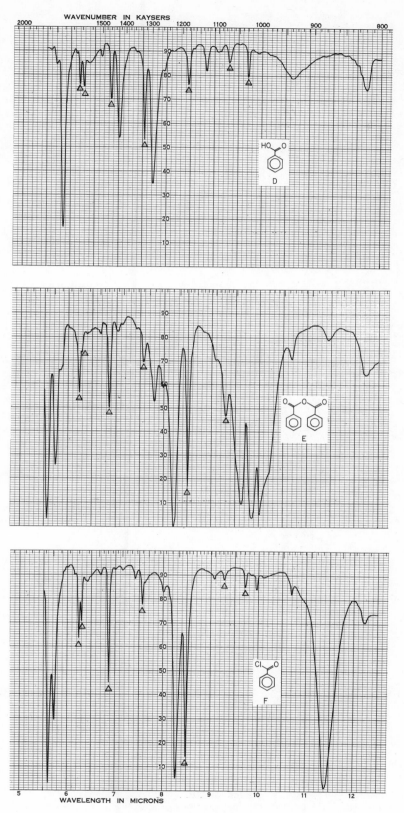

Figure 18 (*cont'd*)

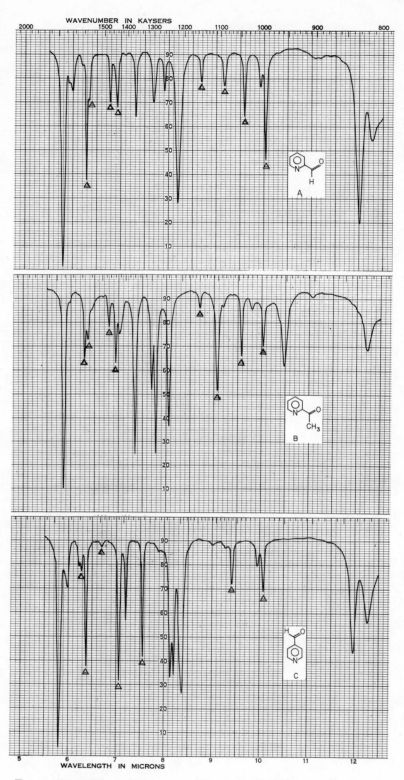

WAVENUMBER IN KAYSERS

WAVELENGTH IN MICRONS

FIGURE 19 (A-F). 5.0–12.5μ region (CCl₄) of 2-, 3- and 4-pyridoyl compounds. (A) Pyridine-2-aldehyde; (B) 2-acetylpyridine; (C) pyridine-4-aldehyde; (D) pyridine-3-aldehyde; (E) 3-acetylpyridine; (F) 4-acetylpyridine.

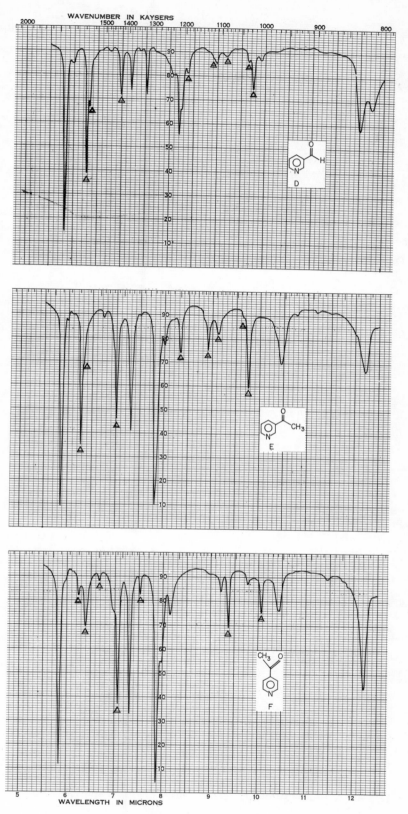

Figure 19 (*cont'd*)

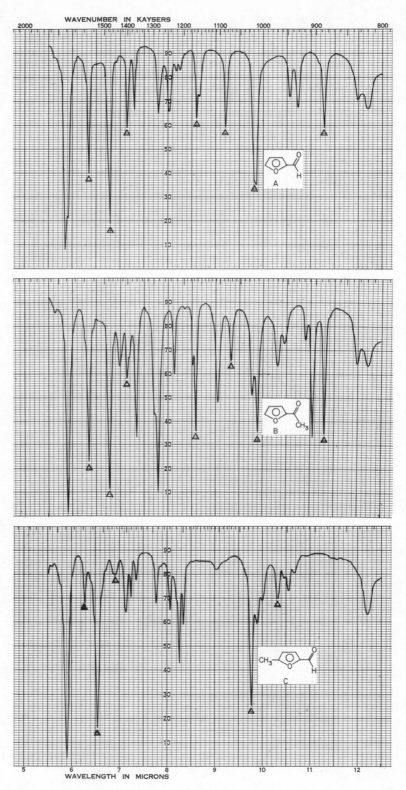

WAVENUMBER IN KAYSERS

WAVELENGTH IN MICRONS

FIGURE 20 (A-F). 5.0–12.5μ region (CCl₄) of furoyl compounds. (A) Furfural; (B) 2-acetylfuran; (C) 5-methylfurfural; (D) furoic acid; (E) furoyl chloride; (F) 5-methyl-2-acetylfuran.

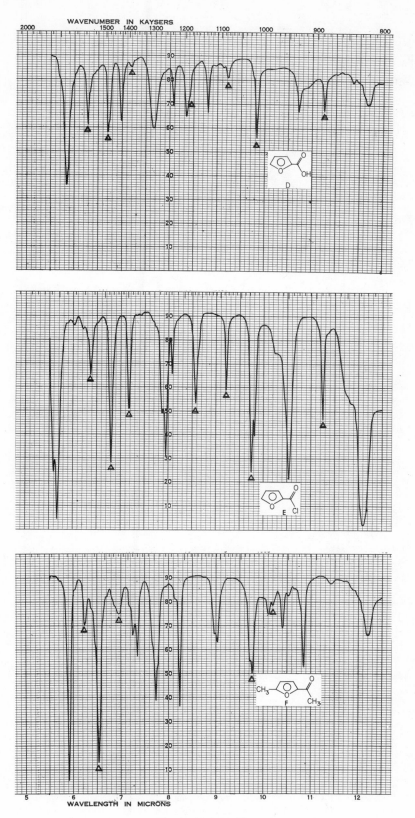

Figure 20 (*cont'd*)

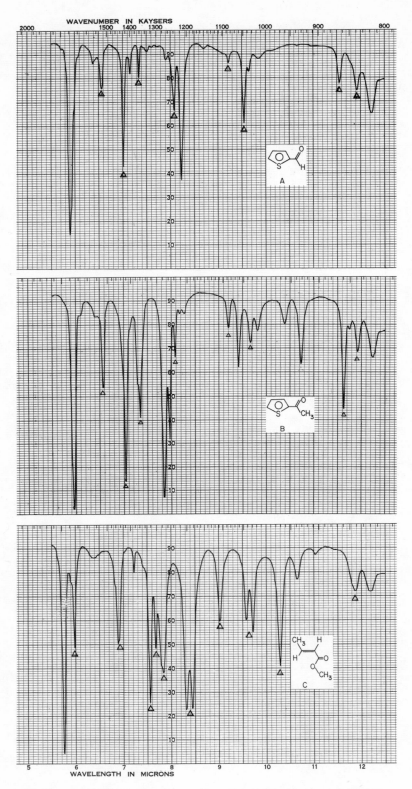

FIGURE 21 (A-F). 5.0–12.5μ region (CCl₄) of: (A) 2-thiophenaldehyde; (B) 2-acetylthiophene; (C) methyl crotonate; (D) methyl β-2-furylacrylate; (E) ethyl β-2-furylacrylate; (F) ethyl crotonate.

78

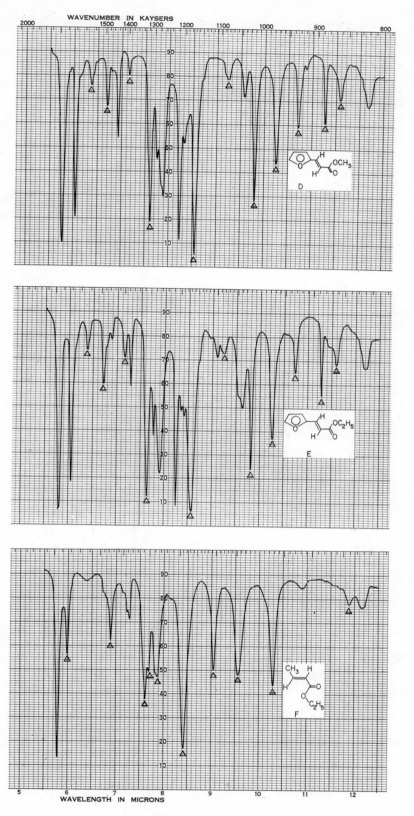

Figure 21 (*cont'd*)

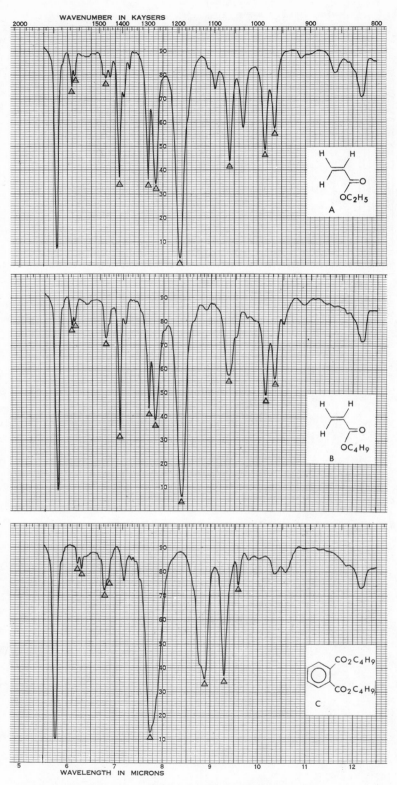

FIGURE 22 (A-F). 5.0–12.5μ region (CCl₄) of: (A) ethyl acrylate; (B) n-butyl acrylate; (C) n-butyl phthalate; (D) methyl benzoate; (E) iso-butyl benzoate; (F) didecyl phthalate.

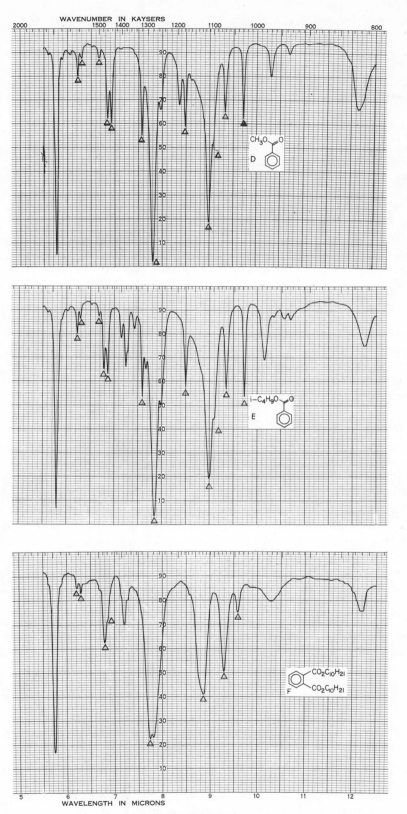

Figure 22 (*cont'd*)

ence of a 2-substituted furanic structure. Furthermore, some information concerning the nature of the substituent can sometimes be rapidly gained, since the relative intensities of some bands of the pattern vary depending on whether the first carbon atom of the substituent chain, i.e., the one connected to the furan ring, is an electron donor or an electron acceptor.

Naturally, some bands of the pattern will be highly sensitive to changes in the substitution on the ring. For example, while some changes are observed in the bands corresponding to ring-stretching and ring-breathing vibrational modes when comparing 2-substituted and 2,5-disubstituted furanic systems, the substitution patterns of the two types are found to be completely different. Without further comment on this point, the reader is invited to compare the spectra of furfural and 2-acetylfuran on one hand and those of 5-methylfurfural and 5-methyl-2-acetylfuran on the other (see Figures 20a, b, c, and f).

Once the origin of the bands present in the spectra of simple furanic compounds is understood, it readily follows that the *pattern characteristic of the particular ring structure and the particular type of substitution* should be found in the spectrum of any molecule, no matter how complex, containing that particular system.

A few spectra, Figures 18 to 22, are presented in order to show the potentiality of the pattern method. The bands found most useful for recognition of each of the molecular units considered, i.e., a benzoyl, a 2-, 3-, or 4-pyridoyl unit, etc., are marked with an asterisk. It should be noted that patterns are also extremely useful in the identification of α, β-unsaturated esters[60] (the data given in standard works furnish little insight into the nature of the acid moiety).

However, it should be kept in mind that *the pattern method must be used with caution*.

4. The Interpretation of Infrared Spectra by the Non-Specialist

The examples given in the previous sections were chosen to illustrate the fact that there are various factors that must be taken into consideration when trying to determine the structure of a compound on the basis of its infrared spectrum. For instance, the first example showed the importance of correlating *band positions* with specific structural features; the importance of interpreting correctly the message that may be conveyed by *band shapes* and intensities was illustrated by the second example; observations upon the *relative intensities* of two bands were put to good use in the third, and the information of diagnostic significance that can sometimes be derived from the study of *weak bands* was emphasized in the fourth. Finally, the fifth and sixth examples showed the application of the use of *patterns* which, in reality, is only an extension of the concept of group frequencies.

However, the foundation of all interpretative work still consists in the accurate determination of band positions, coupled with the ability to predict the wavelength at which a particular structural unit will show absorption when present in a particular molecular environment. Excellent compilations of frequency data are available, such as the admirable book by Bellamy,[13] truly the *vade mecum* of anyone engaged in the interpretation of infrared spectra.* Also available are excellent frequency correlation charts, such as those first published by Colthup.[29] However, it is hardly possible to become proficient in spectral interpretation by merely reading compilations of data or by studying charts; actually, the mechanical use of frequency charts by an inexperienced person can lead to quite erroneous conclusions. On the contrary, the *chemist* who decides that he should be able to interpret his own spectra, rather than relying only upon the specialist, should have no reason for concern, provided he realizes that, when reading spectra, he must not set aside his chemical knowledge. Further, he must keep in mind that many of the concepts familiar to him,

Note added in proof. Several other excellent books have recently appeared (See Selected References).

such as those of resonance, strain, steric hindrance, electric interactions through space, chelation, etc., are not the exclusive domain of chemistry but that, instead, the chemistry of compounds is only a consequence of their physical properties. Moreover, while the parallel between reactivities and certain group frequencies should not be pushed to far, since the infrared spectrum can only give a picture of molecules in the ground state, the chemist who is used to thinking in terms of electron distributions is very well qualified, indeed, to become quite proficient in spectral interpretation. His knowledge of chemicals gives him a decided advantage over the physical specialist. In addition, reasoning by analogy, truly one of the most important tools in his armamentarium, lends him a sure hand in the necessary process of choosing valid model compounds.

Considering what has been said, it is rather surprising that many chemists still rely completely on the specialist for their interpretative work, thus handicapping both themselves and the specialists, who might otherwise devote more time to the search for new useful correlations from which, in turn, the chemist would benefit.

With these facts in mind, the remaining part of this section will be devoted to a discussion of the infrared characteristics of the functional group which is probably the most important in chemistry: the carbonyl. This will afford the opportunity to present a set of self-consistent frequency values, most of them obtained on the same instrument, and, as far as possible, in the same solvent. Also, it is hoped that reading the remaining part of this section and solving the problems at the end of the chapter will give the reticent chemist confidence in the fact that there is nothing specialistic in the interpretation of infrared spectra, or, better, in the kind of interpretation that is of interest to the organic chemist.

The goal proposed is certainly not that of complete coverage of the subject. Rather, it is to give the neophyte a "feeling" for the various known molecular environmental factors that can influence the carbonyl group and of acquainting him with a number of basic phenomena of which one must be well aware when attempting to reason his way into the interpretation of infrared spectra.

While some readers may believe that the explanations offered for many of the phenomena are overly simplified, they should bear in mind that this section is devoted to newcomers to the field and that even what might be considered *ad hoc* explanations constitute a solid foundation for the interpretation of the spectra of many different types of compounds.

5. The Nature of the Carbonyl Group

The carbon atom of the carbonyl group is in its sp^2 hybridization state, with three coplanar orbitals forming angles of approximately 120° with one another; the fourth is a p orbital, perpendicular to the plane formed by the sp^2 orbitals. The carbonyl bond results from the interaction of one of the sp^2 orbitals of the carbon atom with one of the p orbitals of the oxygen (σ bond) and of the other p orbital of the oxygen atom with the p orbital of the carbon (π bond). Because of the different electronegativities of the two atoms, the bonding electrons are not equally distributed in the space between carbon and oxygen and the important contribution of the dipolar form

$$\text{\scriptsize$\diagdown$}C=\bar{O}\text{\small|} \quad \leftrightarrow \quad \text{\scriptsize$\diagdown$}\overset{(+)}{C}-\overset{(-)}{\bar{O}}\text{\small|}$$

to the total structure of the carbonyl group causes the appearance of a marked electrophylic character on the carbon atom of the carbonyl. Equally important in determining the nature of the carbonyl group are the other outside-shell electrons of the oxygen atom, namely the $2s^2$ and the $2p^2$ electrons. These lone-pair electrons are responsible for the formation of hydrogen bonds to the carbonyl group. In an acidic medium, carbonyl compounds may actually be transformed, at least in part, into their conjugate acids, whose carbonyl carbon is much more strongly electrophylic and, consequently, more reactive toward nucleophilic reagents (acid catalysis of additions to carbonyl compounds).

$$\underset{/}{\overset{\backslash}{C}} = \underset{\oplus}{\bar{O}} - H \quad \leftrightarrow \quad \underset{\oplus}{\overset{\backslash}{\underset{/}{C}}} - \bar{O} - H$$

This "basic" character of the carbonyl oxygen atom is unquestionably responsible for the shifts in frequency of the carbonyl stretching absorption which are observed when the spectra of carbonyl compounds are determined in solvents capable of acting as hydrogen donors. These hydrogen-bonding effects on the carbonyl absorption frequencies, even though only slightly larger than less specific solvent effects, are nevertheless real. This is indicated, for instance, by the values of $\nu_s(C{=}O)$ of acetone in the vapor and liquid states and in solution in various solvents (Table 5). In the table, the solvents are listed in order of increasing values of the function $n^2 - 1/2n^2 + 1$, where n is their refractive index; the solvents in which hydrogen-bonding can occur are indicated in boldface character.

In order to minimize these solvent effects, all the frequency values presented in this chapter refer to dilute carbon tetrachloride solutions of the compounds, except in the few

TABLE 5.   Effect of Hydrogen Bonding on the C=O Stretching Mode of Acetone*

Solvent	$n^2 - 1/2n^2 + 1$	$\nu_s(C{=}O)$ (cm^{-1})
Vapor	—	1740
Liquid	$18 \cdot 10^{-2}$	1716
C_2H_5OH	18	*1709*
Ethyl ether	18	1721
Hexane	19	1723
CH_2Cl_2	20	*1713*
$CHCl_3$	21	*1712*
$1,2\text{-}C_2H_4Cl_2$	21	*1714*
CCl_4	22	1719
C_6H_6	23	1716
Toluene	23	1719
$CHBr_3$	25	*1708*
CS_2	26	1717

Data from Pimentel, G. C., and McClellan, A. L., "The Hydrogen Bond," San Francisco, W. C. Freeman and Co., 1960.

*Note that theoretical considerations indicate that the shifts in frequency due to solvent effects must depend upon the characteristics of both the solute and the solvent. Thus, it would be unwise to indiscriminately extrapolate the data given above for acetone to other carbonyl compounds of a different class. On the other hand, it should be kept in mind that the sensitivity of $\nu_s(C{=}O)$ to solvent polarity, and in particular to hydrogen-bonding, constitutes a useful criterion for the differentiation of carbonyl stretching vibrations from ring and $\nu_s(C{=}C)$ modes, which are relatively insensitive to solvent effects. For some applications of this criterion, see Refs. 14, 15, and 57.

cases when poor solubility of the samples in this solvent made it mandatory to determine the spectra on chloroform solutions or, very seldom, on KBr pellets.

Apart from external factors, such as the occurrence of intermolecular hydrogen bonding or other forms of association, various internal ones may perturb the electronic distribution of the carbonyl group. The detailed consideration of these factors and of the way they affect the carbonyl stretching frequencies constitutes the basis for the interpretation of the spectra of substances containing such a group.

Considering the basic structure $\overset{R}{\underset{\underset{O}{\|}}{\diagdown}}\overset{X}{\underset{}{C}}\diagup$, we shall take as the "normal" class, that is, the one in which the interaction between the group X and the carbonyl group is at a minimum, the class represented by the saturated aliphatic ketones. Furthermore, we shall simply state that any factor *tending to increase the double bond character of the carbonyl group, that is, to increase the force constant of the bond, will cause an increase of the frequency (lowering of the wavelength) of the infrared radiation that the group is capable of absorbing.* Naturally, the opposite effect will be caused by any factor tending to diminish the double bond character of the carbonyl group.

The discussion of the factors that perturb the nature of the carbonyl group of compounds of the general formula RCOX will be divided into two main sections, based upon: A) *Effects observed by varying X and holding R constant* (X = $O^{\ominus}$: anions of carboxylic acids; X = —NR$_2$: amides; X = —H: aldehydes; X = —OR: esters; X = —OH, carboxylic acids; X = —Cl: acid chlorides; X = —OCOR: anhydrides of carboxylic acids); B) *Effects observed by varying R and holding X constant* (conjugation of unsaturated groups with the carbonyl, electrical interactions through space, steric strain, chelation, etc.).

5.1. Variations of the Electronic Distribution and of the Wavelength of Absorption of the Carbonyl Group Corresponding to Variations of the Group X. The nature of the group X in compounds of the general formula RCOX may influence the electronic distribution and, consequently, the wavelength of absorption of the carbonyl group because of two fundamental phenomena: *resonance* and *induction*. We shall illustrate this point by considering compounds in which X is NR$_2$ (amides), OR (esters), and Cl (acid chlorides).

5.1a. Resonance Effects. The contribution of structures such as XII, XIV, and XVI to the total structure of compounds of the types XI, XIII, and XV may cause a reduction of the carbonyl character, the magnitude of which is dependent upon the importance of these contributions to the resonance hybrids.

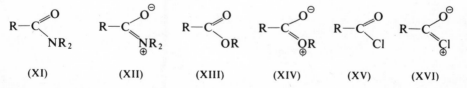

(XI)　　　　(XII)　　　　(XIII)　　　　(XIV)　　　　(XV)　　　　(XVI)

The importance of such resonance forms manifests itself in various ways; for example, in the case of esters, reduced freedom of rotation about the C—OR bond is clearly indicated by dipole-moment measurements and, more specifically, by the temperature independence of the dipole moments of these compounds over a wide range of temperatures. The resonance stabilization of the amide group is still larger than that of the ester group, and the importance of forms such as XII manifests itself in the geometry of the amide group, which is planar, in the lengths of the C=O and C—N bonds (both intermediate to those corresponding to single and double bonds) and also in the low reactivity of amides in reactions initiated by attack of a nucleophile on the carbonyl carbon atom. With reference to the chlorides of carboxylic acids, one may consider, instead, that forms such as XVI cannot be important contributors to the resonance hybrid.

5.1b. Inductive Effects. Superimposed upon the resonance effect between the carbonyl and the group X conjuncted to it, one must also consider the inductive effect, which is due to the different electronegativities of the carbonyl carbon and of the group X. The inductive effect operates, in general, in a sense opposite to that of the resonance effect and can be schematically represented by the following canonical form:

$$R{-}C{=}\overset{\curvearrowleft}{\underset{\underset{X}{\curvearrowleft}}{O}}| \quad \approx \quad R{-}C{\equiv}O^{\oplus} \; X^{\ominus}$$

Thus, while resonance tends to reduce the bond order of the carbonyl, the inductive effect tends to increase it, and what one actually observes is the cumulative effect of the two factors. The unequal balancing of the two effects in different types of carbonyl compounds is reflected by the fact that the frequency corresponding to stretching of the carbonyl group varies, in general, in the order indicated below:

$$RCOO^- < RCONH_2 < (RCOOH)_2 < RCOR < RCHO \leq RCOOR < RCOOH < RCOOCOR$$

Some actual values of $\nu_s(C{=}O)$ are given in Table 6.

TABLE 6. Values of $\nu_s(C{=}O)$ of Various Types of Carbonyl Compounds*

Compound	Typical of **	$\nu_s(C{=}O)$ (cm^{-1})	$\lambda(C{=}O)$ (μ)
Potassium acetate	Salts of carboxylic acids	1575	6.35
N,N-Dimethylacetamide	Amides (3°) of carboxylic acids	1667	6.00
N-Methylacetamide	Amides (2°) of carboxylic acids	1669	5.99
Acetamide	Amides (1°) of carboxylic acids	{1684 / 1718 (shoulder)	{5.94 / 5.84 (shoulder)
Ethyl carbamate	Carbamates	1689	5.92
Butyric acid (dimer)	Carboxylic acids (dimers)	1721	5.81
Butanone	Ketones	1724	5.80
Propyl formate	Esters of formic acid	1733	5.77
Butanal	Aldehydes	1736	5.76
Ethyl propionate	Esters of carboxylic acids	1736	5.76
Methyl propionate	Methyl esters of carboxylic acids	1748	5.72
Diethyl carbonate	Normal carbonates	1751	5.71
Diphenyl carbonate	Vinyl-type carbonates	1761	5.68
Isopropylidene acetate	Vinyl esters of carboxylic acids	1764	5.67
Vinyl acetate	Vinyl esters of carboxylic acids	1770	5.65
Phenyl acetate	Phenyl esters	1770	5.65
Butyric acid (monomer)	Carboxylic acids (monomers)	1776	5.63
Acetyl chloride	Chloride of carboxylic acids	1812	5.52
Acetic anhydride	Anhydrides of carboxylic acids	{1825 / 1754	{5.48 / 5.70

*All values determined in carbon tetrachloride solution, with the exception of those for potassium acetate and ethyl carbamate (KBr pellet) and acetamide (chloroform solution).

**Small variations must be expected for various members of the same class.

A few comments on the values given in Table 6 are appropriate:

(a) The very low "carbonyl" absorption frequency exhibited by salts of carboxylic acids is certainly not surprising, in view of the very large resonance energy of the carboxylate ions, which are much more accurately represented by forms such as XVII than by XVIII. Consequently, the bonds between the two oxygen atoms and the carbon become identical, and the band at 1575 cm^{-1} is only one component of a pair, the second one appearing at about 1412 cm^{-1} (antisymmetric and symmetric stretching).*

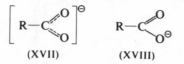

$$(\text{XVII}) \qquad (\text{XVIII})$$

(b) Certainly other factors besides the ones discussed above are instrumental in determining the electronic distribution of the carbonyl groups of amides. This is indicated by the fact that, when the spectra of compounds of this class are determined on very dilute solutions in nonpolar solvents, such as hexane, the carbonyl absorptions occur at frequencies which are considerably different from the ones indicated above.**[70]—The shift to lower frequencies which accompanies alkyl substitution on the nitrogen atom of amides can be related[75] to the stabilizing effect exerted by such groups on resonance forms such as XII (p. 85).—It is of interest to note that a satisfactory explanation has not yet been put forward for the splitting of the carbonyl band observed in the spectrum of acetamide. While the doublets observed in the spectra of some other amides have been attributed to *cis-trans* isomerism,[27] this postulation is not plausible in the case of acetamide itself. The possibility that the phenomenon might be due to an equilibrium between associated and non-associated forms can also be ruled out, since the intensity ratio of the two peaks is not dependent upon concentration.

(c) Carboxylic acids have a strong tendency to exist as dimers, and the strong carbonyl band present in their spectra is, indeed, due to the dimer. This band may be accompanied by a much weaker one due to the carbonyl of the small percentage of monomer present, but often this satellite band appears only as a shoulder on the high-frequency side of the principal absorption. The marked elevation in frequency of the C=O stretching band of monomeric carboxylic acids, as compared with ketones, may be attributed to the strong electron-attracting power of the hydroxyl group.

(d) The fact that the carbonyl absorption of aldehydes occurs at a frequency higher than that of the corresponding ketones may be rationalized by considering that alkyl groups (two in ketones and one in aldehydes) are capable of causing a decrease of the double-bond character of the carbonyl to which they are joined (hyperconjugation).

$$\overset{\oplus}{H} \quad \underset{CH_2}{\overset{R}{C}}-O^{\ominus}$$

(e) Vinyl esters, of the general type RCOOC(R)=CR$_2$, and the analogous phenyl esters deserve special attention, since in the spectra of these compounds both the C=O

*The large variations observed in the infrared spectra when a carboxylic acid is transformed into a salt can be put to good use when some doubt exists as to whether or not a certain carbonyl band should be attributed to a carboxyl group. One may add to the sample a few drops of triethylamine; in the presence of an acid, salt formation will result in a very marked shift of the "carbonylic" band. It should be noted, however, that this technique is successful only if the acid is dissolved in solvents which favor salt formation (chloroform is satisfactory, while carbon tetrachloride is not); moreover, salt formation would be expected to occur also in the case of compounds that contain a group which is vinylogous to a carboxyl group.

**This can be easily determined, of course, only with amides having a sufficiently long hydrocarbon chain to permit solution in nonpolar solvents.

stretching band and the absorption due to complex vibrations of the C—O—R grouping are apparently abnormal; the former occurs at higher frequency, and the latter at lower frequency than the analogous bands of the corresponding non-vinyl compounds. These facts can be rationalized on the basis that forms such as the one indicated below may be important to the resonance hybrid of vinyl esters:

$$R-\overset{\overset{\displaystyle |\bar O}{\|}}{C}-\underset{}{\bar O}-C{=}C \approx R-\overset{\overset{\displaystyle |\bar O}{\|}}{C}-\underset{\oplus}{\bar O}{=}C-\underset{\ominus}{C} \quad (R-\overset{\overset{\displaystyle |\bar O}{\|}}{C}-\underset{\oplus}{\bar O}{=}\underset{\ominus}{R'})$$

This would decrease the tendency of the ethereal oxygen to furnish electrons to the carbonyl carbon, causing an increase of the double-bond character of the carbonyl (relative to that of normal esters), a decrease of the double-bond character of the C—O linkage of the C—OR' grouping, and the acquisition of a certain amount of double-bond character by the linkage between the ethereal oxygen atom and the group R' conjucted to it. It is noteworthy that the increased electrophilic character of the carbonyl carbon of vinyl esters manifests itself also in their higher rate of hydrolysis with respect to the corresponding non-vinyl compounds. For instance, the hydrolysis rate in alkaline solution at 25° is more than one hundred times higher for vinyl acetate than for ethyl acetate. A case akin to that of the vinyl esters is that of many nitrogen-containing compounds such as XIX, which show "ester" carbonyl absorption at abnormally high frequencies.[44]

$$CH_3-C\overset{\displaystyle O}{\underset{\displaystyle O-NH-COCH_3}{<}}$$

$$\nu_s(C{=}O): 1800 \text{ cm}^{-1} (\sim 5.56\mu)$$

(XIX)

In these cases, the observed anomaly is probably due to the demand for electrons (inductive effect) exerted by the amide nitrogen upon the ethereal oxygen of the "ester" moiety; however, a coulombic interaction may also be operative.

(f) The double carbonyl absorption observed in the spectra of anhydrides represents an example of mechanical interaction between two individual C=O vibrations (see p. 111).

It would be wise for the neophyte to eventually commit to memory the set of figures given above and many of those that will be presented in the following sections, since this will permit him to rapidly become oriented when inspecting an infrared spectrum of a carbonyl compound. However, attention should be called to the danger of becoming dogmatic in these matters. The best way to implement this warning is to point out the existence of "exceptions" to the rules. For instance, the carbonyl stretching absorption of N-acetylpyrrole (XX), formally a tertiary amide, occurs at 1724 cm^{-1} (5.80μ), a frequency certainly more indicative of an aliphatic ketone than of an amide. It is not difficult to perceive that the contribution of a resonance form analogous to XII (p. 85) must be practically nil in this molecule, since it could only occur at the expense of the resonance energy of the ring. Even more "abnormal" appear the carbonyl stretching frequencies of 1-acetylglyoxaline (XXI), 4-acetyl-1,2,4-triazole (XXII), and 1-acetyltetrazole (XXIII). This results from increasing withdrawal of electrons into the heterocyclic system with the progressive replacement of the ring-CH groups by nitrogen atoms. It should be noted that the gradual strengthening of the carbonyl and simultaneous weakening of the exocyclic C—N bond is parallelled in these compounds by enhanced reactivity and increased ease of hydrolysis.[76] This constitutes the basis for a novel synthetic procedure for aliphatic or aromatic ketones.[83,84]

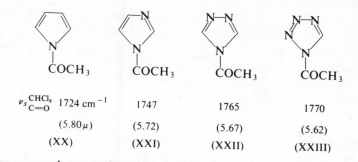

$\nu_s\,{}^{CHCl_3}_{C=O}$ 1724 cm^{-1}	1747	1765	1770
(5.80μ)	(5.72)	(5.67)	(5.62)
(XX)	(XXI)	(XXII)	(XXIII)

Analogously, the unusual properties of N-acylaziridines have been put to good use in a method for the synthesis of aldehydes from the corresponding acids via amides.[26]

N

COR

N-Acylaziridine

ν_s(C=O): 1730 cm^{-1}(5.78μ)

A phenomenon which is quite the opposite of the ones discussed above may be caused by transannular interactions, i.e., occurring through space, between a carbonyl and an amino group which are properly positioned relative to each other. As a consequence of such an interaction, the carbonyl loses some of its double-bond character and the nitrogen some of its basicity (transannular amide-type neutralization). For instance, the ν_s (C=O) of the alkaloid cryptopine (XXIV), *a weak base*, occurs at 1675 cm^{-1} (5.97μ), which is a somewhat low frequency for a keto-carbonyl conjugated with an aromatic ring. Furthermore, the spectrum of the perchlorate of this alkaloid does not show any carbonyl stretching absorption, in agreement with the partial structure [Me—N—C—OH]$^+$ ClO$_4^-$.[7] The fact that cryptopine fails to yield an oxime and does not condense with benzaldehyde or with amyl nitrite may also be a consequence of the interaction of the lone pair of electrons of the nitrogen atom with the carbonyl across the ten-membered ring. A similar situation prevails also with N-methylpseudostrychnidine (XXV); actually, in this case, the transannular interaction is even more evident.

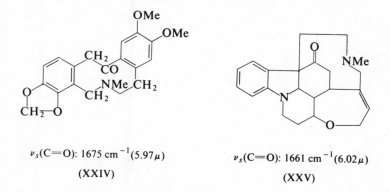

ν_s(C=O): 1675 cm^{-1}(5.97μ) ν_s(C=O): 1661 cm^{-1}(6.02μ)

(XXIV)   (XXV)

These interesting phenomena have been extensively studied with simpler model compounds by Leonard and his collaborators,[64,65,67] who have demonstrated the rather stringent requirements that must be met for transannular interactions to occur. The same author has more recently studied[66] the interactions that can take place between a sulfoxide and a ketone function in an eight-membered ring system, such as that of the sulfoxide of 1-thiacyclooctan-5-one (XXVI). On the basis of infrared, NMR, and other data, the perchlorate of this compound was assigned structure XXVII, with an oxygen bridge between the sulfur and the carbon atom diametrically opposed to it.

A transannular interaction is evidenced in the ultraviolet spectral region, but not in the infrared,* also for cyclodec-5-en-1-one (XXVIII).[69]

| (XXVI) | (XXVII) | (XXVIII) |

5.2. Variations of the Electronic Distribution and of the Wavelength of Absorption of the Carbonyl Group Corresponding to Variations of the Group R. The nature of the group R in compounds of the general formula RCOX may influence the electronic distribution, and consequently, the wavelength of absorption of the carbonyl group as a result of various phenomena which are discussed below.

5.2a. Conjugation Effects. When a carbonyl group is part of a conjugated system, its unsaturated character decreases, since the π-electrons of the unsaturated groups tend to distribute themselves over the entire system (delocalization of electrons). This reduction of the unsaturated character manifests itself—inter alia—with a lowering of the carbonyl stretching frequency. The magnitude of this effect depends upon both the type of conjugation (olefinic, aromatic, heterocyclic, etc.) and upon the type of compound (ketone, acid, aldehyde, ester, etc.).

Olefinic Conjugation. Several examples of the effect of olefinic conjugation upon $\nu_s(C{=}O)$ of various classes of compounds are given in Table 7. It should be observed that the degree and type of substitution on the olefinic linkage play a definite role in determining the frequency (and intensity values) of both C=O and C=C stretching vibrations. In fact, for an accurate interpretation of the spectra of compounds whose carbonyl is conjugated with olefinic systems, it is necessary to take into account the various possible geometrical states. Considering the contribution of polar forms such as $\overset{\oplus}{C}{-}C{=}C{-}O^{\ominus}$ to the total structure of α,β-unsaturated carbonyl compounds, one can understand the possibility of existence of a particular type of geometrical isomerism. This is due to the partial double-bond character of the linkage between the C=C and C=O groups, which is represented in the classical form as a single bond, and is termed *s-cis-trans isomerism, where s- signifies limited rotation about a "single" bond.*

For example, if both the conventional and the *s-cis-trans* isomerisms are taken into account for crotonaldehyde, one must consider the four following forms:

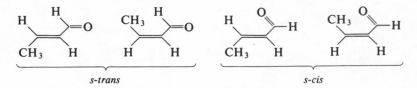

However, dipole moment studies and electronic diffraction measurements show that, at room temperature, crotonaldehyde exists predominantly in the first depicted *s-trans*

---

*It should be borne in mind that the infrared spectrum of a substance is determined by its ground state, while the ultraviolet spectrum is determined by both ground state and electronically excited states.

TABLE 7. Values of ν_s(C=O) of Various Types of Conjugated Carbonyl Compounds (Carbon Tetrachloride Solutions)

Compound	ν_s(C=O) (cm⁻¹)	λ_s(C=O) (μ)	Compound	ν_s(C=O) (cm⁻¹)	λ_s(C=O) (μ)
CH₂=CHCH₂CH₂COCH₃*	1724	5.80	CH₃CH₂CH₂CO₂H*	1721	5.81
CH₂=CHCOCH₃	[1706, 1689]	[5.86, 5.92]	CH₃CH=CH—CO₂H	1709	5.85
(CH₃)₂C=CHCOCH₃	1701	5.88	CH₃CH=C(CH₃)CO₂H**	1701	5.88
(CH₃)₂C=CHCOCH=C(CH₃)₂	[1678, 1637]	[5.96, 6.11]	CH₃CH=CH—CH=CHCO₂H	1698	5.89
CH₃CH₂CHO*	1736	5.76	CH₃CH₂CO₂CH₃*	1748	5.72
CH₂=CHCHO	1706	5.86	CH₃CH=CHCO₂CH₃	1730	5.78
CH₃CH=CHCHO	1701	5.88	CH₃CH=CH—CH=CHCO₂CH₃	[1727, 1739 (sh.)]	[5.79, 5.75]
CH₃CH₂CH₂CH=CH—CHO	1709	5.85	(CH₃CO)₂O*	[1825, 1754]	[5.48, 5.70]
CH₃CH=CH—CH=CH—CHO	1695	5.90	(CH₃CH=CHCO)₂O	[1789, 1739]	[5.59, 5.75]

* Reference compound.
** Tiglic acid.

form.[40] On the other hand, mesityl oxide exists mainly in the *s-cis* configuration, since the *planar s-trans* form of this compound is subjected to severe steric impediments:

An even more complex situation prevails for ketones whose carbonyl group is flanked by two olefinic carbon-carbon double bonds. For instance, there are three possible rotational isomers for phorone:

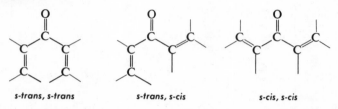

The importance of taking into account the various geometrical forms that are possible for a given unsaturated carbonyl compound resides in the easily understandable fact that the olefinic double bond can perturb the nature of the carbonyl group, and be perturbed by it, to a different extent, depending upon their position in space relative to one another. Moreover, the coexistence of various rotamers of similar energy content but of different polarities may cause the appearance of more than one carbonyl absorption for a given compound. Timmons[87] reported that pent-3-en-2-one exhibits two carbonyl absorptions and suggested that this is due to the presence at equilibrium of both the *s-cis* and *s-trans* rotamers (see also the case of methyl vinyl ketone in Table 7).

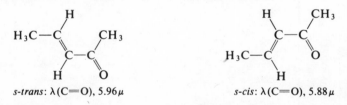

The question of these equilibria has been extensively studied in the case of α,β-unsaturated ketones,[38,72,73] and, aside from the results of theoretical interest, some generalizations of interpretive importance are possible on the basis of these studies. For example, Erskine and Waight[38] have shown that the ratio of the integrated intensities of the C=O and C=C stretching vibrations gives a good indication of the geometry of the unsaturated system, being low in cisoid and high in transoid configurations. In cisoid systems, the intensities of ν_s(C=O) and ν_s(C=C) are actually comparable. Noack and Jones[74] also have presented some useful generalizations concerning the preferred geometry of α,β-unsaturated ketones of the general formula R_1—C—C(R_2)=CR_3R_4
$$\overset{\parallel}{\underset{O}{}}$$
(cisoid, transoid, and equilibrium of the two), as a function of the nature of the substituents R_2, R_3, and R_4.

It may be mentioned at this point that also a cyclopropyl ring can conjugate with the *p*-orbitals of a substituent. For instance, the value of the dipole moment of methyl cyclopropyl ketone (2.84 D) falls between that of methyl vinyl ketone (2.98 D) and that of methyl n-propyl ketone (2.70 D). The carbonyl stretching absorption of methyl cyclo-propyl ketone in carbon tetrachloride solution occurs at 1712 cm^{-1} (5.84μ).

The conjugative effect of an acetylenic group on a carbonyl conjuncted to it has also been studied; for instance, propargyl aldehyde and 1-butyn-3-one are reported[77] to absorb at 1701 cm^{-1} (5.88μ) and 1695 cm^{-1} (5.90μ), respectively. Ethyl propiolate absorbs at 1724 cm^{-1} (5.80μ) and ethylphenylpropiolate at 1718 cm^{-1} (5.84μ).

Finally, it should be remarked that the ultraviolet spectrum of a substance can be much more accurate than its infrared spectrum as a probe of the type and extent of conjugation.

Aromatic Conjugation. When an aromatic ring is conjugated to a carbonyl group either directly or through a carbon-carbon double bond, the unsaturated nature of the carbonyl is again reduced, as observed in olefinic conjugation. This is made clear from considera-tion of the frequency values corresponding to carbonyl stretching vibrations of some typical compounds (Table 8).

The remarkable effect of certain ring substituents upon the carbonyl frequency will be discussed below:

(a) Meta and Para Substituents. Substituents in the meta and para positions of an aromatic ring conjugated to a carbonyl may exert their influence mainly through inductive

TABLE 8. Values of ν_s(C=O) of Various Types of Aromatic Compounds (Carbon Tetrachloride Solutions)

Compound	ν_s(C=O) (cm^{-1})	λ(C=O) (μ)	Compound	ν_s(C=O) (cm^{-1})	λ(C=O) (μ)
Acetic anhydride*	1825 1754	5.48 5.70	α-Methylcinnam- aldehyde	1698 1724(sh.)	5.89 5.80(sh.)
Benzoic anhydride	1802 1739	5.55 5.75	Phenylacetyl chloride*	1808	5.53
Ethyl phenylacetate*	1745	5.73	Benzoyl chloride**	1779** 1739	5.62 5.75
Ethyl benzoate	1727	5.79	Phenyl- Acetic acid*	1718	5.82
Ethyl cinnamate	1727	5.79	Benzoic acid	1704	5.87
Cyclohexyl- carboxaldehyde*	1733	5.77	Cinnamic acid	1698	5.89
Benzaldehyde	1718	5.82	Phenylacetone*	1721	5.81
Pyridine- 2-aldehyde	1727	5.79	Acetophenone	1691	5.91
Pyridine- 4-aldehyde	1724	5.80	2-Acetylpyridine	1709	5.85
Pyridine- 3-aldehyde	1718	5.82	4-Acetylpyridine	1706	5.86
Furfural	1721	5.81	3-Acetylpyridine	1701	5.88
Thiophene- 2-aldehyde***	1695	5.90	2-Acetylfuran	1695	5.90
N-Methylpyrrol- 2-aldehyde	1675	5.97	2-Acetylthiophene	1675	5.97
Cinnamaldehyde	1698	5.89	2-Acetyl- N-methylpyrrole	1667	6.00
			Benzalacetone	1686 1704(sh.)	5.93 5.87(sh.)
			Benzophenone	1669	5.99

* Reference compound.

** For doublet of benzoyl chloride, see p. 106. Similar but less resolved doublets appear in the spectra of several of the hetero-cyclic aldehydes and ketones mentioned in the table.

*** It should be noted that the electron releasing tendency at the 3-position of a 5-membered heterocycle can be quite different from that observed at the 2-position. For instance, the carbonyl stretching absorption of thiophen-3-aldehyde occurs 18 cm^{-1} higher than that of the 2-isomer.[45] An analogous situation prevails with pyrrolic compounds. To the contrary, electron release from the indole ring takes place more easily at the 3- than at the 2-position. For an excellent review of the spectral characteristics of heterocyclic compounds see Ref. f in General References.

effects (meta) or through the combination of inductive and resonance effects (para). Actually, numerous investigators have demonstrated the existence of a linear relationship between carbonyl absorption frequencies of these types of compounds and Hammett reactivity constants (σ), thus pointing to the fact that the same combination of factors may be responsible for differences in reactivities and shifts of carbonyl stretching vibrations. The extent of these substituent effects is shown graphically in Figure 23 which illustrates the relationship between carbonyl stretching frequencies of various classes of carbonyl compounds and the pK values of the corresponding carboxylic acids. The importance of this relationship for the chemist involved in infrared interpretation consists mainly in the fact that, in predicting the expected carbonyl frequencies of meta and para substituted aromatic compounds, he can apply with a reasonable degree of confidence the same very reliable criteria that are generally invoked to explain the difference in pK values of substituted aromatic acids. For example, the difference between the carbonyl absorption frequencies of p-dimethylaminobenzaldehyde (1701 cm^{-1}, 5.88μ), benzaldehyde (1718 cm^{-1}, 5.82μ), and p-nitrobenzaldehyde (1721 cm^{-1}, 5.81μ) can be easily rationalized by

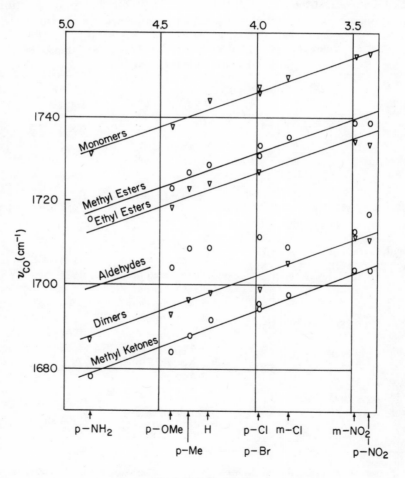

FIGURE 23. Relationship between ν CO of Y-C$_6$H$_4$-COX and pKa of Y-C$_6$H$_4$-CO$_2$H. (G. Egglinton, *J. Chem. Soc.*, Fig. 1, p. 106, 1961.)

considering that the dimethylamino group, forcing electrons into the ring, will tend to stabilize quinoid structures such as:

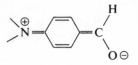

and, consequently, to reduce the double-bond character of the carbonyl. On the contrary, the nitro group, which reduces the electron density of the ring (induction and resonance), will cause an increase of the carbonylic character.* A few typical values for $\nu_s(C{=}O)$ of some meta and para substituted acetophenones are given in Table 9.

TABLE 9.   Effect of Meta and Para Substituents on the $\nu_s(C{=}O)$ of Aromatic Compounds

Compound	$\nu_s(C{=}O)$ (cm^{-1})	$\lambda(C{=}O)$ (μ)	Compound	$\nu_s(C{=}O)$ (cm^{-1})	$\lambda(C{=}O)$ (μ)
p-Aminoacetophenone	1677	5.96	m-Aminoacetophenone	1689	5.92
Acetophenone	1691	5.91	Acetophenone	1691	5.91
p-Fluoroacetophenone	1692	5.91	m-Fluoroacetophenone	1696	5.90
p-Chloroacetophenone	1692	5.91	m-Chloroacetophenone	1696	5.90
p-Nitroacetophenone	1700	5.88	m-Nitroacetophenone	1701	5.88

*All values determined on carbon tetrachloride solutions.
 Data from Ref. 52 and this laboratory.

As it appears from these data, the effects of *meta* and *para* substituents, while real and of unquestionable theoretical interest, may be small. For example, in the case of *p*-fluoro and *p*-chloro substituted acetophenones (resonance and induction operating in opposite sense), the shift in the carbonyl absorption with respect to the norm (acetophenone) amounts to only 1 cm^{-1}, and thus it is of no interest for ordinary diagnostic purposes. However, it is important to be aware of the existence of these phenomena, since consideration of such factors may occasionally be of help in the interpretation of the spectra of aromatic and heterocyclic compounds.

(b) Ortho Substituents.   In aromatic compounds containing substituents ortho to the carbonyl, this group may be perturbed not only through the normal inductive and resonance effects but also through steric effects, dipole interaction through space (field effects), and most importantly, through chelation.

(1) Steric Effects.   A necessary condition for effective electron delocalization in a conjugated system requires that all the atoms that constitute the conjugated system be approximately coplanar. It is then readily apparent that bulky substituents occupying one or both ortho positions of an aromatic carbonyl compound may render conjugation less effective by preventing coplanarity of the carbonyl and the aromatic ring. For example, in the case of 2,3,5,6-tetramethylacetophenone (XXIX), the strong van der Waals repulsions between the ortho methyl groups and the methyl of the acetyl group force the latter into an energetically more favorable configuration, in which the carbonyl is considerably

* It is of interest that NMR spectra of p-N, N-dimethylaminobenzaldehyde and p-N, N-dimethylaminobenzaldehyde-3,5-d$_2$ indicate that at very low temperatures the ortho protons become nonequivalent [Anet, F.A.L., and Ahmad, M. J., J. Amer. Chem. Soc., 86, 119 (1964)]. Note also that the relative abundance of the [CH$_3$CO]$^+$ ion in the mass spectra of p-nitroacetophenone (4.5) acetophenone (1.0) and p-aminoacetophenone (0.26) seem to reflect the different strength of the bond between the carbonyl carbon and the ring in the molecular ions of the three compounds.

diverted out of the plane of the ring. This situation results in a less perfect conjugation of the pi-electrons of the ring with the pi-electrons of the carbonyl, and, consequently, in an increase of the double-bond character of the group, relative, for instance, to that of the carbonyl of acetophenone. The less severe steric hindrance existing in 2,6-disubstituted aromatic aldehydes as compared to the corresponding methyl ketones is illustrated below.

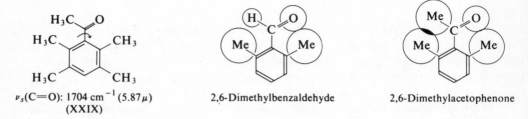

ν_s(C=O): 1704 cm^{-1} (5.87μ)
(XXIX)

2,6-Dimethylbenzaldehyde

2,6-Dimethylacetophenone

It must be noted that the effect of steric hindrance to planarity is considerably more evident in the ultraviolet than in the infrared spectra.*

(2) Field effects. In the case of aromatic carbonyl compounds carrying a polar substituent, such as OR, Cl, Br, or NO_2, in the ortho position, there come into play, beside steric, resonance, and inductive effects, other effects that may be attributed to interactions of dipoles through space. In the infrared spectra, it is possible to see indications of s-cis, s-trans isomerism, due to restricted rotation of the -COR group about the "single" bond which joins this group to the aromatic ring. Thus, an equilibrium of conformers is probably responsible for the appearance of carbonyl doublets in the spectra of some o-substituted acetophenones (XXX).

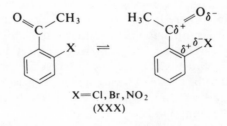

X=Cl, Br, NO$_2$
(XXX)

These are only particular cases of a more general phenomenon that will be treated later (p. 99); additional details can be found in the original literature.[25,52]

(3) Chelation Effects. The most marked effect upon the electron distribution, and therefore upon the carbonyl stretching frequency of o-substituted aromatic compounds, occurs when the substituent is capable of forming a hydrogen bond with the carbonyl. When this occurs, the carbonyl double-bond character is considerably reduced, and this is clearly reflected in the infrared spectrum. However, it is necessary to call attention to the danger involved in *indiscriminately* equating variations in carbonyl stretching frequencies with variations in reactivity of compounds (see Tables 10 and 11).

In general, much more information of interpretive value for the organic chemist can be extracted from spectra measured in solution than from those determined on neat liquids or on solid in KBr, nujol, etc. This is especially true for molecules containing hydroxyl groups and groups capable of acting as acceptors in a hydrogen-bonded system. When spectra of these types of compounds are measured in the condensed state, the intermolec-

---

* It should also be pointed out that this type of steric effect is certainly not limited to aromatic compounds. For instance, the progressive increase reported for ν_s(C=O) of 1-acetyl-cyclohexene, 1-acetyl-2-methylcyclohexene and 1-acetyl-2,6,6-trimethylcyclohexene reflects the progressive increase of steric hindrance to planarity.[21]

TABLE 10. Effect of Hydrogen-Bonding on ν_s(C=O) of Aromatic Compounds*

Compound	ν_s(C=O) (cm^{-1})	λ(C=O) (μ)	Compound	ν_s(C=O) (cm-1)	λ(C=O) (μ)
Benzaldehyde	1712	5.84	Acetophenone	1692	5.91
m-Hydroxybenzaldehyde	1698	5.89	m-Hydroxyacetophenone	1686	5.93
p-Hydroxybenzaldehyde	1692	5.91	p-Hydroxyacetophenone	1675	5.97
o-Hydroxybenzaldehyde	1672	5.98	o-Hydroxyacetophenone	1650	6.06

* All values determined on chloroform solutions.

TABLE 11. Rates of Phenylhydrazone and Oxime Formation of Aldehydes as Related to Hydrogen-Bonding

Aldehyde	Phenylhydrazone Half-time*	Oxime Half-time*
Benzaldehyde	9	0.7
o-Hydroxybenzaldehyde	0.7	0.7
p-Hydroxybenzaldehyde	200	9.0

* Time in minutes for half-completion of the reactions. From Pimentel, G. C., and McClellan, A. L., "The Hydrogen Bond," San Francisco, W. C. Freeman & Co. 1960.

ular and reticular interactions can be so pronounced as to completely preclude the possibility of deriving from the spectra any information of diagnostic significance. To take the simplest example, the differentiation of o-hydroxy-benzaldehyde from its meta and para isomers on the basis of their carbonyl stretching frequencies, which would be a simple task if the spectra were determined in solution, would be hardly possible if they were determined in the condensed state.

In this connection, the information contained in Table 12 is of interest. Although the difference between the carbonyl frequencies of the undissolved compounds and of their solutions in dioxane (a solvent capable of acting as a proton acceptor) is 20 to 40 cm^{-1} for substances with intermolecular hydrogen bonding, the two frequencies are essentially the same for chelated compounds; the largest difference (for salicylic acid) being only 15 cm^{-1}.

This situation can be occasionally turned to advantage in structural studies. For example, by the simple procedure of recording the spectra in both KBr and tetrahydrofuran,

TABLE 12. Inter- and Intramolecular Hydrogen Bonding. Effect of Physical State on ν_s(C=O) *

Compound	Type of H-Bond	ν_s(C=O) (undissolved) (cm^{-1})	(μ)	ν_s(C=O) (Dioxane) (cm^{-1})	(μ)
o-Hydroxybenzaldehyde	Chelat.	1662	6.02[b]	1665	6.01
p-Hydroxybenzaldehyde	Intermol.	1665	6.01[a]	1688	5.92
o-Hydroxyacetophenone	Chelat.	1640	6.09[b]	1640	6.09
p-Hydroxyacetophenone	Intermol.	1658	6.03[a]	1678	5.96
Methyl o-hydroxybenzoate	Chelat.	1675	5.97[b]	1677	5.96
Methyl p-hydroxybenzoate	Intermol.	1680	5.95[a]	1720	5.81
o-Hydroxybenzoic acid	Chelat.	1665	6.01[b]	1680	5.95
p-Hydroxybenzoic acid	Intermol.	1687	5.92[a]	1718	5.82

[a] Liquid.
[b] KBr.
*Data from Ref. 2.

it was determined that one of the carboxyl groups of pannaric acid (XXXI) is in close proximity to an OH group (and chelated to it), while the other is not.[2]

Compound	ν_s(C=O)(cm^{-1}) (KBr)	ν_s(C=O)(cm^{-1}) (Tetrahydrofuran)
Pannaric acid	1662	1658
	1690	1710
Dimethyl pannarate	1657	1660
	1688	1715

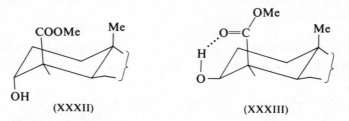

(XXXI)

It must be noted, however, that this criterion is not necessarily applicable to substances containing intramolecular hydrogen bonds not as strong as the ones typical of conjugated chelated systems.

While detection of intramolecular hydrogen bonding can be extremely useful in structural studies of a great variety of complex organic molecules, the subject is too vast to be treated in detail in this chapter. However, consideration of a few examples taken from the literature can give some idea of the potentialities of this approach to delicate problems of structural elucidation. For instance, differentiation between the triterpenoid 3-α-hydroxyurs-12-en-24-oate and its 3-β-epimer (XXXII and XXXIII) is possible by realizing that the carbonyl stretching absorption of the former occurs at 1723 cm^{-1} (5.80 microns), while that of the latter, as a consequence of hydrogen bonding, falls at 1709 cm^{-1} (5.85 microns).[28] This example illustrates, also, the fact that the effect of simple chelation is very small when compared to that of conjugated chelation, such as the one prevailing in aromatic ortho-hydroxy carbonyl compounds, or, for instance, in the enols of β-diketones (see p. 109).

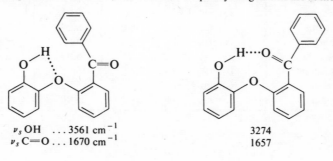

It is important to be aware of the fact that hydrogen bonding can also occur between proton donors and such units as aromatic and cyclopropanic rings and acetylenic and olefinic bonds.[10,12,81,82,89] An interesting example of molecules in which an —OH group can form hydrogen bonds at various sites of the same molecule is represented by the compound shown below, for which the frequency assignments are as indicated:[17]

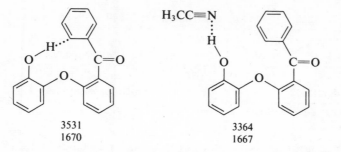

3531
1670

3364
1667

This case also illustrates that, while it is often assumed that intramolecular hydrogen bonding occurs only when a 5- or 6-membered quasi-ring results, formal ring size is certainly not the only determining factor.

Other very remarkable applications of the study of hydrogen bonding were recently reported by Fales and Wildman,[39] who were able to differentiate between haemanthamine and epihaemanthamine on the basis of the observation that, upon hydrogenation of the 1,2-olefinic double bond, the —OH stretching frequency of one of the epimers remained unchanged, while the corresponding vibration of the other moved to higher frequency. After inspection of molecular models, this phenomenon was rationalized by considering that the hydroxyl group at C-11 is situated favorably for hydrogen bonding with the pi-electrons of the olefinic double bond in one of the epimers and with the pi-electrons of the aromatic ring in the other. Consequently, it was reasoned that the —OH stretching frequency of only one of the two epimers should shift upon hydrogenation of the olefinic double bond, and this permitted structural assignments (XXXIV).

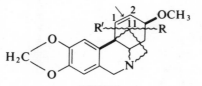

(XXXIV)

Haemanthamine: R=OH, R′=H; Hydroxyl stretching: 3598 cm^{-1} (2.78 μ)
                 Hydroxyl stretching
                 of dihydroderivative: 3625 cm^{-1} (2.76 μ)

Epihaemanthamine: R=H; R′=OH; Hydroxyl stretching: 3560 cm^{-1} (2.81 μ)
                   Hydroxyl stretching
                   of dihydroderivative: 3560 cm^{-1} (2.81 μ)

(The spectra were measured in high dilution in carbon tetrachloride with a double-beam, prism-grating spectrophotometer.)

5.2b. Field Effects.

Mono-, di-, and trichloroacetic acid are all considerably stronger acids than the parent compound. While acetaldehyde, at equilibrium at 20°, is hydrated to the extent of 58 per cent, chloral forms a stable crystalline hydrate. Finally, in aqueous solution at 25°, ethyl monochloracetate is hydrolyzed more than one thousand times faster than ethyl acetate. These phenomena are all related, in a more or less direct manner, to the same physical property, i.e., the increased double-bond character of the carbonyl group of compounds carrying electron-attracting substituents in the α-position. Thus, it is certainly not surprising that such a physical property manifests itself also with an increase of the carbonyl stretching frequency of these compounds relative to those of the parent substances. (Table 13).

These facts, if separately examined, could easily be attributed to simple inductive effects of the electron-attracting groups upon the electronic distribution of the carbonyls. However, evidence has been accumulating in recent years in support of the view that these phenomena must be considered, at least in part, as manifestations of electrical interactions of a coulombic nature, which are transmitted through space rather than through

TABLE 13.   Influence of Halogen α-Substitution on ν_s(C=O)*

Compound	ν_s(C=O) (cm^{-1})	λ_s(C=O) (μ)	Compound	ν_s(C=O) (cm^{-1})	λ_s(C=O) (μ)
Acetaldehyde	1736	5.76	Methyl acetate	1748	5.72
Trichloracetic aldehyde	1767	5.66	Methyl trichloracetate	1776	5.63

* Values determined on carbon tetrachloride solutions.

chemical bonds. For instance, the spectra of various monohalo- and dihalo-carbonyl compounds exhibit two bands in the carbonyl stretching region (Table 14). This double carbonyl absorption can be explained on the basis of the possibility of rotational isomerism for compounds containing the groupings —CO—CH$_2$X or —CO—CHX$_2$. This means that, of the infinite number of conformations which are formally possible by rotation of the —CH$_2$X or the —CHX$_2$ groups about the single bonds which join them to the carbonyl, some are energetically more favorable than others. For example, in the case of compounds of the general type RCOCH$_2$X, the two preferred rotamers are believed to be the ones displaying *cis* and *gauche* conformations.

(A)   (B)
cis   *gauche*

Consideration of the two conformers will promptly reveal, if the possibility of electrical interactions through space is taken into account, that the reciprocal influence of the C—X and the carbonyl dipoles must be different in A and B. In the case of conformer A, the partial negative charge present on X will tend to induce a partial charge of the opposite sign on the carbonyl oxygen atom, thus contrasting the normal polarization of the group and causing a considerable increase in the carbonyl stretching frequency. On the other hand, if conformer B is also present at equilibrium, the appearance of a second carbonyl

TABLE 14.   Manifestations of Field Effects in Mono- and Dihalogenated Carbonyl Compounds

Compound	ν_s(C=O)* (cm^{-1})		λ_s(C=O)* (microns)	
	ν_1 (cm^{-1})	ν_2 (cm^{-1})	λ_1 (μ)	λ_2 (μ)
Methyl acetate		1748		5.72
Methyl monochloracetate	1776	1751	5.63	5.71
Methyl dichloracetate	1776	1757	5.63	5.69
Acetophenone		1691		5.91
ω-Chloroacetophenone	1714	1694	5.84	5.90
ω,ω-Dichloroacetophenone	1716	1693	5.83	5.90
ω,ω,ω-Trichloroacetophenone		1717		5.82
ω-Bromoacetophenone	1709	1688	5.85	5.92
ω,ω-Dibromoacetophenone	1707	1682	5.86	5.95
ω,ω,ω-Tribromoacetophenone		1704		5.87

* Values determined on carbon tetrachloride solutions. Data from Ref. 54 and this laboratory.

stretching band, at a frequency which is generally slightly higher than that of the parent non-halogenated compound, can also be explained. While in this conformation the field effect of the C—X dipole on the electron distribution of the carbonyl group should be negligible, the halogen atom can still exert its normal inductive effect, which is independent of orientation. It should be noted, however, that the frequency of ν_2 is considerably affected by the mass of the substituent (see Table 14 and Ref. 54).

That the band at higher frequency actually pertains to the more polar *cis*-form can be deduced from the study of the variations of the relative intensities of the two bands with the polarity of the solvent in which the spectra are determined. It is known that solvents of high dielectric constant favor the more polar conformers, and, consequently, it is reasonable to expect that the intensity of the carbonyl band corresponding to them should increase, at the expense of the second carbonyl absorption, with increasing polarity of the medium. Figure 24 illustrates this point. It is also of interest that the higher thermo-

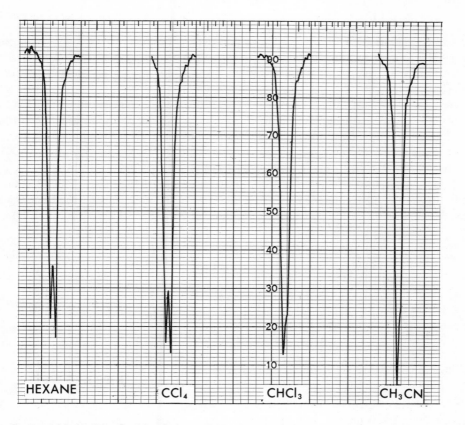

FIGURE 24 (A-D). Carbonyl absorption of methyl dichloracetate. (A) Hexane; (B) CCl_4; (C) $CHCl_3$; (D) CH_3CN.

dynamic stability of the more polar conformers, such as A, has been demonstrated in the case of some open-chain α-halogenated compounds by determining the relative intensities of the two carbonyl bands at various temperatures.[16, 20, 54] Since in this conformation the halogen and oxygen atoms approach each other as closely as possible, in spite of the repulsions that might be expected to exist between them, some stabilizing factor must be involved.

The situation may be different and more complex in the case of α-halocyclanones. The bromine atom in 2-bromocyclohexanone (XXXV) is axial and the compound exhibits a carbonyl stretching frequency only 4 cm^{-1} greater than that of cyclohexanone itself. To the contrary, the carbonyl frequency of 2-bromo-4,4-dimethylcyclohexanone (XXXVI) is hypsochromically shifted 16 cm^{-1} compared with the parent compound, suggesting that the bromine is equatorially oriented. (Minimization of non-bonded interactions.) The problem concerning the conformations of α-halocyclohexanones has been discussed in detail by Corey and collaborators.[32,33]

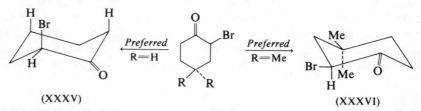

(XXXV)   (XXXVI)

The spectral properties of medium and large ring carbocyclic carbonyl compounds, with special reference to 2-bromo substituted substances, have been studied by Leonard.[68] For a study of polar effects in α-halocyclopentanones, the reader is referred to the work of Sandris and Ourisson.[80]

It should be noted that the effect of polar groups properly oriented relative to a carbonyl manifests itself also in those molecules whose carbonyl group is already perturbed by some other factor. The combined effects of conjugation and dipolar interactions, acting in an opposite sense, can be observed in the spectrum of tribromosantonine (XXXVII).[91] The carbonyl absorption frequencies (CHCl$_3$) are compared below to those of an appropriate model compound (XXXVIII); the bulk of the shift of the ketocarbonyl absorption of the halogenated substance may be attributed to the presence of an equatorial bromine atom in the α-position, with a possible additional contribution of the bromomethyl group.

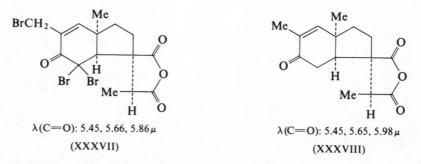

λ(C=O): 5.45, 5.66, 5.86 μ   λ(C=O): 5.45, 5.65, 5.98 μ

(XXXVII)   (XXXVIII)

Finally, it should be stressed that field effects, whose stereospecific character clearly differentiates them from normal inductive effects, are of rather general occurrence and certainly are not limited to α-halogenated substances. For instance, the double carbonyl absorptions observed have been attributed to rotational isomerism, determined at least partially by field effects, in the following types of compounds: aroyl ethylene oxides,[50] glycidic esters,[18] α-methoxymethyl aryl ketones,[35] and α-aminoketones.[34] The last case is particularly interesting because, while the carbonyl band assigned to the *cis* conformer occurs at a frequency higher than that of the corresponding parent compound, the second carbonyl stretching band, assigned to the isomer in the gauche conformation, falls at a frequency lower than that of the carbonyl of the parent compound. This has been attributed to an intramolecular effect related to the previously described transannular interactions occurring in some azacyclanones (p. 89).

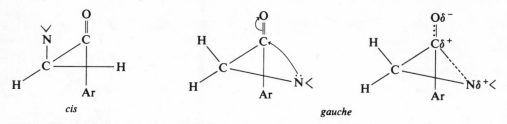

cis   *gauche*

5.2c. Effects of Steric Strain. Typical chemical and physical properties are associated with various types of carbonyl compounds which have in common the characteristic that the angle defined by the carbonyl carbon and the two groups conjuncted to it deviates from the "norm." For instance, while the value of the $\overset{C}{\underset{O}{>}}CO$ angle can be estimated to be approximately 120° for δ-valerolactone, the corresponding angle for the molecule of β-propiolactone has been found to be 94°.[22] More generally ketones, lactones, carbonates, lactams, anhydrides, and some less common types of substances whose carbonyl group is part of a ring of five or fewer members belong to this class of compounds.

A rehybridization of the orbitals of the carbonyl carbon corresponds to the particular kind of geometry of strained carbonyl compounds, resulting in the acquisition of an increased s character by the σ bond of the carbonyl. A shortening of the carbonyl bond, an increase of its force constant, and thus, a rise of the carbonyl stretching frequency relative to that of the corresponding unstrained substances would stem from this.[47] However, it must be mentioned that a general equation has been proposed which relates the carbonyl stretching frequency of strained structures only to that of the corresponding unstrained substance and to the value of the $\overset{C}{\underset{X}{>}}CO$ angle of the anomalous compound.[30] Moreover, Halford[46] has shown that a change in frequency can occur without a corresponding change in the force constant of the carbonyl bond. Whatever the explanation for the anomalous carbonyl stretching frequencies of strained compounds, the phenomenon, as shown in Table 15, is very real.*

An interesting extension of the data given in Table 15 is represented by the observation[80] of the carbonyl stretching frequencies of various strained cyclic ketones, in which one of the CH₂ groups of the ring is substituted by a heteroatom. Some typical values are given below and seem to parallel quite closely the variations in steric strain. Note that acylation of the amino group of the azacompound, resulting in the introduction in the molecule of another unit endowed with a certain trigonal character (resonance of the amido group), causes a further increase in the carbonyl stretching frequency relative to that of the parent substance:

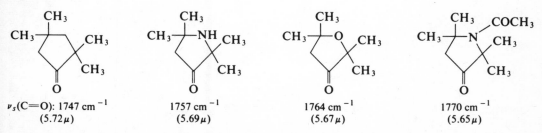

| $\nu_s(C=O)$: 1747 cm⁻¹ | 1757 cm⁻¹ | 1764 cm⁻¹ | 1770 cm⁻¹ |
| (5.72μ) | (5.69μ) | (5.67μ) | (5.65μ) |

* It should be noted that the effect of strain can be observed also in compounds having other types of exocyclic double bonds. For instance, while the C=C stretching of methylenecyclohexane occurs at 6.09 μ, methylenecyclobutane absorbs at 5.96 μ. On the other hand, when the double bond is part of the ring, the effect of strain is reversed; thus, cyclohexene, cyclopentene, and cyclobutene absorb at 6.08, 6.21, and 6.38 μ, respectively.[71]

TABLE 15.   Effect of Steric Strain on $\nu_s(C=O)$ *

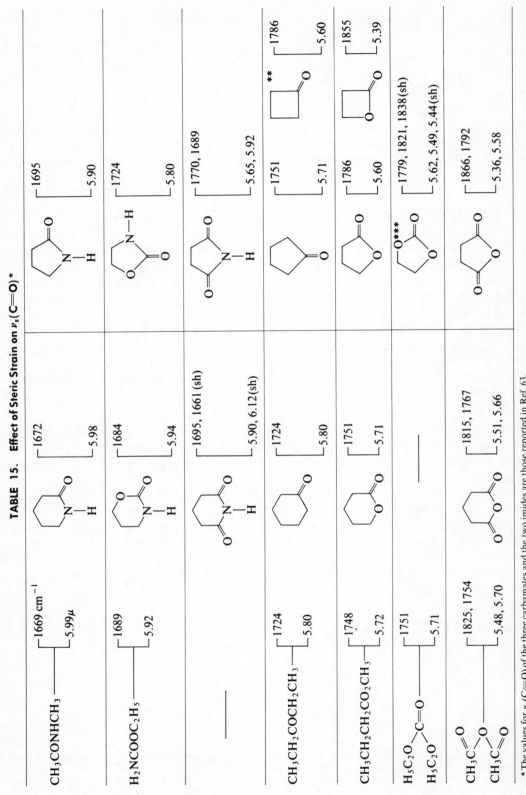

Acyclic	6-membered ring	5-membered ring	4-membered ring
CH₃CONHCH₃ — 1669 cm⁻¹ / 5.99μ	1672 / 5.98	1695 / 5.90	
H₂NCOOC₂H₅ — 1689 / 5.92	1684 / 5.94	1724 / 5.80	
——	1695, 1661 (sh) / 5.90, 6.12 (sh)	1770, 1689 / 5.65, 5.92	
CH₃CH₂COCH₂CH₃ — 1724 / 5.80	1724 / 5.80	1751 / 5.71	1786** / 5.60
CH₃CH₂CH₂CO₂CH₃ — 1748 / 5.72	1751 / 5.71	1786 / 5.60	1855 / 5.39
H₅C₂O, H₅C₂O >C=O — 1751 / 5.71	——	1779, 1821, 1838 (sh) / 5.62, 5.49, 5.44 (sh)***	
(CH₃CO)₂O — 1825, 1754 / 5.48, 5.70	1815, 1767 / 5.51, 5.66	1866, 1792 / 5.36, 5.58	

* The values for $\nu_s(C=O)$ of the three carbamates and the two imides are those reported in Ref. 63.

** It is of interest to note that some recently synthesized cyclopropenones show carbonyl absorption at approximately 5.40 μ.[23]

*** The complex absorption of ethylene carbonate has been attributed to Fermi resonance (see p. 106).

The cumulative action of various inductive, resonance, and steric strain effects is, instead, apparent in the carbonyl stretching frequencies of the two compounds indicated below (XXXIX and XL) [compare with $\nu_s(C=O)$ of oxazolidone (Table 15).[63]]

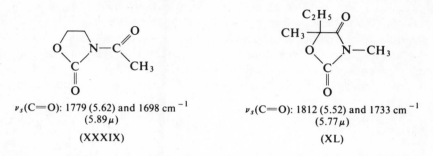

$\nu_s(C=O)$: 1779 (5.62) and 1698 cm^{-1}
(5.89 μ)

(XXXIX)

$\nu_s(C=O)$: 1812 (5.52) and 1733 cm^{-1}
(5.77 μ)

(XL)

It must be recognized that quite the opposite phenomenon (decrease of carbonyl stretching frequency) is to be expected for those compounds in which steric factors cause a spreading of the $\overset{C}{\underset{X}{\diagdown}}C=O$ angle beyond the normal value, i.e., di-t-butyl ketone shows carbonyl stretching absorption at 1692 cm^{-1}(5.91 μ). This is, however, rather uncommon.

This brief discussion of the effects of strain upon carbonyl stretching vibrations permits pointing out that, while the effects of the various factors that can influence $\nu_s(C=O)$ are generally additive (see Table 16 for some examples), some caution is necessary in applying this very useful criterion to the prediction of the frequency at which a carbonyl group should show absorption. For instance, while the carbonyl stretching frequency is greater for α-angelicalactone (XLI) than for butyrolactone (XLII) (vinyl effect), the influence of conjugation in β-angelicalactone (XLIII) seems to be rather limited. This has been rationalized by considering that the introduction of a carbon-carbon double bond in the already strained ring may cause, as a secondary effect, a further decrease of the internal valency

TABLE 16.   Additivity of Effects on $\nu_s(C=O)$

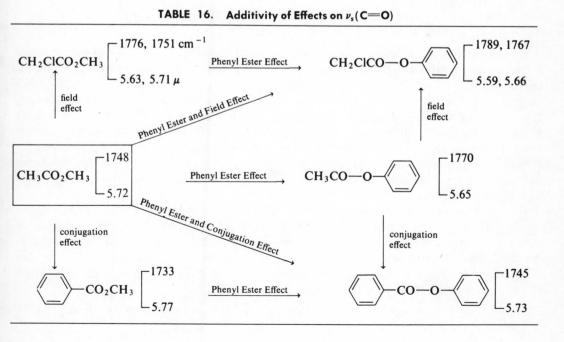

angles, that is, a further increase in strain, which might somewhat counteract the primary effect of conjugation.[51] The situation is again "normal" in the case of unsaturated δ-lactones.[62]

These facts are illustrated by the data given below, which also show the result of competing conjugation and vinyl effects in α-pyrone (XLVII) and coumarin (XLVIII). Compare also the behaviour of γ-pyrone (XLIX) with that of α-pyrone, where the high resonance energy of the former's dipolar form causes a very marked bathochromic shift in the carbonyl stretching frequency. (For the same reason, the carbonyl stretching frequency of γ-pyrones is much less affected than that of α-pyrones by ring substitution.)

ν_s(C=O): 1812 cm^{-1}
(5.52μ)

(XLI)

1786 cm^{-1}
(5.60μ)

(XLII)

1782, 1765 (sh.)
[5.61, 5.67 (sh.)]

(XLIII)

1770 cm^{-1}
(5.65μ)

(XLIV)

1751 cm^{-1}
(5.71μ)

(XLV)

1710 cm^{-1}
(5.85μ)

(XLVI)

1752, 1715 (sh.) cm^{-1}
[5.71, 5.83 (sh.) μ]

(XLVII)

1757, 1743
(5.69, 5.74)

(XLVIII)

1678
(5.96)

(XLIX)

It is also noteworthy that the spectra of numerous α,β-unsaturated 5- and 6-membered lactones show doublets in the carbonyl stretching region (see β-angelicalactone, α-pyrone, and coumarin, above). The relative intensities of the two bands are dependent upon both the polarity of the solvent and the temperature, but are independent of the concentration, thus satisfying some of the conditions for the presence of an equilibrium of conformers and excluding the possibility of an equilibrium between associated and unassociated molecules. However, since it is not plausible for this type of compound, an equilibrium of conformers cannot be invoked as an explanation of the phenomenon, and this has led Jones and collaborators[51] to attribute the occurrence of the doublets to some type of intramolecular vibrational effect.

It must be noted that the occurrence of doublets in the carbonyl stretching region has been observed also for various other types of compounds for which it is not possible to postulate an equilibrium of conformers. Among these are cyclopentanone,[9] ethylene carbonate,[8] 5-membered cyclic unsaturated anhydrides,[31] benzoyl chloride,[42,79] and certain Δ^2-cyclopentenones.[92] Fermi resonance has been invoked as the most plausible explanation of the phenomenon in all these cases.

When the energy of an overtone or combination level happens to coincide with the fundamental level of a different vibration, a phenomenon of resonance can occur. One may think of the molecules as gradually transferring their energy from the fundamental mode to the combination tone and back again. As a consequence of this, if certain conditions are met, the resonance will originate *a pair of transitions of similar intensity* at frequencies that are approximately equidistant from that at which, in absence of resonance, both the fundamental and the combination would occur. The phenomenon, whose occurrence is widespread, is known as Fermi resonance.

In the case of certain Δ^2-cyclopentenones, corroboration of the occurrence of Fermi resonance between the carbonyl stretching mode and the overtone of a low-lying vibration attributed to C—H bending has been sought and found in deuteration studies.[92]

5.2d. Interaction Between Carbonyl Groups. *α-Dicarbonyl Compounds.* If α-dicarbonyl compounds existed in the *cisoid* conformation, such as the one represented below, it would be reasonable to expect the occurrence of a certain degree of interaction between the two dipoles, possibly resulting in increased carbonyl character or, when possible, in enolization.

cisoid   transsoid

However, no such interaction is apparent in the infrared spectra of *acyclic* α-dicarbonylic substances; for instance, the $\nu_s(C{=}O)$ of diacetyl (1724 cm^{-1}, 5.80 μ) is exactly the same as that of a normal monoketone. This behavior, rather general for acyclic α-dicarbonyl compounds, can be explained by assuming that these substances exist in the energetically more favorable transoid conformation, in which dipole interactions are essentially nullified.*

In the *cyclic* analogues the two polar groups would be held more or less rigidly, depending upon ring size, in the highly energetic cisoid conformation. As a result, the stimulus is probably furnished for the marked enolization observed in cyclic α-dicarbonyl compounds with rings of the more common sizes. This is represented below for the molecule of cyclopentane-1,2-dione (L), which could be more descriptively named cyclopent-2-en-2-ol-1-one. In this case, the angle between the two carbonyl dipoles of the non-enolized form would be of approximately 65°.

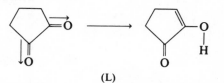

(L)

The greater flexibility of 6-membered α-dicarbonyl compounds permits the two polar groups to rotate more freely about the bond which joins them, leading to a reduction of their mutual interaction which is, however, still adequate to cause a pronounced enolization. The values of enolization constants given in Table 17 clearly reflect the situation prevailing in aqueous solution with acyclic, 5-membered and 6-membered α-dicarbonylic substances. However, the infrared spectra indicate that, in less polar solvents, both cyclopentane-1,2-diones and cyclohexane-1,2-diones exist almost exclusively in the enolic form (Table 18.)**

It should be added that, in the spectra of those cyclic α,β-dicarbonyl compounds in which the high interaction energy of the two polar groups cannot be relieved by enoliza-

---

*Note that the absorption observed corresponds to the antisymmetric stretching of the two carbonyls; the symmetric stretching mode is infrared inactive (no net dipole-moment change during the vibration).

**The carbonyl stretching frequency of the yellow-colored cyclodecane-1,2-dione is almost the same as that of a normal aliphatic monoketone.

TABLE 17.   Enol Content of some 1,2-Diketones*

Compound	K_T** (Water)	% Enol (Water)
Diacetyl	negligible	—
3-Methylcyclohexane-1,2-dione	1.50	60
3-Methylcyclopentane-1,2-dione	∞	100

*Data from Hammond, G. S., in: Newman, M. S., "Steric Effects in Organic Chemistry," p. 449, New York, John Wiley & Sons, 1956. For the possible role of hydration of the dicarbonylic form of cyclic 1,2-diketones on the keto-enol equilibrium, see Refs. 11 and 69.
**K_T = [Enol]/[Keto]

tion, the interaction of the two carbonyls is evidenced by high carbonyl absorption frequency and by the appearance of doublets. For instance, the frequencies indicated have been reported for the compounds shown below,[4] whose enolization would involve the formation of a double bond at a bridge-head.

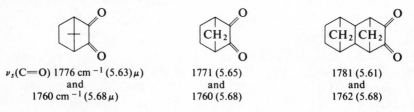

ν_s(C=O) 1776 cm^{-1} (5.63)μ)   1771 (5.65)   1781 (5.61)
and   and   and
1760 cm^{-1} (5.68μ)   1760 (5.68)   1762 (5.68)

That the high carbonyl frequencies reported for these compounds are not simply an effect of the added strain resulting from the fusion of two rings can perhaps be deduced from the fact that the carbonyl absorption of camphor is normal for a 5-membered ring ketone. [It may be parenthetically observed that, in contrast to this, the spectra of compounds containing a carbonyl group as a *p*-bridge in a 6-membered ring show abnormally high carbonyl stretching frequencies (1773 cm^{-1})].[5]

TABLE 18.   Values of ν_s(C=O) and ν_s(C=C) for some Cyclic Ketones, Diketones, and Derivatives (CHCl$_3$)

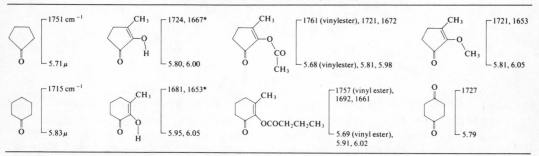

*For the position and shape of the O—H stretching absorption of this compound, see Figure 7.

β-Dicarbonyl Compounds.   Contrary to the case of α-dicarbonylic substances, where a distinction must be drawn between cyclic and acyclic molecules, most β-dicarbonyl compounds, be they cyclic or not, are enolized to a certain appreciable extent. This occurs, of course, when the carbon atom joining the carbonylic functions is connected to at least one hydrogen atom. However, the position of the equilibrium between the keto tautomer, A, and the enol tautomer, B, is sensitive to a number of factors.

For instance, the non-bonded interactions between R and R'', which are small in the non-enolized form of β-ketoesters, become quite important in β-diketones; consequently,

(A)   (B)

the equilibrium generally favors tautomer A in the case of β-ketoesters and tautomer B in β-diketones. These facts are clearly reflected in the IR spectra; actually, infrared spectroscopy has been widely used to study tautomeric systems. Nuclear magnetic resonance is also a very valuable tool for these studies.

It should be of interest to compare the spectra of 2,5-hexanedione and 2,4-pentanedione (Figures 25 and 26). The former, a γ-diketone, is not appreciably enolized, and its spectrum is completely compatible with a substance containing two non-interacting carbonyls; were it not for the very low intensity of the C—H stretching bands, this spectrum could be easily taken for that of an aliphatic methyl monoketone.* To the contrary, the spectrum of 2,4-pentanedione (Figure 26) shows, besides a band of weak intensity at 5.81 μ (probably due to the small fraction of non-enolized molecules present at equilibrium), a very intense and broad band centered at about 6.15 microns, corresponding to the chelated system of the enol.

It should be noted that enolization is favored by the fact that the enol tautomers can form strong hydrogen bridges; for instance, it has been estimated that hydrogen bonding stabilizes the enol of 2,4-pentanedione to the extent of 5 to 10 kcal/mole, and conjugation further stabilizes the system by 2 to 3 kcal/mole. Consequently, any structural feature that hinders coplanarity of the chelated system will reduce enolization; for instance, 3-methyl-2,4-pentanedione is considerably less enolized than 2,4-pentanedione, and this is clearly reflected in the IR (and NMR) spectra.**

The situation prevailing with the less strongly enolized ethyl acetoacetate is illustrated in Figure 27; while the two bands near 5.71 and 5.79 μ must pertain to the ester and keto carbonyls of the non-enolized molecules, the bands at 6.02 and 6.09 μ must be attributed to the small fraction of enolized molecules present at equilibrium. These latter bands would be expected to be hardly noticeable in the spectrum of *methyl* acetoacetate, a molecule in which there is probably hardly any interference between R and R'' in the keto form.

Cyclic β-dicarbonyl compounds, such as cyclohexane-1,3-dione (LI), are also strongly enolized, even though their geometric characteristics do not generally permit the formation of intramolecular hydrogen bonds. The pronounced enolization of these substances, whose enols are probably strongly associated, must again derive from the fact that in this state the unfavorable electrostatic interactions are minimized and the resonance stabilization is still high.†

The comparison of the spectra of 1,2- and 1,3-cyclohexanedione, particularly in the C=O and OH stretching regions, can be instructive. The OH stretching absorption of the α-dicarbonyl compound (Figure 28), even though falling at a high wavelength, is not

---

*Remember that, when a methyl or methylene group is adjacent to a carbonyl, the intensity of the C—H stretching bands is reduced (see Table 3).

For a recent study of keto-enol tautomerism by NMR see: Burdett, J. L., and Rogers, M. T., *J. Amer. Chem. Soc.*, **86, 2105 (1964).

† For the "abnormal" chemical and physical properties of some unique cyclic 1,3-diketones whose geometry permits the formation of intramolecular H-bonds [Decaline-1,8-dione (LII) and related compounds], see Refs. 41 and 85.

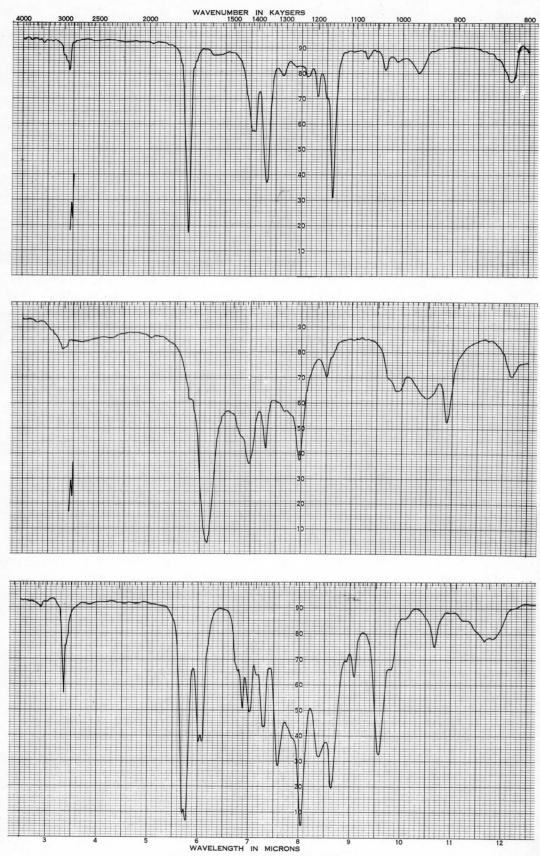

WAVELENGTH IN MICRONS

FIGURE 27. Ethyl acetoacetate (CCl₄).

110

(LI)   (LII)

too abnormal. The analogous absorption of the β-dicarbonylic substance (Figure 29) is, instead, broad and indefinite, as in the case of 2,4-pentanedione. It is noteworthy from an interpretive point of view that this is the type of OH stretching absorption which is encountered in the spectra of carboxylic acids as well as in those of some compounds which contain groups that are vinylogous with the carboxyl group.‡ Note that the carbonyl band of the non-enolized molecules of cyclohexane-1,3-dione, near 5.8 microns, is split. This is probably due to an interaction which has been observed also in the spectra of a number of 2,2-disubstituted cyclohexane-1,3-diones.[6] Finally, it will be noted that the carbonyl absorption of cyclohexane-1,4-dione is essentially normal (see Table 18); the experimental evidence available[2a] indicates that this compound exists predominantly in the boat form LIII.

Of definite interest is tetramethylcyclobutane-1,3-dione (LIV) whose carbonyl stretching is quite clearly under the influence of some type of coupling (Figure 30).

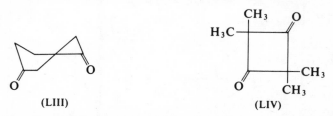

(LIII)   (LIV)

That the apparent abnormalities of the spectrum of this compound are not in some way connected with overcrowding caused by the four methyl groups is shown by the fact that a similar spectral behavior is exhibited by the recently synthesized cyclobutane-1,3-dione.[88] Incidentally, this compound is reported to be only slightly enolized in chloroform, but considerably enolized in aqueous solution.

Anhydrides of Carboxylic Acids. The problem of the double carbonyl absorption present in the spectra of anhydrides has been recently studied by Bellamy and collaborators,[14] who have offered convincing evidence that the phenomenon must be attributed to mechanical coupling, which causes the appearance of both in-phase and out-of-phase vibrations. The data given in Table 4 (p. 62) indicate that, as the carbonyl groups become more nearly colinear, the symmetric mode (higher frequency band) becomes progressively weaker. If the two carbonyl groups were completely colinear, the symmetric mode would be forbidden in the infrared.

In the preceding sections, it has been shown that, aside from the obvious case represented by molecules containing more than one type of carbonyl group, the spectra of many substances containing either a single $>C=O$ or two formally identical ones may show a doublet in the carbonyl stretching region. This phenomenon has been attributed in the various cases to the occurrence of (a) an equilibrium between associated and non-associated forms of the same compound, (b) an equilibrium of conformers, (c) Fermi resonance, and (d) mechanical coupling.

‡Note, however, also the case of compounds containing some types of strong O—H · · N hydrogen bonds (see Figure 7d).

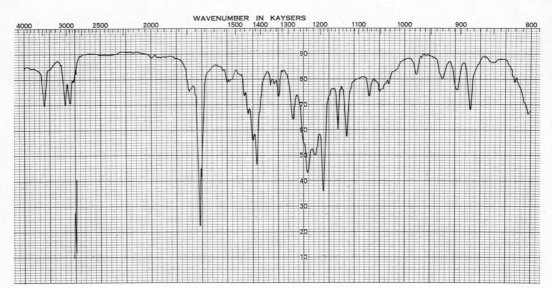

FIGURE 28. Cyclohexane-1,2-dione (CHCl₃).

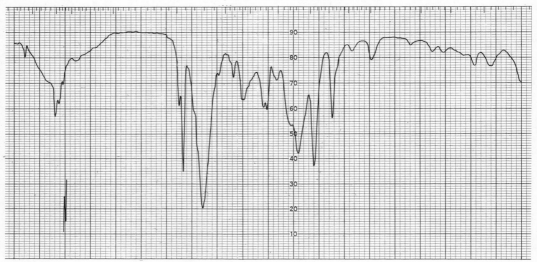

FIGURE 29. Cyclohexane-1,3-dione (CHCl₃).

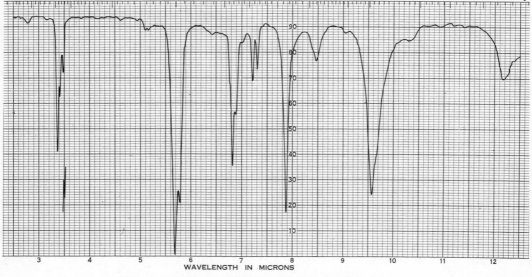

WAVELENGTH IN MICRONS

FIGURE 30. Tetramethylcyclobutane-1,3-dione (CCl₄).

These various possible sources of doublets in the carbonyl stretching region should always be kept in mind when interpreting spectral data, since ignorance of these factors could lead to quite erroneous conclusions. On the other hand, serious mistakes could also be made by rashly attributing the doublets observed to one or another of the phenomena which have been described. For some useful guides, the reader is referred to publications of Bellamy's[14] and Jones' groups.[51]

PROBLEMS

1. The equation $\nu = (k/4\pi^2 c^2 m_A)^{1/2}$ correlates the frequency of an A-B vibration, when A is much lighter than B, with the mass of A (m_A) and with the force constant of the bond (k). What should be the *free* O-D stretching frequency of C_2H_5OD? [C_2H_5OH, in *fairly* dilute solution, absorbs at 2.72 and 2.88 microns (3676 and 3472 cm^{-1}).*

2. The great width of the "O—H stretching" band of compounds containing carboxyl groups renders difficult a study of the underlying C—H stretching bands. Suggest an easy way of obviating this difficulty [Bigley, D. B., *J. Chem. Soc.*, 876, (1964)].

3. The spectrum of the compound shown below shows only one band in the O—H stretching region, irrespective of concentration. Explain.

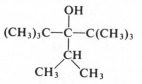

4. How do you rationalize the fact that H-bonding causes a decrease of the frequency of O—H stretching vibrations? What is the relationship between the strength of the H-bond and the ν_s(OH, bonded) value of the group acting as H-donor? How should "strain" in the quasi-ring formed upon intramolecular H-bonding affect the strength of the H-bond? For which of the three isomeric butanediols A, B, C would you expect the largest value of $\Delta\nu_s$(OH)? [$\Delta\nu_s$(OH) = ν_s(OH, free) − ν_s(OH, bonded) in dilute solution]. For a discussion of the various factors to be taken into consideration with regard to H-bonding in glycols, see: Kuhn, L. P., von Schleyer, P., Baitinger, W. T. and Eberson, L., *J. Am. Chem. Soc.*, **86**, 650 (1964); see also: Kuhn, L. P. and Wires, R. A., *ibid.*, **86**, 2161 (1964).

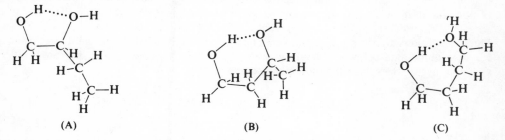

(A)   (B)   (C)

5. Would the spectra of Figures 4 and 5 be compatible with triphenyl carbinol? (Consider both the C—O and C—H stretching regions). Observe the O—H stretching regions in the spectra of benzyl alcohol and of benzhydrol (they were determined at the same molar concentration). What can you expect with regard to the ratio of the free and bonded O—H stretching bands in the spectrum of triphenyl carbinol?

6. Which of the three structures, A, B, or C, is compatible with a strong, sharp band at 2.82 microns (3546 cm^{-1}, CCl$_4$ solution)? Would this band shift upon dilution? What should be the appearance of the O—H stretching region of the other two isomers? Would this be concentration dependent? How would the O—H stretching region of the three isomers compare if the spectra were determined in dioxane solution?

*Assume identical force constants for O—H and O—D.

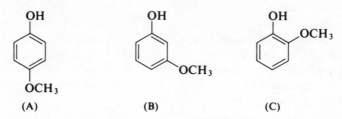

(A)   (B)   (C)

7. What can you expect in the O—H and C=O stretching regions of the isomers A to E in CHCl₃ solution? Indicate the compounds whose spectra would be the least changed in going from the undissolved state to dilute solutions.

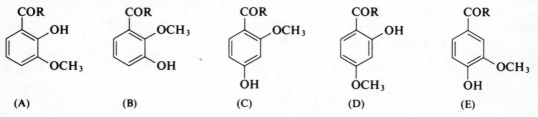

(A)   (B)   (C)   (D)   (E)

8. At a practical but rather low concentration in CHCl₃, catechol (A) and pyrogallol (B) absorb at 2.79, 2.82, and 3.04 microns (3584, 3546 and 3289 cm⁻¹). Explain. How would resorcinol (C) absorb under the same conditions?

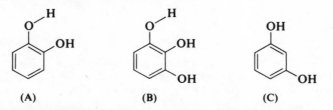

(A)   (B)   (C)

9. In the spectrum of 2-hydroxydiphenyl *in very dilute solution*, one can observe two bands, at 2.77 and 2.80 microns (3609 and 3568 cm⁻¹). The first is the free ν(OH) of the *trans* form; the second, considerably stronger than the other, is attributed to the ν(OH) of the *cis* form (H-bonded to the π-electron cloud of the aromatic ring in the ortho position). In going from 2-hydroxy-diphenyl to 2-hydroxy-4′-nitrodiphenyl, one observes a change in the relative intensity of the two bands. In what direction does this change occur? Would you expect a corresponding shift of ν(*cis* OH)? Remember that the stronger the H-bond, the greater the Δνₛ(OH). [See Beckering, W. J., *J. Phys. Chem.*, **65**, 206 (1961).]

10. Under conditions of high dilution and very good dispersion, the bands indicated were observed for the compounds below [Schleyer, von P. *et al.*, *J. Am. Chem. Soc.*, **80**, 6691 (1958)]. Can you suggest an explanation for these phenomena?

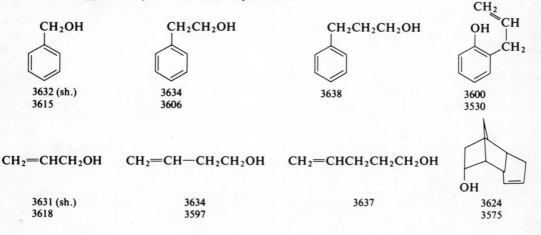

11. The question of whether compound A would predominantly enolize as in B or as in C was clarified when the spectrum of the substance in $CHCl_3$ showed a sharp band at 2.85μ (3509 cm^{-1}) and a broader, but well defined, band at 3.0μ (3333 cm^{-1}). On the basis of this datum alone, which would you favor, B or C? What should be the appearance of the O—H stretching absorption of the other form? [Gianturco, M. A., *et al.*, *Tetrahedron*, 2039, 2051 (1963).]

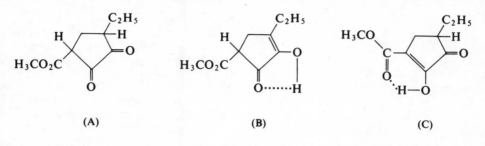

(A)   (B)   (C)

12. The spectra of compounds of type A show strong absorption at 2.85, 5.68, and 5.88μ (3510, 1760 and 1700 cm^{-1}). What does this indicate? Assign the bands. In what way should the high-frequency region and the double-bond stretching region of the spectra of compounds of type A and B differ?

(A)   (B)

13. The occurrence of an equilibrium between non-enolized and enolized (dimeric or polymeric) forms is evident in the spectrum of cyclohexane-1,3-dione (Figure 29). How would you expect the bands in the 5.5 to 6.5μ region to change relative to each other upon dilution?

14. Lithium aluminum hydride reduction of normuscarone (A) yields a mixture of B, C, D and E. What region of the IR spectra of the four compounds (dilute solution) would permit differentiation of B from C and of D from E? Explain. What carbonyl stretching frequency would you expect for compound A? Which bands would suggest the presence of a dimethylamino group in compound A?

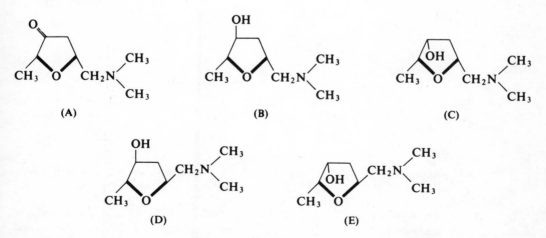

(A)   (B)   (C)

(D)   (E)

15. How could you explain the fact that the spectrum of pyridoin does not show any carbonyl stretching absorption, while those of benzoin and furoin indicate normal behavior? What differences would you expect in the O—H stretching region of the three compounds?

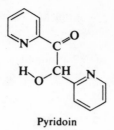

Pyridoin

16. How would you explain that the spectrum of 3-hydroxypyran (dil. CCl_4) shows bands of approximately equal intensity at 2.76 and 2.77μ (3620 and 3604 cm^{-1})? (Consider the possible conformations.) The corresponding 2-OH isomer shows absorption at 2.76μ only. What would you expect in the case of 2-hydroxymethylpyran? [See Barker, S. A., Brimacombe, J. S., Foster, A. B., Whiffen, D. H., and Zweifel, G., *Tetrahedron*, **7**, 10 (1959).]

17. What do the data given below (valid for very dilute solutions) indicate with regard to the conformations of A, B, C? [See Mite, G., Smissman, E. E., and West, R., *J. Am. Chem. Soc.*, **82**, 1207 (1960).]

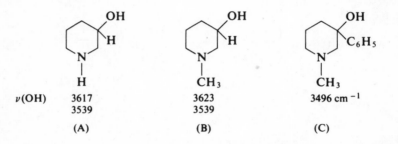

	(A)	(B)	(C)
ν(OH)	3617 3539	3623 3539	3496 cm^{-1}

18. Which of the orientations A-D (vicinal glycols) pertains to:
    (a) OH(a) − OH(e) in a 6-membered ring.
    (b) OH(a) − OH(a) in a 6-membered ring.
    (c) OH(e) − OH(e) in a 6-membered ring.
    (d) *trans* OH's in a 5-membered ring.
    (e) *cis* OH's in a 5-membered ring.

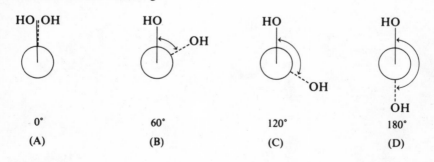

0°	60°	120°	180°
(A)	(B)	(C)	(D)

What would you predict with regard to the O—H stretching absorptions of compounds whose OH's were locked in each of the above orientations (dilute solutions)? [See Kuhn, L. P., *J. Am. Chem. Soc.*, **80**, 5950 (1958) and preceding papers.]

19. Using the data in the graph below and considering that the C=O is the site of H-bonding in lactones, arrange β-propiolactone, γ-butyrolactone and δ-valerolactone in order of increasing "basicity" of the carbonyl. [Graph from Searles, S., Tamres, M., and Barrow, G. M., *J. Am. Chem. Soc.*, **75**, 71 (1953).]

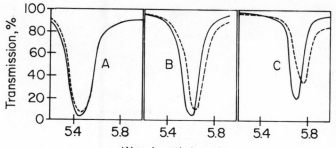

Effect of hydrogen bonding on carbonyl bands of lactones: A, β-propiolactone; B, γ-butyrolactone; C, δ-valerolactone; solid lines, 10 per cent solutions in carbon tetrachloride; dotted lines, same with equimolecular amount of methanol added.

20. The spectrum of 2,6-dimethyl-4-pyrone (A) in CCl_4 shows bands at 1678 and 1639 cm^{-1}. In $CHCl_3$ solution, absorption occurs at 1677 and 1630 cm^{-1}; in ethanolic solution, at 1670 and 1597 cm^{-1}. The complex of A with $ZnCl_2$ absorbs at 1660 and 1530 cm^{-1}, while the spectrum of the "hydrobromide" of A displays bands at 1645 and 1488 cm^{-1}. Which of the two bands, the one at 1678 or the one at 1639 cm^{-1}, should be attributed to the carbonyl group of A in CCl_4? [See Cook D., Can. J. Chem., **39**, 1184 (1961).]

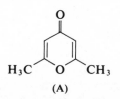

(A)

21. Consider the following values for $v_s(C{=}O)$ in CCl_4 solution. Do you find a good parallellism between these values and those of the corresponding oxygen analogues? [Frequency values from Nyquist, R. A., and Potts, W. J., Spectrochim. Acta, 514 (1959).]

	cm^{-1}	μ
R—C(=O)—SR′	1690	5.92
Ph—C(=O)—SR	1665	6.01
R—C(=O)—S—Ph	1710	5.85
Ph—C(=O)—S—Ph	1685	5.93

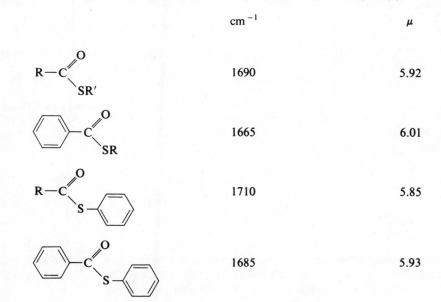

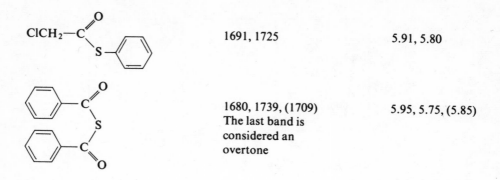

ClCH$_2$—C(=O)—S—(phenyl)	1691, 1725	5.91, 5.80
(dibenzoyl)—C(=O)—S—C(=O)	1680, 1739, (1709) The last band is considered an overtone	5.95, 5.75, (5.85)

Note that while one can be easily tempted to ascribe the lower ν_s(C=O) of the thiocompounds (with respect to the corresponding oxygen analogues) to the importance of resonance forms such as A, this view cannot be reconciled with the fact that the "basicity" of the thiocompounds is apparently *lower* than that of the corresponding oxygen compounds. It has been recently suggested that the lower "basicity" and lower ν_s(C=O) of the thiocompounds should be explained on the basis of resonance forms such as B (with 10 electrons in the outside shell of sulfur). [See Baker, A. W., and Harris, G. H., *J. Am. Chem. Soc.*, **82**, 1923 (1960).]

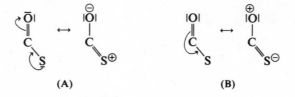

(A)   (B)

22. Are either structure A or B compatible with a strong absorption at 1724 cm^{-1} (5.80μ)? Place A, B, C, D, and E in order of the expected increasing C=O stretching frequencies.

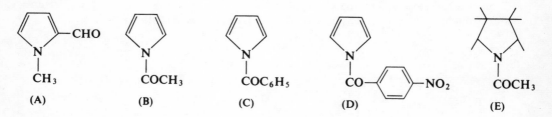

(A)   (B)   (C)   (D)   (E)

23. Rationalize the small differences in ν_s(C=O) of the three acetylpyridines (see Table 8). Can you explain the high C=O stretching frequency reported for compound A (1796 cm^{-1}, 5.57μ)? [Kampa, W., *Angew. Chem.* (Intern. Ed.) 2,479 (1963)]. Compare this value with that observed for diphenyl carbonate (Table 6).

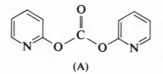

(A)

24. How do you rationalize the fact that the spectrum of compound A is reported to show two carbonyl stretching bands? [Fuson, R. C. and House, H. O., *J. Org. Chem.*, **18**, 496 (1954)]. To which of the carbonyls would you ascribe the band at higher frequency?

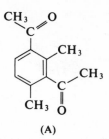

(A)

25. What explanation might be considered for the following observed C=O frequencies? [See Cannon, G. W., Santilli, A. A., and Shenian, P., *J. Am. Chem. Soc.*, **81**, 1660 (1959).]

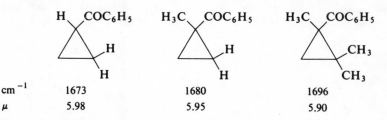

cm⁻¹	1673	1680	1696
μ	5.98	5.95	5.90

26. 2-Pyrrolaldehyde in CCl_4 solution is partially associated, probably to a dimer, A. The spectrum of the compound shows $\nu_s(C=O)$ at 1665 and 1655 cm^{-1} (6.01 and 6.04μ). Which of the two bands should be attributed to the monomeric form? How could you test your hypothesis?

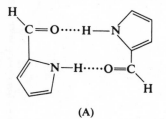

(A)

27. Is the structure of protopine compatible with a carbonyl absorption at 1658 cm^{-1} (6.03μ)? Which could be a suitable model compound to prove or disprove this point? Note that the spectrum of the perchlorate of the alkaloid has a band at 3385 cm^{-1} (2.95μ), but no $\nu_s(C=O)$ absorption. [See Marion, L., Ramsey, D. A., and Jones, R. N., *J. Am. Chem. Soc.*, **73**, 305 (1951); Mottus, E. H., Schwarz, H., and Marion, L., *Can. J. Chem.*, **31**, 1144 (1953).]

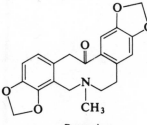

Protopine

28. Can you rationalize the fact that the spectra of the perchlorates of many α,β-unsaturated amines (such as Δ^2-tetrahydropyridines) show no band attributable to the $-N^{\pm}-H$ group, but show instead a double-bond absorption at a frequency much higher than that of the corresponding bases? For instance, compound A absorbs at 1649 cm^{-1} (6.06) μ), but its perchlorate absorbs at 1690 cm^{-1} (5.92μ). Can you write a structure for the salt? [See Leonard, N. J., and Hauck, F. P., Jr., *J. Am. Chem. Soc.*, **79**, 5279, (1957).]

(A)

29. The calculated (infrared) value of the ratio Ng/Nt, defining the position of the equilibrium between the *gauche* and the *trans* conformers of ethylene chloride, at 25°, is 1.3. For 0.77 and 1.23 M solutions of tetrabutyl-ammonium perchlorate in ethylene chloride, the values found for Ng/Nt are 1.69 ± 0.05 and 1.92 ± 0.07, respectively. Explain. [See Inami, M. A., and Ramsay, J. B., *J. Chem. Phys.*, **31**, 1297 (1959). For a study of the effect of changes in the dielectric constant of the medium upon the *frequencies* of the carbon-halogen (and carbonyl) stretching absorptions of halogenated ethanes (and of chloroacetone), see: Hallam, H. E. and Ray, T. C., *J. Chem. Soc.*, **318**, 1964.]

30. The spectrum of furfural shows a split carbonyl stretching band (see Figure 20A). Do you see the possibility of a field effect being operative?

31. Can you differentiate, on the basis of carbonyl stretching frequencies, between a 3- and a 17-ketosteroid? Is it possible to distinguish, on the same basis, a 2- and a 3-ketosteroid? [Note that the latter differentiation is possible via the mass spectra of the corresponding ethylene ketals (see Budzikiewicz, H., Djerassi, C., and Williams, H., "Interpretation of Mass Spectra of Organic Compounds," p. 54, San Francisco, Holden-Day, 1964).]

32. Match the following sets of absorptions with the structures given below: (a) 1647, 1615 cm^{-1}; (b) 1685, 1677 cm^{-1}; (c) 1737, 1685, 1650, 1620 cm^{-1}; (d) 1741, 1673, 1654, 1623 cm^{-1}. (See p. 162 of Ref. i of General References.)

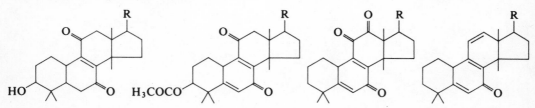

33. Can you arrange the following compounds in the expected order of increasing "carbonyl stretching" frequency? [Mecke, R., Mecke, R., and Lüttringhaus, A., *Chem. Ber.*, **90**, 075 (1957).]

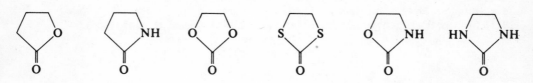

34. Considering the principle of vinology, indicate which of the two partial structures, A or B, should have the lower carbonyl stretching frequency.

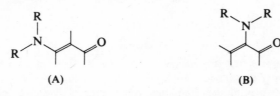

(A)   (B)

35. Rationalize the following values of $\nu_s(C{=}O)$, keeping in mind both the possibility of H-bonding and the principle of vinology. [For a large number of data concerning the spectra of substituted anthraquinones, see Bloom, H., Briggs, L. H., and Cleverley, B., *J. Chem. Soc.*, 178 (1959).]

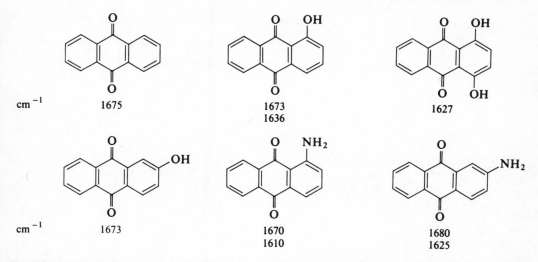

cm^{-1} 1675   1673   1627
                     1636

cm^{-1} 1673   1670   1680
                     1610   1625

36. What kind of correlation would you expect between ν_s(C=O) of quinones and their oxidation-reduction potentials? [For data on the spectra of quinones with electron-attracting substituents, see Bagli, J., *J. Am. Chem. Soc.*, **84**, 177 (1962).]

37. Making use of the patterns of Figures 18 to 22, postulate an unique structure for the compound of molecular formula $C_7H_6O_3$, whose spectrum is given in Figure 31. How would the spectra of the two possible mono-oximes of the compound differ in the ν_s(C=O) region? Do you find absorptions at 5.93 and 5.73μ, respectively, in agreement with the structures of two of the three possible methyl ketals of the compound of Figure 31? [Gianturco, M. A., *et al.*, *Tetrahedron*, **20**, 2951 (1964).]

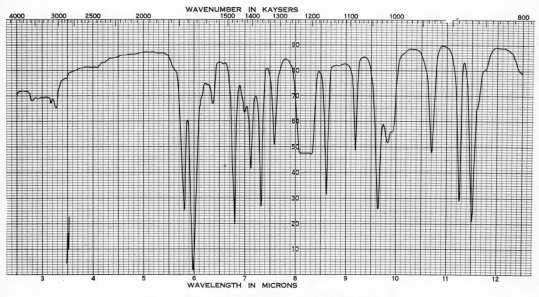

FIGURE 31. Substance of Problem 37 ($CHCl_3$).

38. Knowing that the spectrum of a bromoacetophenone shows a doublet in the C=O stretching region, would you consider more likely that the compound is *o*-, *m*-, or *p*-bromoacetophenone? Or could it be $C_6H_5COCH_2Br$? Which part of the spectrum would you examine to differentiate the four isomers?

39. Which of the two partial structures A and B is in better agreement with two bands of about equal intensity in the double-bond stretching region?

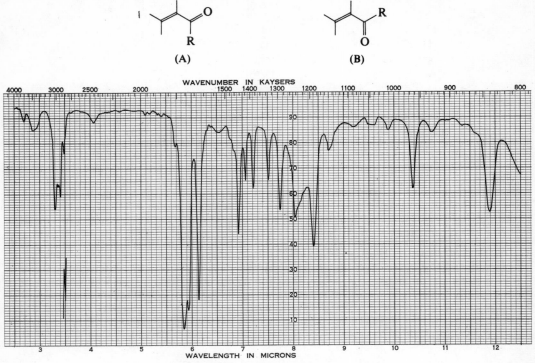

FIGURE 32. 4-Methylcyclopent-2-en-1-one (CHCl₃).

40. The spectrum of Figure 32 is that of 4-methylcyclopent-2-en-1-one. Could you offer a tentative explanation for the doublet in the C=O stretching region? (See Problem 47.)

41. In addition to greatly enhanced intensity of the double-bond stretching absorption, the spectra of several vinyl ethers show a distinct doublet in the ν_s(C=C) region. For instance, in the spectrum of n-butyl vinyl ether one observes strong bands at 1640 and 1613 cm⁻¹ (6.10 and 6.20 μ). This has been attributed to Fermi resonance with the first overtone of the out-of-plane deformation band of the CH₂=C< group, which in the spectra of vinyl ethers falls at approximately 800 cm⁻¹. Considering the possibility of π-p conjugation between the π-electron cloud of the C=C and the p-electrons of the oxygen, can you postulate an alternative explanation for the phenomenon? [See Popov, E. M., Andreev, N. S., and Kagan, G. I., *Optics and Spectroscopy*, **12**, 37 (1962).]

42. Can you postulate structures for the compound of molecular formula C₅H₈O₂ (Figure 33), which emerges from a non-polar GLC column well ahead of butyrolactone? Can it be an α-, a β-, or a γ-diketone? Why would you say that it cannot be a vinyl ester? [Gianturco, M. A., Friedel, P. and Giammarino, A. S., *Tetrahedron*, **20**, 1763 (1964).]

43. Explain the following absorptions in the spectra of compound A and of its *cis* isomer, B. To what vibration would you attribute the band at 1668 cm⁻¹ (6.0μ) in the spectrum of B? Why is the band absent in the spectrum of A?

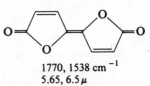

1770, 1538 cm⁻¹
5.65, 6.5 μ

(A)

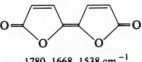

1780, 1668, 1538 cm⁻¹
5.62, 6.0, 6.5 μ

(B)

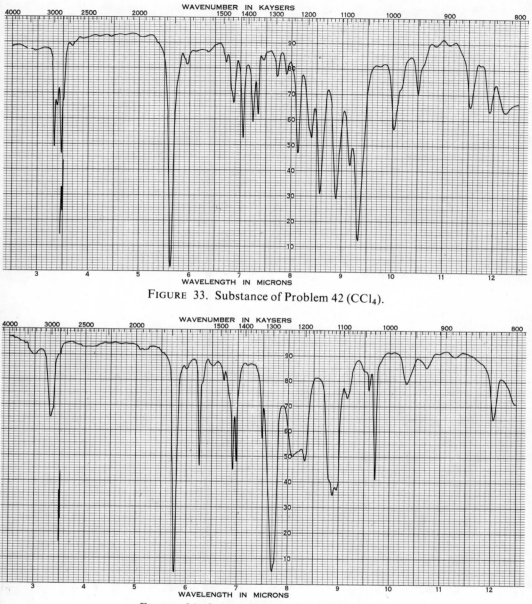

FIGURE 33. Substance of Problem 42 (CCl_4).

FIGURE 34. Substance of Problem 44 ($CHCl_3$).

44. Postulate a structure for the substance of Figure 34, a product of the pyrolysis of trigonelline (Hint: Write two molecules of trigonelline head-to-tail and compare Figure 34 with the patterns of Figures 18 to 22). Considering the vastly different pK_a values of pyrazine and pyridine, would you expect "anomalies" in the spectrum of nicotinic acid or in that of pyrazinecarboxylic acid?

Trigonelline

45. The following representation of the ring orbitals of vinylcyclopropane shows that they have increased p-character ($sp^{4.12}$ vs the usual sp^3 of the orbitals of tetrahedral carbon) and that they are in a good position for overlap with the p-orbitals of a double bond adjacent to the ring. [Compare ν_s(C=O) of methyl cyclopropyl ketone with that of butanone (p. 93).]   To the high p-character of the ring orbitals of cyclopropanes corresponds the reduced p-character (increased s-character) of the exo-bonds. What is the relationship between this quantomechanical representation and the C—H stretching frequency of cyclopropane derivatives?   (See Table 1.) Considering that the separation between ν_s(C—H) of cyclopropanic derivatives and of other types of compounds is not too large, would you consider it wise to attempt the differentiation of the two types on the basis of the first overtones in the 6000 cm^{-1} region? [See Washburn, W. H., and Mahoney, M. J., *J. Am. Chem. Soc.*, **80**, 504 (1958).]

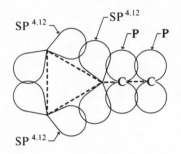

46. It has been shown possible to determine the type of fusion of a quinolizidine ring (*cis*, A, or *trans*, B) on the basis of the observation that the spectra of *trans*-quinolizidines with at least two *axial* H-atoms adjacent to the nitrogen show a prominent band (or group of bands) in the 2800 to 2700 cm^{-1} (3.57 to 3.70μ) region. If this absorption is due to C—H stretching vibrations, at approximately what frequency would you expect the "*trans*-quinolizidine band" in deuterated *trans*-quinolizidines?

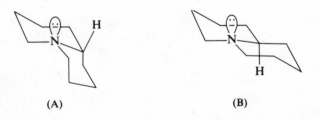

(A)   (B)

47. The spectra of compounds A, B, C, which show a band at 11.6 to 11.7μ (862 to 855 cm^{-1}, olefinic C—H out-of-plane bending), have a split "carbonyl" stretching band at 5.82 and 5.90μ (1718 and 1695 cm^{-1}). The spectrum of D, which has a band at 11.45μ (873 cm^{-1}) but no band at 11.6μ, as well as those of E and F, which show no absorption near 11.6 to 11.7μ, have instead a single band at 5.86μ (1706 cm^{-1}). What explanation might be given to this phenomenon? [Hint: $\frac{1}{2}$(1718 + 1695) = 1706; 2 × 862 = 1724; 2 × 855 = 1710; 2 × 873 = 1746.]

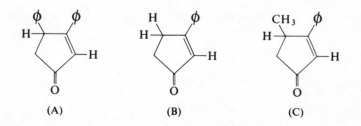

(A)   (B)   (C)

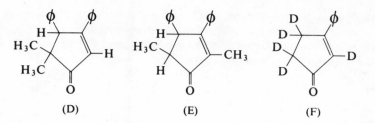

(D)   (E)   (F)

48. How would you go about proving that the low-frequency band in the ν_s(C=O) region of furoyl chloride (Figure 20e) is not due to the presence of furoic acid in the sample? What might be the origin of the doublet?

49. Postulate a structure for the compound $C_4H_4O_2$ (Figure 35). Which band in the low-frequency range might be responsible for the doublet in the carbonyl stretching region?

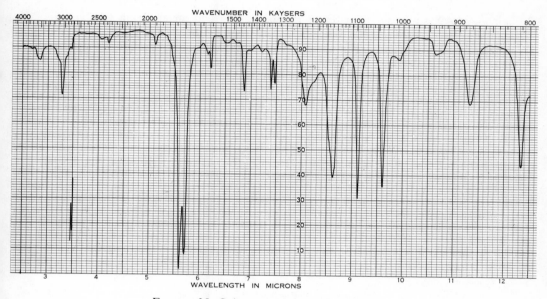

FIGURE 35. Substance of Problem 49 ($CHCl_3$).

50. What carbonyl stretching frequencies would you predict for compound A? (Hint: Upon reduction, one of the benzoyl groups is split off.) How do you rationalize the fact that compound B shows a carbonyl stretching absorption at 5.63 microns?

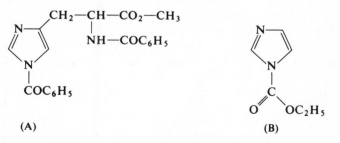

(A)   (B)

51. As pointed out by Fieser (Fieser, L. F., and Fieser, M., "Steroids," p. 173, New York, Reinhold Publishing Corp., 1959), the location of a carbon-carbon double bond in a steroid can often be determined by observation of the infrared spectrum of the product resulting from oxidation of the steroid with osmium tetroxide, reduction of the osmate ester with $LiAlH_4$ and treatment of

the resulting glycol with lead tetraacetate. Considering both the carbonyl stretching frequencies and the eventual C—H absorption of formyl groups of the oxidized products, how could you differentiate the structures A-D? Could D be differentiated from E? [For original data, see Castells, J., and Meakins, G. D., *Chem. Ind.*, 248 (1956).]

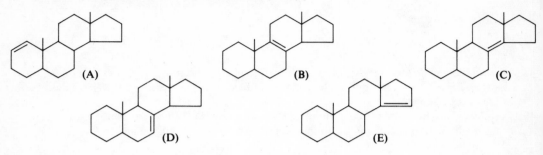

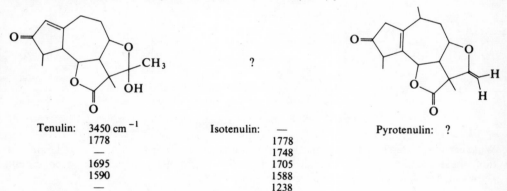

52. Compound A has a ketocarbonyl in a 6-membered ring and an alcoholic OH group. Compound B has a ketocarbonyl in a 5-membered ring and an alcoholic OH group. If you wanted to protect the OH groups and still have a chance of seeing the ketocarbonyl absorptions, would you consider it preferable to prepare the acetate or the benzoate of A and B, respectively? Would your choice be different if the OH groups of A and B were phenolic?

53. Upon short boiling with London tap water (high in bicarbonate), tenulin, which has been assigned the structure indicated below, is transformed into an isomer, isotenulin. On the basis of this fact and of the pertinent absorption bands of the two compounds (nujol, see below), can you postulate a tenable structure for isotenulin? Can you predict the approximate absorption frequencies between 1800 and 1600 cm^{-1} in the spectrum of pyrotenulin? Would you expect strong or weak absorption in the C=C stretching region of the spectrum of pyrotenulin? [See Barton, D. H. R., and deMayo, P., *J. Chem. Soc.*, 142 (1956).]

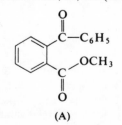

Tenulin:	3450 cm^{-1}	Isotenulin:	—	Pyrotenulin: ?
	1778		1778	
	—		1748	
	1695		1705	
	1590		1588	
	—		1238	

54. Esterification of *o*-benzoylbenzoic acid with diazomethane in ether yields the normal methyl ester, A [λ (CO): 5.82 and 6.00μ]. However, if the preparation is attempted by treating the acid first with thionyl chloride and then with methanol-pyridine, the product is an isomer of A. The carbonyl stretching absorption of this compound occurs at 5.65μ (1770 cm^{-1}). Postulate a structure. [Bonner, W. A., *J. Am. Chem. Soc.*, **85**, 439 (1963).]

$$\begin{array}{c} O \\ \parallel \\ C - C_6H_5 \\ OCH_3 \\ C \\ \parallel \\ O \end{array}$$

(A)

55. To the fungal metabolite geodin was assigned structure A. However, the absorption of the compound in the double-bond region was considered incompatible with this structure (1728, 1665, 1630 and 1610 cm^{-1}). Do you agree? Are the above absorptions in better agreement with the alternative structure B, proposed by Barton and Scott? [Barton, D. H. R., and Scott, A. J., *J. Chem. Soc.*, 1767 (1958).]

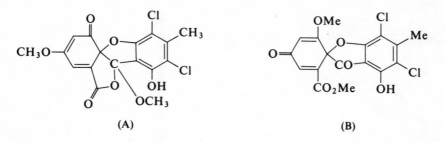

(A)   (B)

56. The thermodynamically more stable orientation of the halogen in 2-bromocholestan-3-one is as in A. In contrast to this, the stable form of 2-bromofriedelin is represented by B. Explain. How should the carbonyl stretching frequencies of A and B compare with those of the corresponding nonhalogenated compounds? [Corey, E. J., and Ursprung, J. J., *J. Am. Chem. Soc.*, **78**, 5041 (1956).]

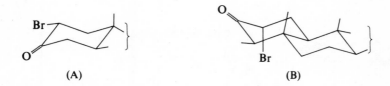

(A)   (B)

57. Hydrogen bonding in a carbonyl compound is generally associated with a decrease in carbonyl stretching frequency. However, there may be exceptions. For instance, which of the two isomers, A or B, would you expect to have the higher carbonyl stretching frequency? Note that an acetate of type A has been found to hydrolize *faster* than the corresponding equatorial acetate. [See Henbest, H. B., and Lovell, B. J., *J. Chem. Soc.*, 1965 (1957).]

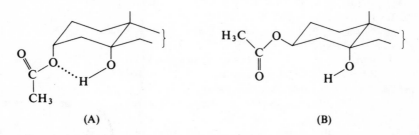

(A)   (B)

58. Among the products of the chromic acid oxidation of tuberculostearic acid, C$_{19}$H$_{38}$O$_2$, were identified azelaic acid, HO$_2$C(CH$_2$)$_7$CO$_2$H, and an unbranched ketone, C$_{10}$H$_{20}$O, whose IR spectrum showed distinct bands at 7.38 and 8.62 microns. On the basis of these data alone, can you identify the ketone and postulate a structure for tuberculostearic acid? [See Gianturco, M. A. and Pitcher, R. G., *Applied Spectroscopy*, **19**, 109 (1965)].

59. The work leading to the synthesis of d,1-caryophyllene, recently described by Corey and collaborators [*J. Am. Chem. Soc.*, **86**, 485 (1964)], shows how modern organic chemists make full use of physical methods to follow the course of reactions. Below are indicated some of the sequences in this synthesis. Can you predict the approximate frequency values of the most critical absorptions of each intermediate? Note that C and D were obtained as mixtures of isomers.

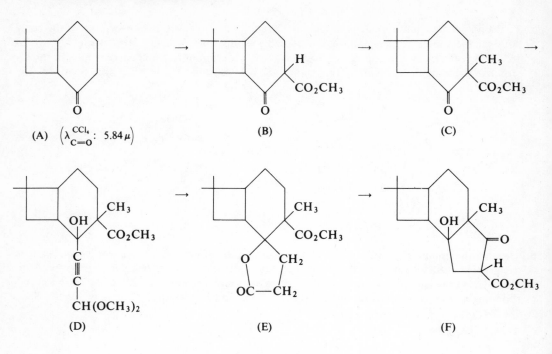

(A) $\left(\lambda_{C=O}^{CCl_4}: 5.84\,\mu\right)$ (B)   (C)

(D)   (E)   (F)

REFERENCES

1. Aaron, H. S., and Rader, C. P., *J. Am. Chem. Soc.*, **85**, 3046 (1963).
2. Akerman, B., *Acta. Chem. Scand.*, **15**, 985 (1961).
2a. Alinger, N. L., and Freiberg, L. A., *J. Am. Chem. Soc.*, **83**, 5028 (1961).
3. Allsop, T. L., Cole, A. R. H., White, D. R., and Willix, R. L. S., *J. Chem. Soc.*, 4868 (1956).
4. Adler, K., Schafer, H. K., Esser, H., Krieger, H., and Reubke, R., *Liebigs Ann. Chem*, **593**, 23 (1955).
5. Allen, C. F. H., Davis, T., Stewart, D. W., and Van Allan J. A., *J. Org. Chem.*, **20**, 306, 310 (1955).
6. Anacenko, L. N., Berezin, T. V., and Torgov, T. V., *Bull. Acad. Sci. U.R.S.S.*, 1644 (1960).
7. Anet, F. A. L., Baily, A. S., and Robinson, R., *Chem. and Ind.*, 944 (1953).
8. Angell, C. L., *Trans. Faraday Soc.*, **52**, 1178 (1956).
9. Angell, C. L., Krueger, P. J., Lanzon, R., Leitch, L. C., Noack, K., Smith, R. D. J., and Jones, R. N., *Spectrochim. Acta*, 926 (1959).
10. Baker, A. W., and Shulgin, A. T., *J. Am. Chem. Soc.*, **80**, 5358 (1958).
11. Bakule, R., and Lang, F. A., *J. Am. Chem. Soc.*, **85**, 2309 (1963).
12. Beckering, W. J., *J. Phys. Chem.*, **65**, 206 (1961).
13. Bellamy, L. J., "The Infrared Spectra of Complex Molecules," London, Methuen and Co., Ltd., 1958.
14. Bellamy, L. J., Connelly, B. R., Philpotts, A. R., and Williams, R. L., *Z. Elektrochem.*, **64**, 563 (1960).
15. Bellamy, L. J., and Rogash, P. E., *Spectrochim. Acta*, **16**, 30 (1960).
16. Bellamy, L. J., Thomas, L. C., and Williams, R. L., *J. Chem. Soc.*, 3704 (1956).
17. Biggins, R., Cairns, T., Eglinton, G., Hasham, H., and Haworth, R. D., *J. Chem. Soc.*, 1750 (1963).
18. Blanchard, E. P., and Buchi, G., *J. Am. Chem. Soc.*, **85**, 955 (1963).
19. Bohlmann, F., *Chem. Ber.*, **91**, 2157 (1958).
20. Bojcov, V. G., and Gotlib, J. J., *Optics and Spectroscopy*, **11**, 691 (1961).
21. Braude, E. A., and Timmons, C. J., *J. Chem. Soc.*, 3766 (1955).
22. Bregman, J., and Bauer, L. H., *J. Am. Chem. Soc.*, **77**, 1955 (1955).

23. Breslow, R., Posner, J., and Krebs, A., *J. Am. Chem. Soc.*, **85,** 234 (1963).
24. Briggs, L. H., Colebrook, L. D., Fales, H. M., and Wildman, W. C., *Anal. Chem.*, **29,** 904 (1957).
25. Brooks, C. J. W., Eglinton, G., and Norman, J. F., *J. Chem. Soc.*, 106 (1961).
26. Brown, H. C., and Taukamota, A., *J. Am. Chem. Soc.*, **83,** 4549 (1961).
27. Brown, T. L., Regan, J. F., Schuetz, R. D., and Sternberg, J. C., *J. Phys. Chem.*, **63,** 1324 (1959).
28. Cole, A. R. H., and Mueller, G. T., *J. Chem. Soc.*, 1224 (1959).
29. Colthup, N. B., *J. Opt. Soc. Amer.*, **40,** 397 (1950).
30. Cook, D., *Can. J. Chem.*, **39,** 31 (1961).
31. Cooke, R. G., *Chem. and Ind.*, 142 (1955).
32. Corey, E. J., *J. Am. Chem. Soc.,* **75,** 2301, 3297, 4832, (1953); *ibid.*, **76,** 171 (1954); *Experientia*, **9,** 329 (1953).
33. Corey, E. J., and Green, R. A., *J. Am. Chem. Soc.*, **75,** 6234 (1953).
34. Cromwell, N. H., Branbury, R. E., and Adelfang, J. L., *J. Am. Chem. Soc.*, **82,** 4241 (1960).
35. Cromwell, N. H., Schumaker, F. H., and Adelfang, J. L., *J. Am. Chem. Soc.*, **83,** 974 (1961).
36. Dauben, W. G., and Williams, W. E., *J. Org. Chem.*, **24,** 1595 (1959).
37. de Vries, L., and Ryason, P. K., *J. Org. Chem.*, **26,** 621 (1961).
38. Erskine, R. L., and Waight, E. L., *J. Chem. Soc.*, 3425 (1960).
39. Fales, H. M., and Wildman, W. C., *J. Am. Chem. Soc.*, **85,** 784 (1963); *ibid.*, **82,** 197 (1960).
40. Fernandez, J. E., and Solomons, T. W. G., *Chem. Reviews*, **62,** 347 (1962).
41. Fieser, L. F., and Fieser, M., "Topics in Organic Chemistry," p. 475, New York, Reinhold Publishing Corp., 1963.
42. Flett, M. St. C., *Trans, Faraday Soc.*, **44,** 767 (1948).
43. Francis, L. A., *J. Chem. Phys.*, **18,** 861 (1950); **19,** 942 (1951).
44. Freeman, J. P., *J. Am. Chem. Soc.*, **80,** 5954 (1958).
45. Gronovitz, L., and Rosenberg, A., *Arkiv. Kemi*, **8,** 23 (1955).
46. Halford, J. O., *J. Chem. Phys.*, **24,** 830 (1956).
47. Hall, H. K., and Linden, F., *J. Am. Chem. Soc.,* **80,** 6428 (1958).
48. Hammond, G. S., in Newman, M. S., "Steric Effects in Organic Chemistry," p. 449, New York, John Wiley & Sons Inc., 1956.
49. Hill, R. D., and Meakins, G. D., *J. Chem. Soc.*, 760 (1958).
50. House, H. O., and Blaker, J. W., *J. Am. Chem. Soc.,* **80,** 6389 (1958).
51. Jones, R. N., Angell, C. L., Ito, T., and Smith, R. J. D., *Can. J. Chem.*, **37,** 2007 (1959).
52. Jones, R. N., Forbes, W. F., and Mueller, W. A., *Can. J. Chem.*, **35,** 504 (1957).
53. Jones, R. N., and Roberts, G., *J. Am. Chem. Soc.*, **80,** 6121 (1958).
54. Jones, R. N., and Spinner, E., *Can. J. Chem.*, **36,** 1020 (1958).
55. Katritzky, A. R., *J. Chem. Soc.*, 4162 (1958); *ibid.*, 2058 (1959).
56. Katritzky, A. R., and Jones, R. A., *J. Chem. Soc.*, 3670 (1959).
57. Katritsky, A. R., and Jones, R. A., *Spectrochim, Acta*, **17,** 64 (1961).
58. Katritzky, A. R., and Lagowsky, J. M., *J. Chem. Soc.*, 4155 (1958).
59. Katritzky, A. R., and Lagowsky, J. M., *J. Chem. Soc.*, 657 (1959).
60. Katritzky, A. R., Lagowsky, J. M., and Beard, J. A. T., *Spectrochim. Acta*, **16,** 964 (1960).
61. Katritzky, A. R., and Simmons, P., *J. Chem. Soc.,* 2051 (1959).
62. Korte, F., Brichel, K. H., and Göhring, L. *Angew. Chem.*, **71,** 523 (1959).
63. Lee, C. M., and Kulmer, W. D, *J. Am. Chem. Soc.,* **83,** 4576 (1961).
64. Leonard, N. J., Fox, R. C., and Oki, M., *J. Am. Chem. Soc.*, **76,** 5708 (1954).
65. Leonard, N. J., Fox, R. C., Oki, M., and Chiavarelli, S., *J. Am. Chem. Soc.,* **76,** 630(1954).
66. Leonard, N. J., and Johnson, C. R., *J. Am. Chem. Soc.,* **84,** 3701 (1962).
67. Leonard, N. J., and Oki, M., *J. Am. Chem. Soc.,* **76,** 3463 (1954).
68. Leonard, N. J. and Owens, F. H., *J. Am. Chem. Soc.*, **80,** 6038 (1958).
69. Long, F. A., and Bakule, R., *J. Am. Chem. Society*, **85,** 2313 (1963).
70. Lord, R. C., and Miller, F. A., *Applied Spectroscopy*, **10,** 115 (1956).
71. Lord, R. C., and Walker, L. W., *J. Am. Chem. Soc.*, **76,** 2518 (1954).
72. Mecke, R., and Noack, K., *Spectrochim. Acta*, **12,** 391 (1958).

73. Mecke, R., and Noack, K., *Chem. Ber.*, **93**, 210 (1960).
74. Noack, K., and Jones, R. N., *Can. J. Chem.*, **39**, 2201, 2225 (1961).
75. Ogata, N., *Bull. Chem. Soc.*, Japan, **34**, 245 (1961).
76. Ottig, W., *Chem. Ber.*, **89**, 1940 (1956).
77. Petrov, A. A., and Semenov, G. J., *J. Gen. Chem., Moscow*, **27**, 2947 (1957).
78. Pimentel, G. C., and McClellan, A. L., "The Hydrogen Bond," San Francisco, W. C. Freeman and Co., 1960.
78a. Pinchas, S., *Anal. Chem.*, **27**, 2 (1955).
79. Rao, C. N., and Venkataraghavan, *Spectrochim. Acta*, **18**, 273 (1962).
80. Sandris, C., and Ourisson, G., *Bull. Soc. Chim. Fr.*, 350 (1958).
81. Schleyer von, P., Trifan, D. S., and Bacskai, R., *J. Am. Chem. Soc.*, **80**, 6691 (1958).
82. Schleyer von, P., Winter, C., Trifan, D. S., and Bacskai, R., *Tetrahedron Letters*, **14**, 1 (1959).
83. Staals, H. A., *Angew. Chem., Intern. Ed.*, **1**, 351 (1962).
84. Staals, H. A., and Jost, E., *Ann.*, **655**, 90 (1962).
85. Stetter, H., Krüger-Hansen, T., and Risk, M., *Ber.*, **94**, 2702 (1961); Stetter, H., and Milkers, V., *ibid.*, **91**, 977 (1958).
86. Thompson, H. W., and Temple, F., *Trans. Faraday Soc.*, **41**, 27 (1945).
87. Timmons, C. J., Proc. of the IV International Meeting of the European Molecular Spectroscopy Group, Bologna, Italy, 1958.
88. Wasserman, H. H., and Dehmlov, E. V., *J. Am. Chem. Soc.*, **84**, 3786 (1962).
89. West, R., *J. Am. Chem. Soc.*, **81**, 1614 (1959).
90. Weniger, R., *Phys. Reviews*, **31**, 388 (1910).
91. Woodward, R. B., Levine, S. G., and Yates, P., *J. Am. Chem. Soc.*, **85**, 557 (1963).
92. Yates, P., and Williams, L. C., *J. Am. Chem. Soc.*, **80**, 5896 (1958).
93. Zeiss, H. H., and Tsutsui, M., *J. Am. Chem. Soc.*, **75**, 897 (1953).

GENERAL REFERENCES

a. Bellamy, L. J., "The Infrared Spectra of Complex Molecules," London, Methuen and Co., Ltd., 1958.
b. Brügel, W., "An Introduction to Infrared Spectroscopy," London, Methuen and Co., Ltd., 1962.
c. Cross, A. D., "An Introduction to Practical Infrared Spectroscopy," London, Butterworths, 1960.
d. Flett, M. St. C., "Physical Aids to the Organic Chemist," New York, Elsevier, 1962.
e. Jones, R. N., and Sandorfy, C., "Chemical Applications of Spectroscopy," (Ed. W. West), New York, Interscience Publishers, Inc., 1956.
f. Katritzky, A. R., "Physical Methods in Heterocyclic Chemistry," Vol II, New York, Academic Press, 1963.
g. Nakanishi, K., "Infrared Absorption Spectroscopy," San Francisco, Holden-Day, Inc., 1960.
h. Silverstein, R. M., and Bassler, G. C., "Spectrometric Identification of Organic Compounds," New York, John Wiley & Sons, Inc., 1963.
i. Weissberger, A., "Elucidation of Structures by Physical and Chemical Methods," New York, Interscience Publishers, Inc., 1963.

3 FAR INFRARED SPECTROSCOPY

James E. Stewart
Beckman Instruments, Inc.
Fullerton, California

1. Introduction

The spectral region called the "far infrared" is not very well defined. To the designer of military heat detection equipment it might begin at 10 μ, while to the solid-state physicist studying energy gaps in superconductors it lies well beyond 50 μ. Until quite recently the typical chemical spectroscopist considered the far infrared to begin at the long wavelength cut-off of his rock salt prism; at about 16 μ. In the present chapter we shall adopt this convention, even though the modern trend is to record the entire 2 to 25 μ spectrum with a single instrument, without changing optical components. Mention should be made of a recent proposal that the spectral region from 0.8 to 2.5 μ be termed the "near infrared," the region from 2.5 to 50 μ the "mid-infrared," and the region beyond 50 μ the "far infrared."

The interest of chemists in the far infrared has been limited by availability of materials suitable for dispersing the radiation into a spectrum. Sodium chloride prisms cannot be used at wavelengths longer than 16 μ. Potassium bromide, in sizes and quality suitable for prisms, became generally available in the early 1940's and extended the spectrum available for chemical use to 25 μ. Thalium bromide-iodide (KRS-5), developed in Germany during World War II, could be used to 40 μ but had poor mechanical properties. CsBr became available in the early 1950's and CsI shortly after, extending the region to 40 and 50 μ, respectively. Although materials are known which transmit at longer wavelengths, e.g. crystal quartz and polyethylene, 50 μ remains the long wavelength limit of prism spectrophotometers. However, the development of inexpensive replica gratings of good quality has made it possible to extend the range of conventional spectrophotometers to 200 μ. We shall use the terms "prism far infrared" and "grating far infrared" to distinguish the regions 16 to 50 μ and 50 to 1000 μ, respectively. We shall also use the common terms "sodium chloride" or "rock salt region" for 2 to 16 μ, "potassium bromide region" for 15 to 25 μ, "cesium bromide region" for 25 to 40 μ, and "cesium iodide region" for 40 to 50 μ.

Today the prism far infrared from 16 to 50 μ is available on a routine basis for chemical studies and, as more information and spectra from this region are published, it is becoming increasingly valuable in the elucidation of molecular structure. There is considerable activity in the grating far infrared beyond 50 μ in a number of chemical laboratories, but because of greater experimental difficulties, this work is of a somewhat less routine nature. The recent application of interferometric instrumentation and techniques to the spectroscopy of the far infrared has eased some of the problems of the field but has introduced some additional complications. The future should see increasing use being made of this approach.

2. Far Infrared Instrumentation[1,2,3]

2.1. Radiation Source.   Two problems, the scarcity of long wavelength radiation and the occurrence of high levels of stray radiation, are the most troublesome aspects of far infrared spectroscopy, and a great deal of effort is being made to overcome them. In the prism far infrared, it is customary to use the same source as is used in the rock salt region. Usually, this is an electrically heated Nernst glower or Globar. At the longer wavelengths of the grating far infrared, a medium pressure mercury arc confined in a quartz envelope is commonly used. This source is much more efficient in the grating far infrared than it is at shorter wavelengths, which helps to suppress the troublesome stray radiation.

2.2. Detectors.   The standard infrared detector for the rock salt region is a blackened thermal detector, usually a thermocouple but occasionally a bolometer. These detectors can be used throughout the prism far infrared provided a suitable window is used, but at much longer wavelengths the black begins to lose effectiveness. Consequently, the Golay detector, a pneumatic device with a thin metal film receiver of uniform absorptivity, is substituted for work in the grating far infrared. A window of crystalline quartz is required.

Recent research has contributed an array of new detectors having far superior sensitivities. These include a carbon bolometer, a germanium bolometer, several superconducting bolometers, and an indium antimonide photoconductor. Unfortunately, these devices suffer from the common inconvenience of requiring liquid helium temperature for effective operation.

2.3. Filters.   The problem of controlling the level of stray radiation in a monochromator by optical filtering becomes more severe at longer wavelengths and is considerably more difficult in the grating far infrared where the use of a fore-prism monochromator is not possible. Furthermore, grating spectroscopy is complicated by the simultaneous occurrence of multiples of a desired frequency in higher order spectra.

In the prism far infrared a fore-prism monochromator or a set of transmission filters is used as the primary filtering system. These are usually augmented by other devices such as roughened reflectors which serve as good mirrors for long wavelengths but scatter the troublesome short wavelengths. Sometimes a fine grating is used for the same purpose.

In the grating far infrared more drastic measures are necessary. The use of selective reflection filters, commonly alkali halide "reststrahlen" filters, is a particularly useful means of reducing stray radiation and of sorting out overlapping grating orders. The crystal quartz window on the detector aids in eliminating radiation from the 4 to 40 μ region and additional transmission filters of various materials are used in appropriate regions. An especially useful type of transmission filter consists of finely divided absorbing powder suspended in polyethylene.

2.4. Sample Handling and Techniques.   The techniques of mounting and handling of samples for spectroscopy in the far infrared are not much different from those used in the rock salt region, except, of course, that appropriate window materials must be used for cells. Generally, the choice of window material is limited to crystal quartz or polyethylene in the grating far infrared and the alkali halides KBr, CsBr, CsI, or KRS-5 in the prism far infrared. Usually, somewhat greater sample thicknesses are required in the far infrared than in the rock salt region because low frequency absorptions tend to be weaker. Just as in the rock salt region, it is often advantageous to record the far infrared reflection spectra of solid samples. Reflection and transmission spectra in the 2 to 50 μ region of a large number of useful infrared materials may be found with a complete bibliography in a recent pair of articles by McCarthy.[4] Polarizers for use in the far infrared can be constructed of silver chloride (useful only to about 20 μ) or polyethylene mounted at the Brewster's angle.

Because of the widespread absorption by water vapor in the far infrared, it is desirable to dry the optical path when working in the 16 to 50 μ region, and it is essential to do so beyond 50 μ. Unless an evacuable instrument is available, this can best be done by flushing with dried air or nitrogen.

An extensive bibliography of far infrared spectroscopy, with emphasis on instrumentation and techniques, has been published by Palik.[5]

3. Applications of Far Infrared Spectroscopy

In the early days of far infrared spectroscopy, the region was the exlusive domain of physicists interested in the optical properties of materials. The celebrated work of Hagan and Rubens in verifying the Drude relationship between electrical conductivity and optical reflectivity was done around the beginning of the twentieth century at wavelengths considerably longer than 50 μ. Palik's bibliography contains references to this and other pioneering work. After a long absence from studies of this nature, the solid state physicists have returned, and today many interesting *physical* problems are being attacked and solved by the techniques of far infrared spectroscopy. A discussion of these investigations would be out of place in this book, but it is tempting to at least mention a few of them. The lattice vibrations of crystalline materials generally fall in the far infrared. The "reststrahlen" reflection bands of the alkali halides for example, are due to lattice vibrations. Measurements of the dielectric properties (e.g., real and complex refractive indices) of materials are now being made in the far infrared, filling the last gap between the visible spectrum and microwaves. These measurements have been particularly important in the case of ferroelectrics for which theory predicts an infrared active vibration of very low frequency. See, for example, the publication of Barker and Tinkham.[5] The absorption by free electrons in semiconductors becomes stronger at long wavelengths, the absorptivity being proportional to the square of the wavelength,[7] making it desirable to extend measurements of the optical properties of semi-conductors into the far infrared. The absorption of radiation accompanying the transition of electrons across an energy gap, from a valence state to the conduction band, for example, is also very often a far infrared phenomenon. Finally, a variety of effects involving the influence of a magnetic field on optical properties of materials have been studied in the far infrared.[8]

The most elementary application of infrared spectroscopy to *chemical* problems is the qualitative identification of a sample by comparison and matching of its infrared spectrum with a standard spectrum. At present there are not enough reference spectra available in the region beyond 25 μ to make this a particularly valuable application of the far infrared. However, there is evidence that the far infrared spectra of very similar compounds are more likely to show differences than the rock-salt spectra. For example, Harrah, Ryan, and Tamborski[9] have shown the spectra of tetraphenyl-, triphenylchloro-, and diphenyldichlorostannane to be qualitatively alike in the 2 to 15 μ region, but to have marked differences in the CsBr region.

The performance of quantitative analyses in the far infrared has been limited by the relatively poor signal-to-noise ratio implicit in long wavelength spectroscopy. Nevertheless, a few successful quantitative analyses have been reported in the 15 to 25 μ region.

The serious investigator of vibrational spectra has as his objectives an understanding of the structure of molecules and also of the forces which bind them together. In order to compute the force constants of a molecule, it is necessary to have a complete assignment of the observed (and unobserved) frequencies to specific species of vibrations. In many cases the observation of one or two low frequencies in the far infrared is all that remains to complete the vibrational assignment for a molecule. A knowledge of the spectral region in which vibrations of various kinds are likely to occur is of great value in such studies. This knowledge comes only through comparative studies of the spectra of similar molecules. In some cases, the spectral region of occurrence of similar vibrations is sufficiently narrow that the occurrence or failure of occurrence of an absorption band between certain wavelengths can be taken as evidence for or against the existence of a certain structural group or configuration in the molecule. We say these vibrations have "characteristic frequencies" or "functional group frequencies." We shall return in the next section to a detailed discussion of those characteristic frequencies which are found in the far infrared.

The rotations of molecules, as well as the vibrations, are quantized and give rise to discrete systems of energy transitions. This causes the well-known rotational structure in the infrared absorption bands of light molecules observed in the gas phase. The pure rotational levels unaccompanied by changes in vibrational state, can also absorb infrared energy, under certain circumstances. Because the rotational levels of molecules are generally much closer together than the vibrational levels, we find the pure rotational spectra at low frequencies in the far infrared. The most serious limitation to the use of the far infrared in studying rotational spectra is that only the lightest molecules have transitions in this region. Molecules which have been studied, in addition to NH_3,[10,11] include the methyl halides: CH_3Cl, CH_3Br, CH_3I, and CH_3F;[12] H_2O;[13] AsH_3 and PH_3;[14] NO_2;[15] O_3 and SO_2;[16] CH_3CN, $CH_3C{\equiv}CH$, HCF_3, $(CH_3)_3N$;[17] and HCl and HBr.[10] The rotational spectra of heavier molecules lie at millimeter wavelengths in the microwave spectrum.

The study of molecules in condensed phases is an important application of infrared spectroscopy, and the far infrared should prove to be particularly useful. Some compounds, such as the acids, which will be discussed later, and the alcohols, form hydrogen bonds. The presence of these weak bonds is known to perturb the location and appearance of absorption bands in the rock salt region and in the prism far infrared.[18,19] Direct observations of vibrations involving the stretching and bending of hydrogen bonds have been made in a few cases at frequencies as low as 40 cm^{-1}. Usually these studies have been made by means of the Raman effect, but several far infrared measurements have also been reported. Hadzi[20] has observed infrared bonds in the 120 to 150 μ region in a series of hydrogen-bonded crystals, such as potassium dihydrogen phosphate. In this unusual case the bands are not due to transitions from one vibrational state to another. The vibrational levels of the O—H oscillator are split by the strong hydrogen bonding, and the bands are due to transitions between the separated components of the vibrational ground state.

The lattice vibrations of the alkali halides were mentioned earlier as a physical problem. Chemists are also interested in these low frequency vibrations. Observations of lattice vibrations have been reported, for example, for the oxides of uranium[21] at frequencies down to 90 cm^{-1} and for the solid methyl halides[22] between 130 and 30 cm^{-1}. The crystalline nature of solids also affects the molecular vibrations observed in other regions of the spectrum. The crystalline portions of polymers often have absorption bands quite distinct from those of the amorphous portions, and these differences are particularly noticeable in the far infrared.[23] Furthermore, different crystal modifications of the same chemical compound may have distinctive spectra.

The reader who is interested in the theory of vibrating and rotating molecules should consult more specialized books, such as Wilson, Decius, and Cross[24] on molecular vibrations, Allen and Cross[25] on molecular rotations, and Herzberg[26] on both subjects.

4. Functional Groups and Characteristic Frequencies

Probably the most widespread use of infrared spectroscopy in the conventional rock salt wavelength region has been in functional groups analysis. It was noted very early in the history of infrared analysis that the occurrence of certain functional groups in different molecules is often accompanied by absorption bands at relatively fixed frequencies, termed group frequencies. It is natural to inquire into the possibility of extending this application into the far infrared. Before turning to specific examples, let us first consider the nature of group frequencies. We are interested in listing the conditions under which characteristic group frequencies can occur. Of course, we can state at once that the dominant force constants, bond angles, and distances in the group should be relatively invariant from one molecule to another. Those parameters, which are sensitive to changes in the rest of the molecule, must be relatively weak or must occur in such a way that their importance is minimized. A corollary to this condition is that forces between unbonded atoms in different groups must be weak.

In general, two similar groups with similar frequencies might interact with an attendant shift in frequency, if they are closely coupled in the molecule. There are conditions under which this interaction itself provides the characteristic nature of the vibrations. For example, in the rock salt region the characteristic frequencies of the out-of-plane vibrations of hydrogen atoms on substituted benzene rings are largely determined by the nature of the coupling between different C—H bonds. We shall see further examples of this in the far infrared.

In more complex structures, simple descriptions are not necessarily valid, as very frequently a normal vibration involves both stretching and bending of many bonds and angles. This is particularly true of the low frequency vibrations in the far infrared. Nonetheless, it is customary to retain the picturesque fiction of pure stretching, deformation, rocking, wagging, torsion, ring puckering, and the like, but always with the implied reservation that these are labels and not necessarily descriptions of the actual vibrational motion. When we speak of vibration as a —C—S—C— deformation, for example, it is with the conviction that the C—S—C angle is indeed underoing a periodic change and that this motion is probably making the greatest contribution to the vibrations, in the sense that its amplitude is large. We should not be surprised, however, to learn that the C—S bonds are stretching simultaneously, that the R—C—S angle is changing, that the bonds making up the R group are vibrating, and even that another group many atoms away from the C—S—C group is undergoing vibrations.

The commonly encountered types of vibration of X_2Y and X_3Y groups are sketched in Figure 1, with the descriptive terms used in this chapter. To simplify the drawings, the central atom is assumed to be so heavy that its motion is very slight. Furthermore, only one component of the degenerate asymmetric vibrations of the X_3Y group is shown.

Now let us turn to some specific examples of characteristic frequencies in the far infrared.

4.1. The Nitrile Group.   We might expect the bending vibration of the RC≡N group of nitriles to be a characteristic frequency. Values of the calculated bending frequency are plotted in Figure 2 as a function of the mass of the R group, assuming, of course, that R can be treated as a structureless mass and that the force constant and interatomic distances remain constant. Hidalgo[47,28] has published spectra of thirty-six aliphatic and aromatic nitriles and has assigned a band of medium intensity in the CsBr region to the bending vibration. Figure 2a contains Hidalgo's experimental values for a number of aliphatic nitriles. They cluster very closely about 370 cm^{-1} (371 ± 11 cm^{-1}) even when R is as light as a methyl group. Even though the force constant used in calculating the theoretical

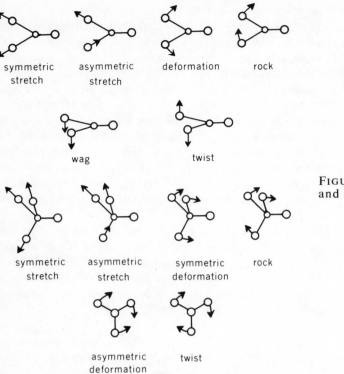

symmetric stretch   asymmetric stretch   deformation   rock

wag   twist

symmetric stretch   asymmetric stretch   symmetric deformation   rock

asymmetric deformation   twist

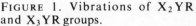

FIGURE 1. Vibrations of X_2YR and X_3YR groups.

curve was chosen to best fit the data for aliphatic nitriles, notice that HCN, DCN, and TCN[29,30] also fall very nearly on the calculated curve. The 370 cm^{-1} band is thus seen to be a good characteristic band for aliphatic nitriles, and we are assured that the $R—C\equiv N$ bending vibration is responsible for its occurrence. Experimental data for aromatic nitriles, including those of the form $\phi—(CH_2)_n—CN$, are plotted in Figure 2b. These compounds also have bands close to 370 cm^{-1}, but with considerably greater variance (362 ± 51 cm^{-1}) than the alkyl nitriles. There are several possible reasons for the greater variation in the case of the aromatic nitriles. First, there is greater opportunity for interactions between the nitrile group and the remainder of the molecule, for the out-of-plane bending vibrations of the benzene ring are also low frequency vibrations and the conjugated nature of the $\phi—C\equiv N$ system tends to introduce interaction force constants. Also, the spectra of aromatic compounds are fairly rich in bands in the cesium bromide region causing some uncertainty in the assignment of bands to specific vibrations. For example, the spectra of the toluene nitriles have bands near 350 cm^{-1} which Hidalgo assigns to methyl-ring vibrations. In p-toluene nitrile this leaves only the band at 413 cm^{-1} available for assignment to the $R—CN$ mode. Whether this assignment is correct, or whether 350 cm^{-1} is really the nitrile band, or indeed whether the absorption at 350 cm^{-1} really contains two unresolved frequencies would be a difficult decision to make. The compound $CH_2\!=\!CH—CN$ is included in Figure 2b. Its frequency falls considerably below the curve. It is probaly that the force constant has been modified by conjugation of the $C\!=\!C$ and $C\equiv N$ bonds.

Figure 2c contains the frequencies of a number of nitriles which disagree somewhat with the group frequency; and, of course, we would like to understand why. Notice first the sequence of halogen cyanides F—, Cl—, Br—, ICN.[31,32] These frequencies form a separate line because niether the force constant nor the $R—C$ bond length is the same for all four compounds.

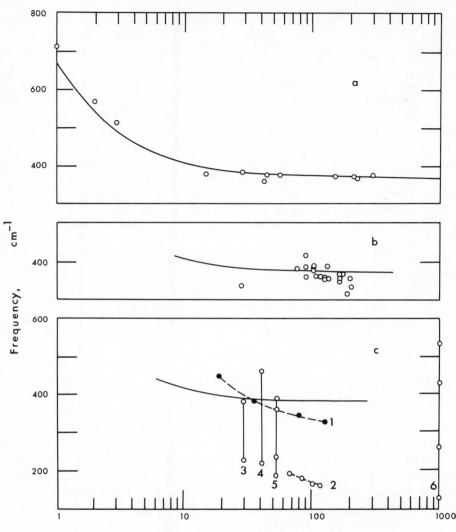

FIGURE 2. RC≡N bond bending frequency of some nitriles. (a) Alkyl nitriles from Hidalgo.[27,28] (b) Aromatic and unsaturated nitriles from Hidalgo.[27,28] (c) The sequence F—, Cl—, Br—, I—CN falls on line 1 (solid circles); the sequence CF_3—, CF_2Cl—, $CFCl_2$— and CCl_3—CN falls on line 2; two frequencies of ethyl nitrile are connected by line 3; two frequencies of cyclopropyl nitrile[38] are connected by line 4; four frequencies of dicyanoethane are connected by line 5; four frequencies of polyvinylnitrile,[39] connected by line 6, are arbitrarily plotted at molecular weight 1000.

The molecules in the sequence CF_3—, CF_2Cl—, CCl_3CN[33-35] do not have frequencies in the 360 cm^{-1} region which can be assigned exclusively to RCN bending, although vibrations occurring near there probably involve a mixture of the C—CN bending mode and bending motions of the carbon-halogen links. Hidalgo observes a band at 439 cm^{-1} in CCl_3CN which he assigns to the bending vibration. Frequencies of much lower value have been assigned to R—C≡N bending in these molecules. We expect to find two frequencies associated with the CN group in some molecules having a plane of symmetry, corresponding to an in-plane and an out-of-plane vibration. All of the remaining molecules included in Figure 2c, in addition to the higher frequency vibrations, do have low frequency vibrations not far from those of the trihalomethyl nitriles (211 ± 48 cm^{-1}). For the most part, these have been observed in the Raman region, rather than in the far infrared.

In molecules containing two nitrile groups, we might expect to find distinct in-phase and out-of-phase frequencies. Two pairs of frequencies are given for dicyanoethane (succinonitrile).[36] The bands at 234 and 357 cm^{-1} have been associated with the rotational isomer of the *gauche* form while 187 and 387 cm^{-1} are due to the *trans* form. This is an illustration of the effects of conformation changes on far infrared spectra, an effect which we will encounter numerous times in other classes of molecules as well. Hidalgo's spectrum of dicyanobutane displays a splitting in the CN band (376 and 360 cm^{-1}) which is possibly also due to *trans* and *gauche* isomers. Several bands of cyanoacetylene and dicyanoacetylene fall in the far infrared, but we do not expect any of these to be associated exclusively with the R—C$\equiv$N group because the —C$\equiv$C— bonds also have characteristic frequencies in this region, as we shall see.

The Ge—C$\equiv$N bending vibration in the compound germyl cyanide, GeH$_3$—CN, has been placed at 221 cm^{-1} (212 cm^{-1} in GeD$_3$CN) by assigning a band at 443 cm^{-1} as the overtone.[37] If this assignment is correct, then by analogy with the alkyl nitriles, it should provide a characteristic frequency for the Ge—C$\equiv$N group.

4.2. The Acetylene Group.   There are two characteristic bending modes of the —C—C$\equiv$C—H group. The —C$\equiv$CH bending vibration is found at 629 ± 51 cm^{-1}, and the —C—C$\equiv$C bending vibration is usually in the region 325 ± 25 cm^{-1}. (See Table 1.) The vibrational frequencies of the aliphatic acetylenes have been reviewed by Nyquist and Potts[40] who find that the C—CH vibrations falls in the considerably narrower region 630 ± 3 cm^{-1}. Just as in the case of the dicyano compounds, the presence of two or more —C$\equiv$C— bonds in a molecule introduces a multitude of frequencies and, as indicated earlier, the vibrations of a —C$\equiv$N and a —C$\equiv$C bond in the same molecule interact to complicate the spectrum. In the molecule propynol (CH$\equiv$C—CH$_2$OH),[41,42] the —C$\equiv$C—H bending frequencies (in- and out-of-plane) are raised to 684 and 662 cm^{-1} while the —C$\equiv$C—C bending frequencies are lowered to 206 and 260 cm^{-1}, probably by the effects of conjugation on force constants. However, in ethynyl benzene, C$_6$H$_5$—C$\equiv$C—H,[43] the in-plane and out-of-plane —C$\equiv$CH bending vibrations are found at 648 610 cm^{-1}, bracketing the normal region, while a band at 351 cm^{-1} falls in the normal region of the C—C$\equiv$C bending vibrations.

TABLE 1.   Frequencies of Bending Vibrations of Some
Acetylenic Compounds

Molecule	Ref.	C$\equiv$CH Bend	C—C$\equiv$C Bend
HC$\equiv$CH	26	729.1	
HC$\equiv$CF	47	578	
HC$\equiv$CCl	47	604	
HC$\equiv$CBr	47	618	
HC$\equiv$CI	47	630	
Alkyl—C$\equiv$CH	40	630 ± 3	~335
CH$_3$C$\equiv$CCl	45		358
CH$_3$C$\equiv$CBr	46		343
CH$_3$C$\equiv$CI	46		343
CH$\equiv$C—COH	41	662, 684	206, 260
C$_6$H$_5$—C$\equiv$CH	43	610, 648	351
HC$\equiv$C—C$\equiv$CH	48	627, 630	220, 482

The stretching frequencies of the —C≡C—halogen bond are found at 575, 464, and 405 cm^{-1} in chloro-, bromo- and iodomethylacetylene,[44-46] and probably are not far from these values in the higher aliphatic acetylenes. The frequencies of the —C≡C—halogen bending vibrations are 184, 171, and 163 cm^{-1} for chlorine, bromine, and iodine. The fact that these frequencies seem to be insensitive to the substituted halogen atom, and the observation in the case of the nitriles that the bending vibration is not sensitive to the mass of the alkyl substituent suggests that 174 ± 10 cm^{-1} might be a useful characteristic frequency for —C≡C—halogen compounds, provided it is sufficiently intense in the infrared spectrum.

4.3. Other R-A-B-C Groups.. The bending vibration of the —N=N=N group in metal azides[49,50] and in the isolated azide ion[51] is in the narrow region 642 ± 8 cm^{-1}. In hydrazoic acid[52] there is an out-of-plane mode at 522 cm^{-1}. In ammonium azide,[53] bands are found at 664 and 652 cm^{-1}. There does not appear to have been a systematic search for the —N=N≡N bending modes in alkyl or aryl azides, but methyl azide[54] has bands at 666 and 55 cm^{-1}.

The low frequency vibrational frequencies of allene[55,56] and of a few allenic molecules,[57] from methyl to butyl, are known and the assignments given in Table 2 are proposed.

TABLE 2. Characteristic Frequencies of Allenic Molecules

Vibration	Frequency
C=C=C bend	331 ± 25 and 203 ± 7 cm^{-1}
HC=C bend	535 ± 12
C—C=C bend	556 ± 8

4.4. The Alkenes. The spectra in the KBr region of a large number of olefinic molecules are to be found in the series of curves distributed by the American Petroleum Institute. From a study of these and other spectra we can formulate the spectra-structure correlations given in Table 3. A somewhat different table has been given by Bentley and Wolfarth,[58] and the form and frequency of characteristic frequencies of olefins has been discussed by Sverdlov.[59]

TABLE 3. Characteristic Frequencies of Alkene Molecules

Structure	Frequencies		
RCH=CRR	543 ± 26	497 ± 28	427 ± 25 cm^{-1}
trans-RCH=CHR	547 ± 32	491 ± 9	452 ± 12
cis-RCH=CHR	603 ± 25	486 ± 12	
RRC=CH$_2$	548 ± 11	454 ± 16	
RCH$_2$—CH=CH$_2$	629 ± 7	552 ± 2	465 ± 21

The spectrum of natural rubber (Figure 3) provides an illustration of the use of these correlations. Rubber[60] has bands at 570, 500, and 430 cm^{-1}, which verify the structure

$$\begin{array}{c} CH_3 \\ | \\ (-CH_2-C=CH-CH_2-) \end{array}$$

as opposed to

$$\begin{array}{c} CH_2 \\ \| \\ (-CH_2-C-CH_2-CH_2-) \end{array}$$

This is in agreement with the conclusions drawn from the infrared spectrum in the rock salt region. The nature of the vibrations of natural rubber and, by extension, those of the smaller alkenes containing $CRR=CHR$ groups, has been investigated by means of polarized radiation.[61] The 570 cm^{-1} vibration is predominantly along the molecular axis and might be described as a rocking motion. The 500 cm^{-1} vibration is perpendicular to the axis and is probably an out-of-plane bending mode. The 630 cm^{-1} vibration of the $-CH=CH_2$ group is known to be an out-of-plane bending mode of the hydrogen atoms.[62-64] A similar correlation has been made for the *cis*-$CH=CH-$ group frequency near 690 cm^{-1} in the rock salt region.[65]

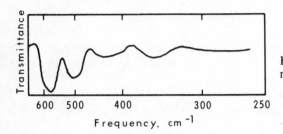

FIGURE 3. Far infrared spectrum of natural rubber (from Linnig and Stewart,[60] CsBr prism).

By analogy with the vibrational motions of the hydrogen atoms of alkenes, which are observed at higher frequencies, we might expect that the vibrations of halogen atoms adjacent to double bonds could provide us with characteristic frequencies in the far infrared. Unfortunately, only the fluoro-, chloro-, and bromo-substituted ethylenes have been studied extensively.[66] The regions of vibrations shown in Table 4 are based on this limited class of compound. The frequencies for the iodine containing compounds have been estimated by extrapolation. It will be interesting to see whether future studies verify or reject these values as characteristic frequencies of halogenated olefins.

TABLE 4.   Tentative Characteristic Frequencies of the Halogenated Alkenes, Based on Frequencies of the Halogenated Ethylenes

Group	Vibration		
	Deformation	Rock	Bend
$=CF_2$	430 ± 85 cm^{-1}	400 ± 55	515 ± 10
$=CFCl$	350 ± 75	370 ± 30	475 ± 45
$=CFBr$	310 ± 15	230 ± 65	415 ± 80
$=CCl_2$	250 ± 15	220 ± 40	410 ± 90
$=CClBr$	220 ± 10	180 ± 50	300 ± 25
$=CBr_2$	160 ± 25	140 ± 20	280 ± 30
$=CFI$	300	260	400
$=CClI$	200	160	310
$=CBrI$	120	80	230
$=CI_2$	100	50	200

4.5. The Alkanes.   The saturated hydrocarbons absorb only weakly in the far infrared, limiting the usefulness of any group frequencies which might be discovered. The straight chain hydrocarbons have weak bands near 455 cm^{-1} and in the 512 ± 27 cm^{-1} region, with the most intense band converging on 540 cm^{-1} as the chain length increases.[58] Figure 4 is a spectrum of a 1 mm thick layer of polyethylene in the CsBr region. The branched

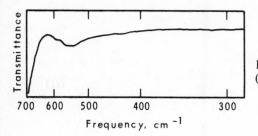

FIGURE 4. Far infrared spectrum of polyethylene (1 mm thick, CsBr prisms).

chains have more distinct bands in the 530 ± 45 cm^{-1} region, and, in fact, correlations between frequency and type of substitution have been given.[58] (See Table 5.)

It is generally accepted that the carbon-halogen stretching vibrations, when the carbon atom is saturated, are found near 1000 to 1300, 560 to 800, 500 to 650, and 480 to 600 cm^{-1} for fluorine, chlorine, bromine, and iodine substitution, respectively.[74] The frequencies

TABLE 5. Characteristic Frequencies of Substituted Alkanes (From Bentley and Wolforth)[58]

Structure	Frequencies	
Monosubstituted	550 cm^{-1}	440 cm^{-1}
Disubstituted	540	
3,3-Disubstituted	530	
2,2-Disubstituted	490	

of the vibrations within these ranges depend on the conformation of the neighboring part of the molecule and on whether the carbon to which the halogen is attached is primary, secondary, or tertiary.[67-75] The correlations of Table 6, from the work of Shipman, Folt, and Krimm,[67] are based on the spectra of some thirty-six compounds. It shows how useful this property can be in the elucidation of molecular structure. If the chlorine is *trans* to another chlorine atom, the frequencies appear to fall in the same regions as though the chlorine were *trans* to a carbon.

The spectrum of polyvinyl chloride —(CH$_2$—CHCl)—[76] is shown in Figure 5. The strong absorption bands at 603 and 638 cm^{-1} lie in the proper region for a chlorine atom

TABLE 6. Characteristic Carbon-Chlorine Stretching Frequency of the Chloroalkanes (From Shipman, Folt, and Krimm)[67]

The following notation is used: P = primary, S = secondary, and T = tertiary carbon atom; H = chlorine atom *trans* to a hydrogen atom; C = chlorine atom is *trans* to a carbon atom.

P$_H$	648–657 cm^{-1}
P$'_H$ (branched)	679–686
P$_C$	723–730
S$_{HH}$	608–615
S$'_{HH}$ (bent)	627–637
S$_{CH}$	655–674
S$_{CC}$	~758
T$_{HHH}$	560–581
T$_{CHH}$	611–632

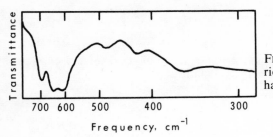

FIGURE 5. Far infrared spectrum of polyvinyl chloride in KBr pellet (from Harvey, Stewart, and Achhammer,[76] CsBr prism).

attached to a secondary carbon and *trans* to a hydrogen atom. The band at 693 cm^{-1}, on the other hand, is due to a chlorine *trans* to a carbon atom. The spectrum of Figure 5 is of a sample of polyvinyl chloride powder, pressed in a potassium bromide pellet. In the spectra of thin films, a band at 615 cm^{-1} can be partially resolved on the side of the 603 cm^{-1} band.[77-79] If the molecular chains are oriented by stretching the film[77] and the spectrum studied with polarized radiation, it is found that the vibrations at 693, 638, and 615 cm^{-1} are predominantly perpendicular to the direction of stretch. The 603 cm^{-1} vibration is parallel in a film stretched to twice its normal length, becoming perpendicular when the stretching is extended to five times or seven times the normal length.

The spectrum of polyvinylidene chloride, "saran" —$(CH_2$—$CCl_2)$— shown in Figure 6, has carbon-chlorine stretching frequencies at 530, 603, 657, and probably 754 cm^{-1}.[78,23] These frequencies fall outside the regions given by Shipman, *et al.*, for a *single* chlorine atom on a tertiary carbon. The band pair 530 and 603 cm^{-1} are due to the in- and out-of-phase vibrations. As a note of caution, it should be noted that in polychlorotrifluoroethylene the carbon-chlorine stretching vibration has an unusually high frequency of 972 cm^{-1}.[80]

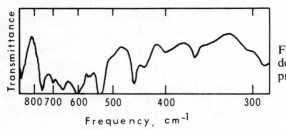

FIGURE 6. Far infrared spectrum of polyvinylidene chloride, "saran" (0.05 mm thick, CsBr prisms).

The *n*-alkyl bromides show a dependence on the conformation of the molecule similar to that of the chlorides. Brown and Sheppard[69] show, for eight compounds from ethyl to *n*-decyl bromide, that the carbon-bromine stretching frequency falls in the 560 to 565 cm^{-1} region when the bromine is *trans* to a hydrogen and 642 to 645 cm^{-1} when it is *trans* to a carbon atom. In tertiary butyl bromide,[81] the carbon-bromine stretch drops to 515 cm^{-1}. Data for alkyl iodides are not plentiful. In *n*-propyl iodide[79] the carbon-iodine stretching vibration occurs at 501 cm^{-1} when the iodine is *trans* to a hydrogen atom and at 593 cm^{-1} when it is *trans* to a carbon atom. In tertiary butyl iodide[81] the carbon-iodine stretching frequency is lowered to 487 cm^{-1}. More experimental work is needed to establish the validity and frequency range for the bromides and particularly the iodides.

Just as the angle-bending vibrational modes of CH, CH_2, and CH_3 groups provide useful group frequencies in the rock salt region of the infrared, we might anticipate the existence of useful group frequencies for the carbon-halogen angular vibrations. The angle bending frequencies of a number of molecules containing CF_3 groups are given in Table 7.

The symmetric deformation modes of CF_3 groups are seen to occur usually near $570 \pm 30 \text{ cm}^{-1}$, except possibly when the group is near an unsaturated bond. The asymmetric deformations are near 635 ± 45 and $530 \pm 25 \text{ cm}^{-1}$, and the asymmetric and symmetric rocking modes are in the considerably less well defined region 200 to 460 cm^{-1}.

TABLE 7.   Deformation and Rocking Vibrational Frequencies of the CF_3 Group

Molecule	Ref.	Deformations			Rocking	
		Asym	Asym	Sym	Asym	Sym
CF_3—CH_2Cl	82	665	520	552	229	202
CF_3—CH_2Br	83	634	526	539	352	312
CF_3—$CHCl_2$	84	672	526	559	—	—
CF_3—CF_2Cl	85	647	558	593	334	260
CF_3—CF_2Br	85, 86	633	548	590	297	297
CF_3—CF_2I	85	621	544	590	433	223
CF_3—$CFCl_2$	87	590	508	558	331	312
CF_3—SH	88, 89		521	463	305	—
CF_3—$C\equiv CH$	90	610	—	—	453	
CF_3—$C\equiv CD$	90	611	—	—	445.4	
CF_3—$C\equiv CF$	90	601	—	—	447	
CF_3—$C\equiv CCl$	90	607	—	—	455	
CF_3—$C\equiv CBr$	90	610	—	—	453	
CF_3—$C\equiv CI$	90	610	—	—	452	

The angular modes of the CF_2 group in polytetrafluoroethylene and polychlorotrifluoroethylene[80] are given in Table 8. The similarity of these frequencies suggests the existence of useful characteristic CF_2 frequencies.

TABLE 8.   Vibration Frequencies of the CF_2 Group in Polytetrafluoroethylene and Polychlorotrifluoroethylene[80]

	—CF_2—	—CF_2Cl—CF_2—
CF_2 rocking	203 and 516 cm^{-1}	235 and 490 cm^{-1}
CF_2 wagging	277 and 636	297 and 580
CF_2 deformation	553	506
CF_2 twisting	321	—

The number of compounds whose spectra are available is much too limited, but there is some evidence that the deformation vibrations of the CCl_3 group occur near 300 ± 70 and $370 \pm 60 \text{ cm}^{-1}$ with a rocking mode near $220 \pm 50 \text{ cm}^{-1}$.

4.6. The Aromatics.   A number of authors have studied the vibrations of substituted aromatic rings in the KBr region. Largely because of the susceptibility of aromatic systems to inductive effects, some of these frequencies are quite sensitive to the nature of the substituent.[91] Indeed, good correlations are often obtained between the frequencies of substituent sensitive bands and certain properties of the substituent, such as Hammett's or Taft's σ constants, electronegativities, or the mass of the substituent.[92,93] Some vibrations of aromatic rings are fairly insensitive to both the mass and the chemical properties of the substituents, but depend on the distribution and number of substituents around the ring. These ring vibrations can serve as group frequencies for determining substitution type, supplementing the out-of-plane vibrations of the hydrogens on an aromatic ring which are observed in the 800 to 650 cm^{-1} region of the rock salt spectrum.[65] A correlation table proposed by Jakobsen[94] on the basis of a study of 279 benzene derivatives is given in Table 9 for single ring aromatic compounds. The higher frequency is an in-plane ring deformation and the low frequency is an out-of-plane bending vibration. The ranges shown are quite broad in some cases and can be reduced considerably when dealing with specific types of substituent. For example, Jakobsen gives the frequency range of the out-of-plane vibration of monosubstituted aromatics: "(1) near 550 cm^{-1} for compounds where the substituents are C=C, C≡C, or C≡N; (2) near 500 cm^{-1} for compounds where the substituents are electron donors such as OH, NH$_2$, etc.; (3) between 440 and 500 cm^{-1} for compounds with halogen or saturated aliphatic substituents; and (4) below 450 cm^{-1} where the substituents are electron acceptors such as NO$_2$, COOH, etc." In meta disubstituted aromatic compounds the out-of-plane vibrations lie in the range 438 ± 23 cm^{-1}, except for compounds with electron accepting substituents, where the frequency rises to 475 ± 15 cm^{-1}. Jakobsen also gives a correlation table for the vibrational frequencies of mono- and disubstituted aromatics with specific types of substituents.

TABLE 9.   Characteristic Frequencies of Substituted Benzenes (From Jakobsen)[94]

Substitution	In-Plane Deformation	Out-of-plane Deformation	Form Unknown
mono	605–626	418–560	
di-1,2	495–555	418–470	
di-1,3	505–560	415–490	
di,1,4	615–650	446–552	
tri-1,2,4		428–476	
tri-1,3,5		500–535	450–470
tri-1,2,3		535–570	
tetra-1,2,3,4			568–585
tetra-1,2,3,5		505–580	
tetra-1,2,4,5			420–470
penta-			558–580
hexa-			385–415

The spectrum of polystyrene film shown in Figure 7 has a typical pair of bands characteristic of a monosubstituted aromatic compound at 760 and 700 cm^{-1} in the rock salt region. In addition, it has a weak band at 622 cm^{-1} and one at 446 cm^{-1} in the potassium bromide region, which verify the identification of a monosubstituted ring. The 446 cm^{-1} band in Figure 7 is partly obscured by the interference fringes but it easily observed in the spectrum given by Liang and Krimm.[23,95] There is also a strong band at 540 cm^{-1} which is not a characteristic band.

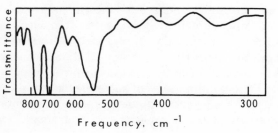

FIGURE 7. Far infrared spectrum of polystyrene (0.025 mm thick, CsBr prisms).

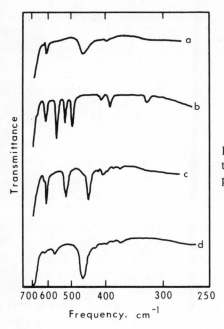

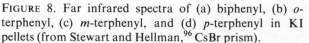

FIGURE 8. Far infrared spectra of (a) biphenyl, (b) *o*-terphenyl, (c) *m*-terphenyl, and (d) *p*-terphenyl in KI pellets (from Stewart and Hellman,[96] CsBr prism).

A study by Stewart and Hellman[96] of a more specialized class of substituted aromatics, the polyphenyls, (see Figure 8) has yielded the frequency correlations shown in Table 10, which are in fair agreement with the correlations of Table 9 except for the displaced low frequency band of the ortho substituted rings and the missing high frequency para substituted ring vibration which overlaps the 614 cm^{-1} band of the monosubstituted rings. Table 10 also contains some correlations given by Dale.[97] The analogous low frequency out-of-plane deformations are found near 475 cm^{-1} in naphthalene,[98-101] 1-alkyl- and 2-alkyl-naphthalenes,[58] and anthracene.[102] Another specialized class of substituted aromatic ring compound, the para substituted phenols, has been studied by Jakobsen and Brewer.[103]

TABLE 10. Characteristic Frequencies of the Polyphenyls
(From Stewart and Hellman,[96] except those in parenthesis which are from Dale[97])

Ring	Frequencies		
	In-Plane	Out-of-Plane	
Monosubstituted	614 ± 4 cm^{-1}	~460 (531 ± 13)	
ortho-Substituted	614 ± 4	503 ± 10 532 ± 10 564 ± 7	
meta-Substituted	614 ± 4	454 ± 20 514 ± 12 563 ± 10	
para-Substituted		471 ± 11 (564 ± 6)	

The spectra of a number of halogenated benzenes have been studied. Of particular importance are the series of fluorinated aromatics investigated in the Naval Research Laboratories and the University of Oklahoma[104-112] and the studies on *p*-dihalobenzenes of Stojiljkovic and Whiffen.[113] The frequencies of those vibrations which can be associated with the ϕ-halogen bond are found to occur in the rather broad regions shown in Table 11.

Harrah, Ryan, and Tamborski[9] have studied the far infrared spectra of a number of phenyl derivatives of Si, Ge, Sn, Pb, P, Sb, and Bi. They find two strong substituent sensi-

TABLE 11. Characteristic Vibrational Frequencies of Halogentated Aromatic Compounds

Vibration	F	Cl	Br	I
Phenyl-halogen stretch and ring deformation	600 ± 80 cm^{-1}	435 ± 65	330 ± 70	225 ± 40
In-plane phenyl-halogen bend	400 ± 25	280 ± 50	260 ± 35	~ 200
Out-of-plane phenyl-halogen bend	290 ± 50	250 ± 85	250 ± 75	235 ± 75

tive bands in the regions 433 to 507 cm^{-1} and 190 to 520 cm^{-1}. The frequencies of these bands, when plotted against the reciprocal of the square root of the phenyl-central atom reduced mass, are found to fall on straight lines. Hence, the frequencies of these vibrations can be considered as characteristic of the metal-phenyl group.

The pyridine molecule is structurally similar to benzene. The far infrared spectra of forty-three monosubstituted pyridines have been studied by Isaac, Bentley, Sternglanz, Coburn, Stephenson, and Wilcox.[114] They find bands at 618 ± 17 cm^{-1} and at 401 ± 16 cm^{-1} in the spectra of 2- and 3-substituted pyridines, while the spectra of 4- substituted pyridines resemble the spectra of monosubstituted benzenes.

4.7. Nonaromatic Cyclic Molecules.   The series of *unsaturated* ring compounds of the type R—CH=CH—CH=CH, where R=CH$_2$, NH, O, S, and Se have infrared absorption bands at 467, 480, 516, 452, and 460 cm^{-1}, respectively. These vibrations are out-of-plane deformations of the rings, and they seem to persist when one or more of the hydrogens on the rings are substituted. The spectra of thirty-three mono-, di-, tri-, and tetra-substituted thiophenes have appeared in the literature,[115,116] and all have bands in the region 490 ± 40 cm^{-1}. The spectra of five mono-and dimethyl substituted selenophenes reported by Chumaevskii, Tatevskii, and Iurev[117] have bands in the region 425 ± 12 cm^{-1}.

The Raman spectrum of cyclopentene[118] has a line at 603 cm^{-1} attributed to an in-plane bending of the ring. Similar vibrations produce an infrared band at 584 cm^{-1} in 4,4-dimethylcyclopentene[119] and in the region 597 ± 18 cm^{-1} in a series of nine 1- and 2- mono-, and 2,3-dialkyl substituted cyclopentenes studied by Sverdlov and Krainov.[118] There is also an out-of-plane vibration at 415 ± 25 cm^{-1}.

The spectra of ten substituted 3,3-diphenylphthalides and of phthalide itself

reported by Jakobsen and Wyant[120] have bands at 503 ± 13 and 479 ± 9 cm^{-1} which are characteristic of the phthalide ring. In addition, the 3,3-diphenylphthalides have bands at 632 ± 6, 530 ± 9, and 370 ± 15 cm^{-1}. The position of the 370 cm^{-1} band is dependent on the nature of the substituents on the 3,3-phenyl rings.

Molecules with saturated rings also have vibrational frequencies in the KBr region. Group frequencies have been established for the alicyclic rings near 500 cm^{-1} by Bentley and Wolfarth,[58] based on the spectra of over one hundred compounds. Their correlations are given in Table 12. These vibrations probably are ring deformation modes.

Because of the greater sensitivity of low frequency molecular vibrations to structural differences we find that characteristic far infrared frequencies quite often occur over a much wider frequency range than the group frequencies of the rock salt region. However,

**TABLE 12.   Characteristic Frequencies of Alicyclic Compounds
(From Bentley and Wolfarth[58])**

Molecular Type	Frequency Range
Cyclohexanes	$500 \pm 70 \text{ cm}^{-1}$, strong
Cyclopentanes	538 ± 45, strong
Alkyl cyclopentanes	556 ± 27, strong
Cyclopropanes	520 ± 20, variable
Alkyl cyclopropanes	520 ± 20 and 468 ± 5, strong

as more and more molecules are studied, it is often possible to subdivide the region of occurrence of a group frequency according to the nature of other portions of the molecule. Some of the low frequency vibrations, indeed, probably most of them, are not confined to a localized portion of the molecule. We realize that a "ring vibration" involves a certain amount of movement of the substituents as well, but we call it a ring vibration because it is correlated with the presence of a ring structure and occurs in a fairly well defined spectral region. On the other hand, the far infrared spectra of the pyranose sugars are very rich in bands which appear to be distributed at random between 15 and 40 μ and hardly seem characteristic of any particular structure. (See Figure 9.) Nevertheless, Isbell and Tipson[121-124] have found it possible by statistical means to correlate absorptions in certain regions with the α- or β-conformation of the pyranose ring C—C—C—C—C
                                                                                      └——— O ———┘

of a given configuration or type of sugar. The actual form of the vibrations responsible for these absorptions is not known, and it would be unduly presumptuous to term them "ring vibrations."

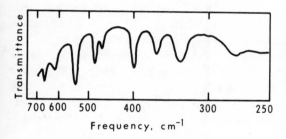

FIGURE 9. Far infrared spectrum of methyl-α-D-lyxopyranoside (from Tipson and Isbell,[121] KCl pellet, CsBr prism).

Other heterocyclic saturated rings which seem to have characteristic absorptions in the far infrared are *m*-dioxane, C—O—C—O—C, which absorbs at $309 \pm 2 \text{ cm}^{-1}$ when fused
                                     └——— C ———┘
to a pyranose ring[125] and the epoxy ring —C—C—, which contributes a band near
                                              \O/

370 cm^{-1}.[126]

An uncompleted study by Ulrich[127] of barbiturates and related compounds containing the

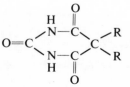

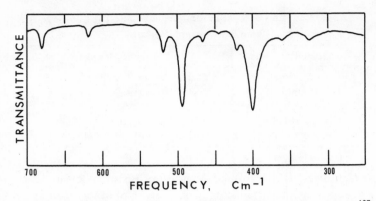

FIGURE 10. Far infrared spectrum of butabarbital (from Ulrich,[127] nujol mull, CsI prism-grating spectrophotometer).

ring structure shows the existence of two characteristic bands near 400 and 500 cm^{-1} (see Figure 10). These bands are strong and should prove useful in the study and identification of this important class of compounds.

4.8. The Amines.   Because of the heavy end groups involved and the relative weakness of the bond-bending force constants, we expect the C—N—C bending vibrations of secondary aliphatic amines to fall somewhere in the far infrared. Furthermore, for large alkyl groups, heavier than the nitrogen atom, we might expect that most of the motion during the vibrations will be done by the nitrogen atom with the alkyls remaining relatively fixed in position. If this is the case, then the C—N—C bending frequency might be a characteristic frequency. The far infrared spectra of four dialkyl amines studied by Stewart[128] do indeed have a band at 427 $\pm$ 14 cm^{-1}, not far from the 400 cm^{-1} Raman line of dimethylamine which Kohlrausch[129] assigned to the bending mode. We feel justified therefore, in naming the 427 cm^{-1} band as a characteristic frequency for secondary amines Unfortunately, the band is not very useful because it is extremely weak and diffuse.

The spectra of twelve primary alkyl amines[128] have medium intensity bands at 469 $\pm$ 24 cm^{-1} and much stronger bands at about the limit of the useful range of the CsI prism, or about 200 cm^{-1}. (See Figure 11.) The internal rotation of the NH$_2$ group around the C—N bond has been reported for methyl amine to be at 269.5 cm^{-1}.[130] The effect of substituting a heavier alkyl group in place of the methyl with no change in the barrier to internal rotation is calculated to decrease the torsional oscillation to about 235 cm^{-1}. The band at 469 cm^{-1} is, therefore, probably the overtone of an internal rotation funda-

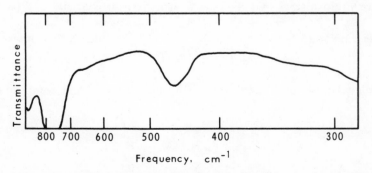

FIGURE 11. Far infrared spectrum of *n*-propylamine (0.1 mm cell, CsBr prisms).

mental at roughly 200 to 220 cm^{-1}. The primary amines in the liquid phase have very intense, broad bands with maxima at frequencies lower than 290 cm^{-1}. These bands become much weaker in solution, which is probably an indication of the effects of hydrogen bonding on the amino group in the liquid phase. A similar strong band has not been observed in liquid aniline.

4.9. The Amides. Because of their importance in biochemistry, a great deal of effort has gone into studies of the structure of amides, and infrared spectroscopy has been a very important tool in these studies. Of the seven characteristic frequencies of amide molecules, three are in the far infrared.[132-137] The amide IV band, due to a deformation of the O=C—N bond angle, lies near 650 cm^{-1}, on the edge of the rock salt region. The amide VI band is associated with an out-of-plane C=O bending mode and occurs near 576 ± 39 cm^{-1}. The amide VII vibration, a torsional oscillation about the C—N bond, is the most sensitive of the amide characteristic bands to changes in conformation of the amide structure. In polyglycine I, the anti-parallel chain extended conformation, it is found at 217 cm^{-1}, while in polyglycine II, the helical conformation, it lies at 365 cm^{-1}.[137] Thus, the amide VII band can prove to be very useful in the elucidation of polypeptide conformations.

4.10. Nitroparaffins. The infrared spectra of four nitroparaffins were recorded by Smith, Pan, and Nielsen[138] some time ago. Their frequencies, together with those reported by Jonathan[139] for sodium nitromethane and sodium-2-nitropropane and the frequencies of tetranitromethane given by Lindenmeyer and Harris,[140] are tabulated in Table 13. A strong absorption band with a characteristic frequency in the 606 to 693 cm^{-1} region, converging on 619 ± 13 cm^{-1} for moderately heavy alkyl groups has been assigned to the NO_2 angle deformation vibration. However, Jakobsen[141] has found that assignments for the nitroparaffins are complicated by the presence of rotational isomers.

The spectra of two organic nitrates (methyl-[142] and polyvinylnitrate[143]) have NO_2 deformation vibrations at higher frequencies than those of the nitro compounds and fall in the NaCl prism region.

TABLE 13. Vibrational Frequencies of Some Nitro Compounds

Molecule	Frequencies	
	Deformation	Rocking
CH_3NO_2	658 cm^{-1}	605, 477
CD_3NO_2	632	560, 424
$C_2H_5NO_2$	621	495
$(CH_3)_2CHNO_2$	630	526
$CH_3CH_2CH_2NO_2$	610	477
$C(NO_2)_4$	693, 668, 606	413, 398, 357
Na^+ $[CH_2NO_2]^-$	690, 677	536
Na^+ $[(CH_3)_2CHNO_2]^-$	624	

4.11. Esters and Acids. The acetate group in methyl acetate[144] absorbs at 639 (O—C—O bend), 615 (out-of-plane distortion of the CH_3—COO group), 429 (C—C—O bend), 303 (C—O—C bend), and 213 cm^{-1} (torsion about the O—C bond).[137] The KBr spectrum of amyl acetate has similar bands at 635, 606, and 436 cm^{-1} (see Figure 12). Sodium acetate[145] also has bands at 651, 620, and 463 cm^{-1}. The spectra of over 40 acetylated pyranose sugars[122, 124] have bands at 647 ± 21 and 605 ± 7 cm^{-1} which correspond to the methyl acetate bands at 639 and 615 cm^{-1}. They also have bands at 385 ±

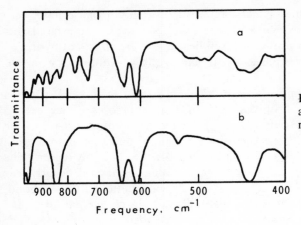

FIGURE 12. Far infrared spectra of (a) amyl acetate and (b) methyl acetate (0.1 mm cell, KBr prisms).

20 cm^{-1} probably due to the C—C—O bending vibration observed at 429 cm^{-1} in methyl acetate. Because of the large number of bands present in the CsBr spectra of the sugars, characteristic frequencies are not easily identified. (See Figure 13.) In methyl formate[144] the C—O—C bending vibration and the torsional oscillation coincide at 325 cm^{-1} in the gas phase and split into separate bands at 348 and 319 cm^{-1} in the solid. In the spectrum of polyethylene terephthalate, "Mylar" (Figure 14), a number of the bands are assigned to the ester group, namely 502, 437, 383, and 355 cm^{-1}.[23,146] Although one of these, 437 cm^{-1}, is in the region of acetate absorption, we should not be surprised that the others do not agree. The vibrations of the ester group are very likely to be sensitive to the nature of the adjacent group.

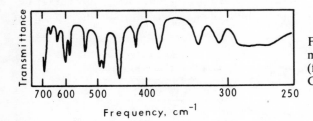

FIGURE 13. Far infrared spectrum of methyl-α-D-lyxopyranoside triacetate (from Tipson and Isbell,[122] KCl pellet, CsBr prism).

Lucier and Bentley[147] recorded the spectra of about 120 aliphatic esters including formates, acetates, propionates, butyrates, isobutyrates, valerates, isovalerates, hexanoates, heptanoates, and methyl-, ethyl-, propyl-, isopropyl-, *n*-butyl-, isobutyl-, *sec*-butyl-, *tert*-butyl-, and neopentyl esters. Most have bands in the 575 to 645 cm^{-1} region and in the 300 to 350 cm^{-1} region. The alkyl and acyl groups determine the location of bands within fairly narrow limits in these and in other spectral regions of the far infrared. It appears

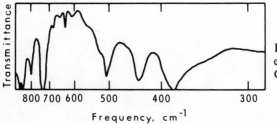

FIGURE 14. Far infrared spectrum of polyethylene terephthalate, "Mylar" (0.05 mm thick, CsBr prisms).

to be quite feasible to identify the acyl and alkyl components of esters from the characteristic frequencies discussed in this paper. In a continuation of this work,[189] the two strong acetate bands between 600 and 650 cm^{-1} were verified. Other types of esters have their own characteristic vibration bands. A correlation chart distinguishes formates, acetates, propionates, butyrates, isobutyrates, valerates, isovalerates, hexanoates, heptanoates, methyl-, ethyl-, propyl-, isopropyl-, butyl-, isobutyl-, sec-butyl-, tert-butyl-, and neopentyl esters.

The torsional oscillations observed at 213 cm^{-1} in methyl acetate and at 325 cm^{-1} in cis-methyl formate are analogous to the torsions of similar frequency in the amides and are quite sensitive to the conformation of the molecule. The torsional mode of trans-methyl formate has been calculated to lie at 233 cm^{-1}.[137] Because there is no band with more than 5 per cent absorption in the vicinity of 233 cm^{-1} in the spectrum of methyl formate, Miyazawa deduced on the basis of the intensity of the 325 cm^{-1} band that less than 1 per cent of the molecules are trans isomers at room temperature and that, therefore, the energy difference between the two forms is greater than 2.7 kcal/mole.

The carboxyl group of acids should also have vibrations in the far infrared. A series of saturated long chain fatty acids, including those with odd numbers of carbon atoms from C_7 to C_{17} and even number of carbons from C_8 to C_{22} were studied by Crisler and Fenton.[148] They have bands at 683 ± 8, 543 ± 8, and 504 ± 9 cm^{-1}. By analogy with the acetates we surmise that the highest and lowest of these are in-plane vibrations, and the remaining band is the out-of-plane vibration.*

Carboxylic acid molecules are loosely dimerized or polymerized through a network of hydrogen bonds, e.g., $O=C-OH \cdots O=C-OH \cdots$. Hydrogen bonds are weak, and the coupled molecules are massive, so the vibrations of these systems are expected to have very low frequencies. The vibrations of the various structures have been calculated to range from 46 to 193 cm^{-1} in acetic acid and 60 to 248 cm^{-1} in formic acid by Miyazawa and Pitzer.[149] Bands observed at 237 and 188 cm^{-1} in formic and acetic acid, respectively, are assigned to a $O \cdots H$ stretching vibration, and a band at 160 cm^{-1} in formic acid is ascribed to an out-of-plane $O-H \cdots O$ bending mode.

4.12. Ketones. The symmetric and asymmetric in-plane skeletal deformation vibrations of acetone are at 523 and 490 cm^{-1} respectively (see Figure 15), and the out-of-plane mode is at 393 cm^{-1}. Katon and Bentley[150] have reported a study of forty-two ketones in the 700 to 350 cm^{-1} region and have proposed the correlations given in Table 14.

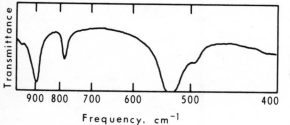

FIGURE 15. Far infrared spectrum of acetone (0.1 mm cell, KBr prisms).

---

* An investigation of the cesium bromide prism spectra of twenty-eight aliphatic monocarboxylic acids has recently been reported [Bentley, F. F., Ryan, M. T., and Katon, J. E., Spectrochim. Acta **20**, 685 (1964)]. The following correlations have been proposed:

Straight chain	590–675 cm^{-1}	465–495 cm^{-1}
C_4—C_{13} straight chain	590–610, 620–640, 655–675	465–495
α-Branched	610–625, 630–640, 645–665	520–555
β- and γ-Branched	600–700	465–495

All bands are strong

It is clear that the characteristic bands for the ketone group are strongly dependent on the nature of the overall molecular structure but that, within a group of molecules of similar structure, they are relatively constant. Katon and Bentley cite the compounds 2-hex-

TABLE 14. Characteristic Frequencies of Ketones
(From Katon and Bentley[150])

s = strong, m = medium, v = variable

Type of Molecule	Frequencies
Aliphatic methyl ketone	580–600(s), 510–530(m–s), 385–420(v)
Aromatic methyl ketone	580–600(s)
Aromatic ketone	no correlation
Aliphatic ketone, α-branched	565–580(m–s), 550–560(v)
Aliphatic ketone, no α-branching	620–630(s), 515–540(s)
Cyclic ketone	480–505(s)

anone, 3-hexanone, 2-methyl-3-hexanone, and cyclohexanone as examples. The group frequencies found in the rock salt spectra of these compounds identify them as ketones but do not permit further classification. However, once labeled as ketones, the characteristic far infrared spectra identify them as an aliphatic methyl ketone, an aliphatic ketone without α-branching, one with α-branching, and a cyclic ketone. See Figures 16 and 17 for KBr spectra of cyclohexanone and 2-butanone.

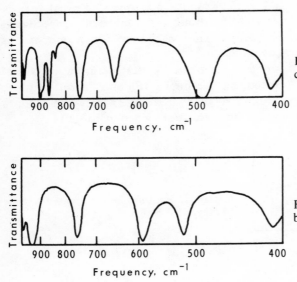

FIGURE 16. Far infrared spectrum of cyclohexanone (0.1 mm cell, KBr prisms).

FIGURE 17. Far infrared spectrum of 2-butanone (0.1 mm cell, KBr prisms).

It is interesting to note that the symmetric deformation vibration of acetone itself is an exception to the frequency range given for the aliphatic methyl ketones. Methyl ethyl ketone has a band at 584 cm^{-1}, and all of the higher aliphatic methyl ketones fit the assigned range. It is not unusual to find that the lightest member of a homologous series does not have its vibrations in a characteristic region defined by the larger molecules. This is an illustration of the dangerous and all too common procedure of attempting to deduce group frequencies for large molecules from the vibrations of light molecules. This is particularly risky in the far infrared. The reader will recognize that we have been guilty of this very practice in the present chapter on a number of occasions, notably in the case of the halogenated ethylenes.

4.13. Ethers. The C—O—C angle deformation vibration of dimethyl ether[151] is observed in the infrared at 412 cm^{-1}, close to the corresponding frequency of the similar molecule dimethylamine. It would not be surprising to find a characteristic frequency for the higher alkyl ethers near 430 cm^{-1} by analogy with the secondary amines, but these bands might also be too weak to be useful.

The vibrational frequencies of polyoxymethylene, $(-CH_2-O-)_n$, and polyethylene glycol, $(-CH_2-CH_2-O-)_n$, have been studied theoretically as well as experimentally by Miyazawa and his co-workers[152,153] and also by Tadokoro and his co-workers.[154,155] The sensitivity of the low frequency skeletal oscillations to conformation of polymer chains is very marked, and Miyazawa has taken advantage of this in deducing models for polymer structures which are consistent with the infrared spectra. Figure 18 shows some of Miyazawa's[152] calculated frequencies for polyoxymethylene, as functions of the internal rotation angle from one polymer unit to the next. The observed values of 633 cm^{-1} for ν_7, and 458 cm^{-1} for ν_8 are consistent with an internal rotation angle of about 75°. These vibrations are certainly not useful chracteristic frequencies in the usual sense because of their extreme variation. Nevertheless, once the variation with molecular geometry is established, they can be very useful in the elucidation of molecular structure. The higher frequency group vibrations, on the other hand, are relatively invariant to internal rotation; and, although they are invaluable in establishing the ether structure of the compound, they are of no use in determining the chain conformation.

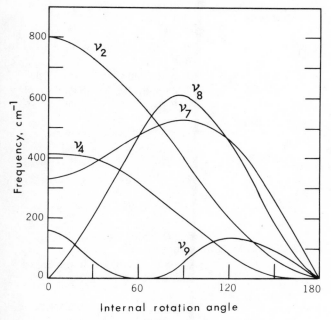

FIGURE 18. Calculated low frequency vibrations of polyoxymethylene as a function of the angle of internal rotation about the C—O bond (from Miyazawa[152]).

4.14. Organophosphorus Compounds. The application of far infrared spectroscopy to the elucidation of molecular structure is expected to be particularly useful in the case of compounds containing heavy atoms. The organophosphorus compounds have been extensively studied, and a fairly complete knowledge of their characteristic frequencies is available.

In a recent study Ferraro, Peppard, and Mason[156] reported the spectra in the 650 to 270 cm^{-1} region of over 90 organophosphorus compounds, including hydrogen phosphonates, GOG'PO(OH); acid phosphates, (GO)$_2$PO(OH); and phosphonates, (GO)$_2$G'PO; with either alkyl or aryl groups at G and G'. In the alkyl substituted compounds, the bands in the 500 to 600 cm^{-1} region shift to higher frequencies as the size of the alkyl chain is increased. A series of dialkyl phosphonates was also studied by Meyrick and Thompson[157] some time ago. In general, in the compounds containing alkyl groups, the spectra are relatively simple while the spectra of aryl compounds contain more bands, partly because of the characteristic aromatic ring absorptions which fall in this region. An absorption correlated with P—O—ϕ group is found near 600 cm^{-1} and one associated with the P—ϕ group is in the 530 $\pm$ 20 cm^{-1} region. Ferraro recommends the use of these bands, in combination with characteristic bands in the NaCl region, to distinguish compounds containing P—O—ϕ links from those with P—ϕ bonds. More specific characteristic frequency correlations are given in Table 15.

TABLE 15.   Characteristic Frequencies of Organo-Phosphorus Compounds

s = strong,   m   =   medium,   w = weak

Compound Type	Reference	Frequencies (cm^{-1})
Acid Phosphate, (GO)$_2$PO(OH)	156	380–400w (not found in phosphonates)
Aryl G		580–600s (somewhat sensitive to phenyl ring substituent), 535–565s, 500–515s, 470–490s
Alkyl G		460–590 broad bands
Hydrogen phosphonate, GOG'PO(OH)	156	
Aryl G and G'		570–605s, 535–550s, 485–495m, 460–465m, 420–430w–m, 350–370w, 290–315w
Aryl-(CH$_2$)$_m$- or alkyl G, aryl G'		530s, 570s, 430w, 350–360w, 310w
Alkyl G and G'		540–570m broad, 450–500m broad, 300–320w
Phosphate (GO)$_3$PO	156	
Aryl G		578–625s, 540–570s, 490–510s, 430–460m–w
Alkyl G		520–595m broad, 465–495m broad, 415–430w, 360–395w
Phosphonate, (GO)$_2$G'PO	156	
Aryl G and G'		600–618m, 515–535s, 480–500vw, 415–425vw
Alkyl G, Aryl G'		565–585s, 520–530s, 420–435w, 310–320w
Alkyl G and G'		500–570m broad, 410–490m broad, 400–440w
Phospite, (GO)$_3$P	158	
Alkyl G		510–560m, 400–540s, 295–385s
Hydrogen Phosphite, (GO)$_2$POH	158	
Alkyl G		545–560s, 505–540w–m
Metal Phosphorodithioate, M—S—P(OG)$_2$S	159	
Alkyl G		537–556
M = Zn, Cd, or Ni		635–637s
M = K		537–556s

A series of eight alkyl phosphites $(GO)_3P$, and four alkyl hydrogen phosphites $(GO)_2POH$ has been studied by Stewart[158] who proposed some characteristic frequencies which are included in Table 15. Just as in the compounds studied by Ferraro, the frequencies of these compounds increase as the size of the alkyl group increases (see Figure 19); and, in fact, the two hydrogen phosphite frequencies appear to converge on a single frequency for very heavy alkyl groups, as do the two higher frequency phosphite bands.

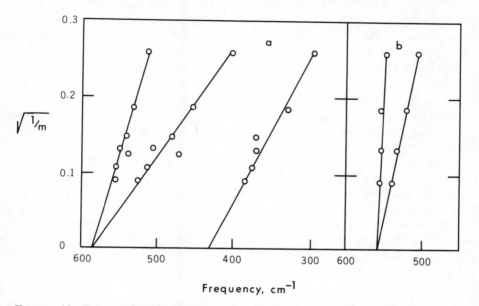

FIGURE 19. Frequencies of some far infrared bands of (a) trialkyl phosphites and (b) dialkyl hydrogen phosphites plotted against the reciprocal of the square root of the molecular weight of the alkyl group.

TABLE 16.   Group Frequencies of Organo-Phosphorus Molecules

Group	Ref.	Frequency
O—O—PCl$_2$	171	465–474, 495–507 cm^{-1}
O—O—PSCl$_2$	171	537–558
R—O—PSCl$_2$	171	~533
N—PSCl$_2$	171	490–524
O—O—POCl$_2$	171	~587
R—O—POCl$_2$	171	~570
R—NH—POCl$_2$	171	~558
O—NH—POCl$_2$	171	522–544
POS$^-$	172	560–652
PS$_2^-$	172	548–583
P=S	172	568–675
PS—C	172	510–620
PS—H	172	510–620
P—S—P	172	450–500
P=Se	172	473–577
P—Cl	172, 173	435–587
P—Br	173	400–485
(R—O)$_2$PSR	174	607–667

A series of 18 metal dialkylphosphordithioates, M—S—P(OG)$_2$S, containing zinc, potassium, cadmium, copper, or nickel has been studied by Rockett,[159] who reported some characteristic frequencies which are also included in Table 15. Rockett attributes the high frequency band to the P=S bond stretching vibration placed at 633–660 by Hooge and Christen[160] in molecules of the type XYZ—P=S and the lower frequency band to the P—S—M group. A band in the same general region, 510–575 cm$^-$, has been found by McIvor, Grant, and Hubley[161] in a number of phosphorodithioc acids and attributed to the P—SH group.

Nyquist[162] has studied the spectra of a large number of phosphorus compounds, and has given group frequency correlations found in Table 16.

Thomas and Chittenden[163] have provided further correlations, based on over 500 compounds, and these are included in Table 16. Also tabulated in Table 16 are some earlier correlations of Corbridge[164] and one of Maiants, Popov, and Kabachnik.[165]

The P—O—G bond in organo-phosphorous compounds is bent, and the barrier to internal rotation about the P—O bond is not too high to prevent rotational isomerism. This phenomenon has been studied by Mortimer[166] and by Maiants, *et al.*[165]

4.15. Organosulfur Compounds. The stretching vibration of the S—S link in organic disulfides occurs with a frequency between 400 and 500 cm^{-1}. It produces a very strong line in the Raman spectrum but, unfortunately for infrared spectroscopists, is extremely weak in the infrared. This should really not be unexpected, as the S—S stretching motion, particularly with identical substituent groups, can involve no appreciable change in the electric dipole moment necessary for the absorption of electromagnetic radiation. In general, when observable, the S—S frequency occurs in the 510 ± 10 cm^{-1} region in dialkyl disulfides.[167] It is found with somewhat greater intensity in aromatic compounds in the 460 ± 30 cm^{-1} region.[168]

The C—S stretching vibration is observed in the infrared with greater intensity than the S—S vibration and is found between 570 and 705 cm^{-1} in both sulfides and mercaptans. The frequency range depends on the substituent as shown in Table 17, according to Sheppard.[169] Mercaptans tend to absorb at slightly higher frequencies (about 10 cm^{-1}) than the corresponding sulfides. Conjugation of the C—S bond with a double bond lowers the C—S frequency by about 60 cm^{-1}. The bending frequencies of sulfides have been observed for only a few compounds. The C—S—C bending vibration occurs near 250 cm^{-1} in 2-thiabutane[170] and 3,3-dimethyl-2-thiabutane,[171] and the C—C—S bending vibration near 325 cm^{-1} in the same compounds.

TABLE 17. Characteristic Frequencies of Sulfides and Mercaptans
(From Sheppard[169])

Group	Frequency
ϕ—S—	688 ± 15 cm^{-1}
Methyl—S—	695 ± 10
RCH$_2$—S—	645 ± 15
RR'CH—S—	615 ± 15
RR'R''C—S—	585 ± 15

Some characteristic frequencies of organic carbonates having a sulfur atom adjacent to the carbonyl have been given by Nyquist and Potts[172] (see Table 18).

Malewski and Weigmann[173] have studied a series of nineteen aromatic mono- and disulfonylchlorides. They place the C—S stretching vibration in a very broad region from

TABLE 18. Characteristic Frequencies of Sulfur-
Containing Carbonates
(From Nyquist and Potts[172])

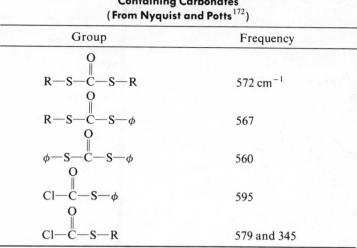

Group	Frequency
R—S—C(=O)—S—R	572 cm^{-1}
R—S—C(=O)—S—ϕ	567
ϕ—S—C(=O)—S—ϕ	560
Cl—C(=O)—S—ϕ	595
Cl—C(=O)—S—R	579 and 345

652 to 775 cm^{-1}, but the SO_2 rocking and deformation vibrations are observed as very strong bands at 551 ± 19 and 588 ± 23 cm^{-1}, respectively. These SO_2 bending modes have also been observed by Geiseler and Bindernagel[174] at about 545 and 590 cm^{-1} in a series of aliphatic sulfonyl chlorides, with the C—S stretching vibration near 690 cm^{-1}.

The spectra of a series of arsine sulfides were investigated by Zingaro, McGlothin, and Hedges[175] in the 15 to 30 μ region. They found a very strong band at 480 ± 7 cm^{-1} in the spectra of seven trialkylarsinesulfides and attributed it to the arsenic-sulfur stretching vibration. The frequency is slightly sensitive to the mass of the alkyl group and, in fact, is proportional to the reciprocal of the square root of the mass.

The characteristic frequencies of the SOS group have been considered by Gillespie and Robinson[176] for a variety of compounds of the type RSOSR'. They find the symmetric S—O—S stretching vibration falling between 256 and 346 cm^{-1} and the S—O—S bending vibration between 125 and 157 cm^{-1}. Both frequencies fall close to straight lines when plotted against the reciprocal of the square root of the mass of the SR group.

4.16. The Organometal Compounds. The nature of the "sandwich" compounds presents an interesting problem in modern chemistry. Compounds of this class consist of a heavy metal atom coordinated between two parallel cyclopentadiene or benzene rings. The infrared active low frequency vibrations of the dibenzene compounds are an a_{2u} mode in which the metal atom is supposed to move perpendicular to the rings in an asymmetric ring-metal-ring stretching vibration and two e_u modes, a symmetric ring tilt, and a lower frequency vibration in which the metal atoms move in a direction parallel to the planes of the two rings.[177,178] The frequencies which have been reported are given in Table 19. The bands are generally strong. The a_{2u} frequencies fall in the 383 ± 77 cm^{-1} region. The higher frequency e_u vibrations occur at 434 ± 56 cm^{-1}. The low frequency e_u band is probably near 140 cm^{-1} In the case of dibenzene compounds, the two higher frequencies are metal sensitive.

In the compound benzene chromium tricarbonyl,[179] in which a chromium atom is coordinated between three C=O groups and a benzene ring, a vibration described as a stretching motion of the benzene ring against the $Cr(CO)_3$ structure is found at 298 cm^{-1}. The ring tilt vibration has a frequency of 330 cm^{-1}.

The compounds ferrocene, nickelocene, and ruthenocene[180-182] also have infrared active

TABLE 19.   Infrared Frequencies of Some "Sandwich" Compounds

Compound	Ref.	Frequencies		
		Asym. Stretch	Ring Tilt	Bending
$Cr(C_6H_6)_2$	177	459 cm^{-1}	490 cm^{-1}	140 cm^{-1}
$Cr(C_6D_6)_2$	178	421	481	—
$Cr(C_6H_6)_2I$	177	415	466	144
$V(C_6H_6)_2$	177	424	470	—
$Mo(C_6H_6)_2$	177	362	424	—
$Mo(C_6H_6)_2I$	177	333	410	—
$W(C_6H_6)_2$	177	331	386	
$W(C_6H_6)_2I$	177	306	378	
$Fe(C_5H_5)_2$	180	478	492	170
$Fe(C_5D_5)_2$	180	457	485	162?
$Ru(C_5H_5)_2$	180	446	528	185?
$Ni(C_5H_5)_2$	180	355	355	125?

vibrations in the regions $417 \pm 62 \text{ cm}^{-1}$, $442 \pm 87 \text{ cm}^{-1}$, and probably $155 \pm 30 \text{ cm}^{-1}$. The nature of these vibrations is similar to those of the dibenzene compounds in the same regions. In this case, however, the frequencies do not appear to correlate with the atomic mass of the central metal atom. The cyclopentadienyl ring itself has out-of-plane vibrations at 614 and 314 cm^{-1} in ferrocene.[183]

The phthalocyanine molecule,[184] alone and with central metallic atom of Mg, Zn, Cu, Fe, Co, or Ni, has medium-to-weak bands at $436 \pm 12 \text{ cm}^{-1}$. Phthalocyanine without a metal atom absorbs at 557, 616, and 620 cm^{-1}. When a metal atom is present these bands shift to *ca.* 575, 642 ± 4, and $643 \pm 3 \text{ cm}^{-1}$.

4.17. Internal Rotations and Torsional Oscillations.   The rotation of one portion of a molecule, such as a methyl group, about a bond connecting it to the rest of the molecule can be virtually unrestricted so that the group rotates freely like a top. On the other hand, it can be so highly restricted by forces between unbonded atoms that the motion of the group is confined to torsional oscillations of small amplitude about an equilibrium position. In either case the fundamental frequency is expected to fall in the far infrared. No examples of free internal rotation have been observed by infrared measurements. This is natural when we realize that, in order to absorb radiation, a freely rotating group must have a permanent electric dipole moment, and an atomic group with a substantial dipole will almost certainly be acted upon by neighboring molecular bonds to restrict its rotation.

The torsional oscillations of a number of molecules have been studied. It is hoped that these investigations might lead to a better understanding of the forces which hinder the rotation of groups within molecules. We have already discussed the torsional vibration of the NH_2 group in primary amines and have suggested that it might be sufficiently invariant in frequency to serve as a characteristic frequency. Some of the methyl torsion frequencies measured by Fateley and Miller[185–187] are given in Table 20. In general, the frequencies cover a wide range, but some tentative observations can be made. First of all, in the hydrocarbons or when the methyls are connected to the molecule through small atoms such as oxygen or nitrogen, the vibrations are often found at relatively high frequencies: 220 to 270 cm^{-1}. However, when a sulfur atom intervenes between the methyl and the rest of the molecule, the frequency is lowered to 182 cm^{-1}. When the methyl is adjacent to a carbonyl group, the torsional mode is found at even lower frequencies, in the 100 to 150 cm^{-1} range.

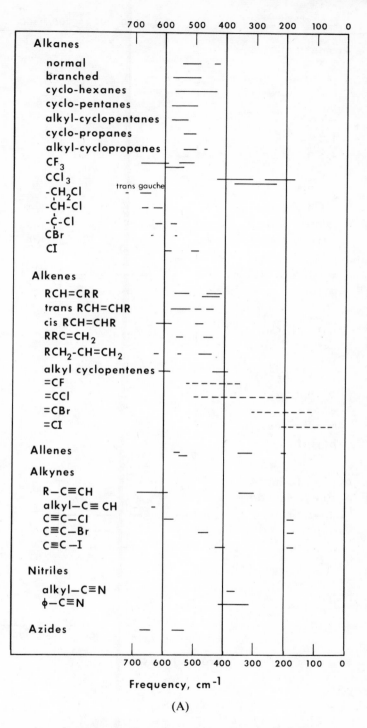

Frequency, cm^{-1}

(A)

FIGURE 20(A, B, C, D, E). Far infrared spectra-structure correlation chart.

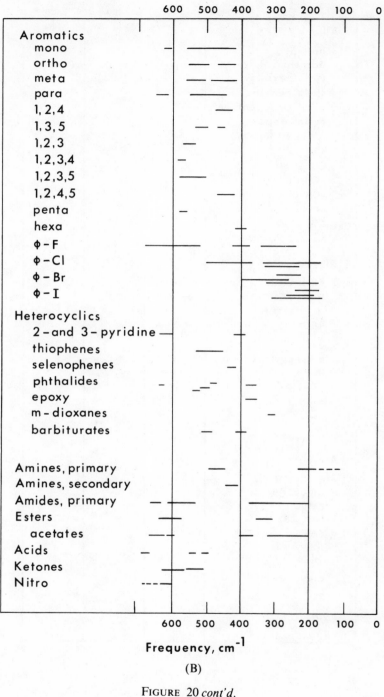

Frequency, cm^{-1}

(B)

FIGURE 20 *cont'd.*

Frequency, cm^{-1}

(C)

FIGURE 20 *cont'd.*

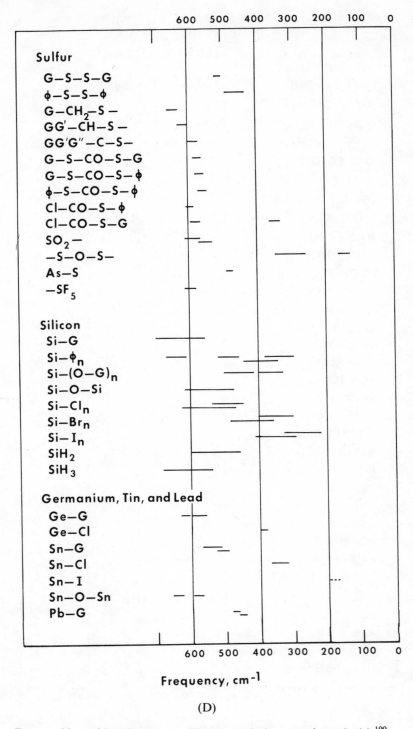

(D)

FIGURE 20 *cont'd.* (The organo-silicon correlations are from Smith[190]).

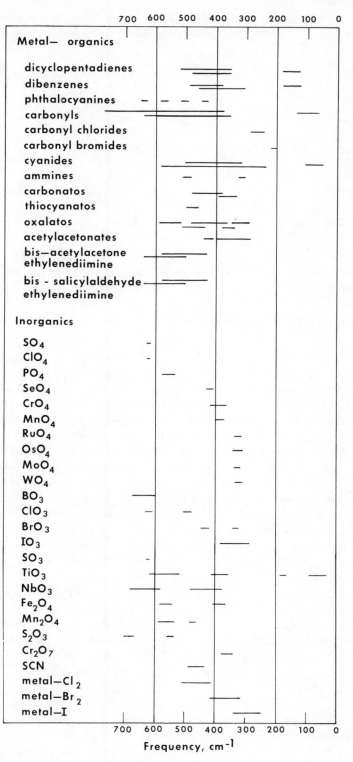

(E)

FIGURE 20 *cont'd.* (Many of the inorganic correlations are from Miller, Carlson, Bentley, and Jones[191]).

TABLE 20. Fundamental Torsional Frequencies of Methyl Rotors
(From Fateley and Miller[185-187])

Molecule	Frequency	Molecule	Frequency
CH_3CH_2Cl	251.5 cm^{-1}	$(CH_3)_2C{=}CH_2$	181
CH_3CHF_2	222	$CH_3CF{=}CH_2$	191
$(CH_3)_2O$	242	$CH_3CH{=}CH_2$	188
$(CH_3)_3N$	269	CH_3CHO	150
$(CH_3)_2NH$	257	$HCOOCH_3$	130
$(CH_3)_2ND$	252	CH_3N_3	126
$(CH_3)_2S$	182	CD_3N_3	90
$CH_3{-}CH{-}CH_2$ $\diagdown O \diagup$	200	CH_3NCO	143
		CH_3NCS	128
$CH_3{-}CH{-}CH_2$ $\diagdown S \diagup$	223.6	CH_3SCN	131
		$(CH_3)_2CO$	109

The torsional oscillations of a few other groups have been reported. For example, NO_2 torsion has been observed in the Raman spectrum of tetranitromethane[140] at 72 cm^{-1} and possibly in the infrared spectrum of polyvinylnitrate[143] at about 50 cm^{-1}. The hindered rotation of the C—O—H group in gaseous methanol[188] is observed as a series of lines in the far infrared, with the fundamental torsional oscillation at 270 cm^{-1}.

5. Conclusion

The vibrational frequencies discussed in the preceding section as well as those for metal-organic and inorganic compounds are summarized in the form of a chart in Figure 20. The reader is strongly urged *against* accepting these values indiscriminately. To be sure, the existence of several well defined characteristic frequencies has been demonstrated. However, much of the material presented in the chart is only tentative. In many cases, it is based on evidence from much too small a sample. New far infrared spectra are being recorded and published at an increasing rate, and as this material becomes circulated and correlated we can be confident that some of these tentative assignments will be more firmly established, although not necessarily with the boundaries given here, and that new characteristic frequency correlations will be discovered. As the far infrared spectra of more compounds are reported, we shall undoubtedly find that some of the very broad characteristic frequency ranges shown in the chart can be subdivided on the basis of molecular configuration, in the manner of the carbon-chlorine vibrations.

It has been pointed out that the idea of a "group-frequency" vibration confined to one functional group of atoms is not generally appropriate to far infrared spectroscopy, because the low frequency vibrations are inclined to involve a large portion of the molecule or all of it. Because of this, it is remarkable that characteristic frequencies occur at all in the far infrared. For successful infrared analysis, and particularly when dealing with the far infrared, the spectroscopist must resist the temptation to overinterpret his spectra. By this we mean the attempt to treat each band in a spectrum as a characteristic frequency, and to associate it with a functional group. The occurrence of a band in a region where characteristic frequencies are found does not in itself prove the existence of any molecular configuration. Furthermore, because of the tendency of the low frequency characteristic absorptions to have variable intensities, the lack of bands in a characteristic frequency region does not prove that any molecular configuration is absent. As in any other form of molecular structure analysis, evidence from as many different sources as possible should be considered along with the evidence obtained from the far infrared spectrum.

If the usefulness of far infrared spectroscopy in chemical analysis were to be judged solely on the basis of its role as a supplement to the rock salt infrared region, we would have to assign it a relative value of only about one-sixth, which is the ratio of the widths in frequency of the two regions. However, the real value of the far infrared lies in the special information it provides.

It has been stressed that the low frequency molecular vibrations found in the far infrared are particularly sensitive to changes in the overall structure of the molecule involved. We have tried to show in this chapter that, far from being a disadvantage, it can be one of the important advantages of far infrared spectroscopy. We would be guilty of oversimplifying were we to state that the rock salt region provides basic information on the types of functional groups present in a molecule, while the far infrared is largely a tool for studying the conformation of the molecule as a whole. Nevertheless, we have seen cases where the far infrared bands differ in a predictable manner for different isomeric forms of the same basic compound, while information regarding the conformation of the molecule is not present in the rock salt spectrum. The far infrared frequencies of metal-organo compounds are often sensitive to the metal ion or atom, and this, too, can be used advantageously in the study of coordination bonds. Moreover, far infrared spectroscopy seems to be particularly well suited to the study of metal-organo or inorganic compounds whose atoms are heavy and whose bonds are inclined to be weak. We can expect that organic chemists as well as their inorganic counterparts will find far infrared spectroscopy to be an increasingly useful tool in the elucidation of chemical structure.

REFERENCES

1. Plyler, E. K., and Acquista, N., *J. Research NBS*, **56**, 149 (1956).
2. Plyler, E. K., and Blaine, L. R., *J. Research NBS*, **60**, 55 (1958).
3. Lord, R. C., and McCubbin, T. K., *J. Opt. Soc. Am.*, **47**, 689 (1957).
4. McCarthy, D. E., *Appl. Optics*, **2**, 591, 596 (1963).
5. Palik, E. D., *J. Opt. Soc. Am.*, **50**, 1329 (1960).
6. Barker, A. S., Jr., and Tinkham, M., *J. Chem. Phys.*, **38**, 2257 (1963).
7. Moss, T. S., "Optical Properties of Semi-Conductors," London, Butterworths, 1959.
8. Palik, E. D., *Appl. Opt.*, **2**, 527 (1963).
9. Harrah, L. A., Ryan, M. T., and Tamborski, C., *Spectrochim. Acta*, **18**, 21 (1962).
10. Hansler, R. L., and Oetjen, R. A., *J. Chem. Phys.*, **21**, 1340 (1953).
11. McCubbin, T. K., and Sinton, W. W., *J. Opt. Soc. Am.*, **40**, 537 (1950).
12. Palik, E. D., and Rao, K. N., *J. Chem. Phys.*, **26**, 1401 (1957).
13. Randall, H. M., Dennison, D. M., Ginsburg, N., and Weber, L. R., *Phys. Rev.*, **52**, 160 (1937)
14. Stroup, R. E., Oetjen, R. A., and Bell, E. E., *J. Opt. Soc. Am.*, **43**, 1096 (1953).
15. Bird, G. R., Danti, A., and Lord, R. C., *Spectrochim. Acta*, **12**, 247 (1958).
16. Danti, A., and Lord, R. C., *J. Chem. Phys.*, **30**, 1310 (1959).
17. Robinson, D. W., and McQuarrie, D. A., *J. Chem. Phys.*, **32**, 556 (1960).
18. Pimental, G. C., and McClellan, A. L., "The Hydrogen Bond," Chapter 3, San Francisco, Freeman, 1960.
19. Stuart, A. V., and Sutherland, G. B. B. M., *J. Chem. Phys.*, **20**, 1977 (1952).
20. Hadzi, D., *J. Chem. Phys.*, **34**, 1445 (1961).
21. Tsuboi, M., Terada, M., and Shimanouchi, T., *J. Chem. Phys.*, **36**, 1301 (1962).
22. Lafferty, W. J., and Robinson, D. W., *J. Chem. Phys.*, **36**, 83 (1962).
23. Krimm, S., *Fortschr. Hochpolym. Forsch*, **2**, 51 (1960).
24. Wilson, E. B., Jr., Decius, J. C., and Cross, P. C., "Molecular Vibrations," New York, McGraw-Hill Book Co., Inc., 1955.
25. Allen, H. C., Jr., and Cross, P. C., "Molecular Vib-Rotors," New York, John Wiley & Sons, Inc., 1963.

26. Herzberg, G., "Molecular Spectra and Molecular Structure II Infrared and Raman Spectra of Polyatomic Molecules," New York, D. Van Nostrand, 1945.
27. Hidalgo, A., *Compt. rend.*, **249**, 395 (1959).
28. Hidalgo, A., *Anales real soc. espon. de fis. y quim. (Madrid)*, **58**, (A) 71 (1962).
29. Bartunek, P. F., and Barker, E. F., *Phys. Rev.*, **48**, 516 (1935).
30. Staats, P. A., Morgan, H. W., and Goldstein, J. H., *J. Chem. Phys.*, **25**, 582 (1956).
31. Dodd, R. E., and Little, R., *Spectrochim. Acta.*, **16**, 1083 (1960).
32. Freitag, W. O., and Nixon, E. R., *J. Chem. Phys.*, **24**, 109 (1956).
33. Wait, S. C., Jr., and Janz, G. J., *J. Chem. Phys.*, **26**, 1554 (1957).
34. Edgell W. F., and Ultee, C. J., *J. Chem. Phys.*, **27**, 543 (1957).
35. Edgell, W. F., and Potter, R. M., *J. Chem. Phys.*, **24**, 80 (1956).
36. Fitzgerald, W. E., and Janz, G. J., *J. Mol. Spect.*, **1**, 49 (1957).
37. Goldfarb, T. D., *J. Chem. Phys.*, **37**, 642 (1962).
38. Daly, L. H., and Wiberley, S. E., *J. Mol. Spec.*, **2**, 177 (1958).
39. Liang, C. Y., and Krimm, S., *J. Polym. Sci.*, **31**, 513 (1958).
40. Nyquist, R. A., and Potts, W. J., *Spectrochim. Acta*, **16**, 419 (1960).
41. Brand, J. C. D., and Watson, J. K. G., *Trans. Faraday Soc.*, **56**, 1582 (1960).
42. King, G. W., and Moule, D., *Spectrochim. Acta*, **17**, 286 (1961).
43. Evans, J. C., and Nyquist, R. A., *Spectrochim Acta*, **16**, 918 (1960).
44. Daykin, P. N., Sundaram, S., and Cleveland, F. F., *J. Chem. Phys.*, **37**, 1087 (1962).
45. Davidson, D. W., and Bernstein, H. J., *Can. J. Chem.*, **33**, 1226 (1955).
46. Meister, A. G., *J. Chem. Phys.*, **16**, 950 (1948).
47. Hunt, G. R., and Wilson, M. K., *J. Chem. Phys.*, **34**, 1301 (1961).
48. Ferigle, S. M., and Weber, A., *J. Chem. Phys.*, **21**, 722 (1953).
49. Gray, P., and Waddington, T. C., *Trans. Faraday Soc.*, **53**, 901 (1957).
50. Papazian, H. A., *J. Chem. Phys.*, **34**, 1614 (1961).
51. Bryant, J. I., and Turrell, G. C., *J. Chem. Phys.*, **37**, 1069 (1962).
52. Dows, D. A., and Pimentel, G. C., *J. Chem. Phys.*, **23**, 1258 (1955).
53. Dows, D. A., Whittle, E., and Pimentel, G. C., *J. Chem. Phys.*, **23**, 1475 (1955).
54. Mantica, E., and Zerbi, G., *Gazz. chim. ital.*, **90**, 53 (1960).
55. Blanc, J., Brecher, C., and Halford, R. S., *J. Chem. Phys.*, **36**, 2654 (1962).
56. Shuler, W. E., and Fletcher, W. H., *J. Mol. Spec.*, **1**, 95 (1957).
57. Sverdlov, L. M., and Borisov, M. G., *Opt. i. Spekt.*, **9**, 227 (1960).
58. Bentley, F. F., and Wolfarth, E. F., *Spectrochim. Acta*, **15**, 165 (1959).
59. Sverdlov, L. M., *Akad. Nauk SSSR Doklady*, **112**, 706 (1957).
60. Linnig, F. J., and Stewart, J. E., *J. Research NBS*, **60**, 9 (1958).
61. Stewart, J. E., and Linnig, F. J., unpublished work, 1958.
62. Brown, J. K., and Sheppard, N., *Trans. Faraday Soc.*, **51**, 1611 (1955).
63. Lord, R. C., and Venkateswarlu, P., *J. Opt. Soc. Am.*, **43**, 1079 (1953).
64. Scherer, J. R., and Potts, W. J., *J. Chem. Phys.*, **30**, 1527 (1959).
65. Bellamy, L. J., "The Infrared Spectra of Complex Molecules," New York, John Wiley & Sons, Inc., Second Edition, 1958.
66. Mann, D. E., Fano, L., Meal, J. H., and Shimanouchi, T., *J. Chem. Phys.*, **27**, 51 (1957).
67. Shipman, J. J., Folt, V. L., and Krimm, S., *Spectrochim. Acta*, **18**, 1603 (1962).
68. Brown, J. K., and Sheppard, N., *Trans. Faraday Soc.*, **48**, 128 (1952).
69. Brown, J. K., and Sheppard, N., *Trans. Faraday Soc.*, **50**, 535 (1954).
70. Brown, J. K., and Sheppard, N., *Trans. Faraday Soc.*, **50**, 1164 (1954).
71. Mizushima, S., Shimanouchi, T., Nakagawa, I., and Miyake, A., *J. Chem. Phys.*, **21**, 215 (1953).
72. Mizushima, S., Shimanouchi, T., Nakamura, K., Hayashi, M., and Tsuchiya, S., *J. Chem. Phys.*, **26**, 970 (1957).
73. Hayashi, M., Ichishima, I., Shimanouchi, T., and Mizushima, S., *Spectrochim. Acta*, **10**, 1, (1957).
74. Nakagawa, I., and Mizushima, S., *J. Chem. Phys.*, **21**, 2195 (1953).

75. Ichishima, I., Kamiyama, H., Shimanouchi, T., and Mizushima, S., *J. Chem. Phys.*, **29,** 1190 (1958).
76. Harvey, M. R., Stewart, J. E., and Achhammer, B. G., *J. Research NBS*, **56,** 225 (1956).
77. Shimanouchi, T., and Tasumi, M., *J. Chem. Phys.*, **34,** 687 (1961).
78. Krimm, S., and Liang, C. Y., *J. Polym. Science*, **22,** 95 (1956).
79. Tasumi, M., and Shimanouchi, T., *Spectrochim. Acta*, **17,** 731 (1961).
80. Liang, C. Y., and Krimm, S., *J. Chem. Phys.*, **25,** 563 (1956).
81. Mann, D. E., Acquista, N., and Lide, D. R., Jr., *J. Mol Spec.*, **2,** 575 (1958).
82. Theimer, R., and Nielsen, J. R., *J. Chem. Phys.*, **27,** 887 (1957).
83. Nielsen, J. R., and Theimer, R., *J. Chem. Phys.*, **27,** 891 (1957).
84. Nielsen, J. R., Liang, C. Y., and Smith, D. C., *J. Chem. Phys.*, **21,** 1060 (1953).
85. Risgin, O., and Taylor, R. C., *Spectrochim. Acta*, **15,** 1036 (1959).
86. Klaboe, P., and Nielsen, J. R., *J. Chem. Phys.*, **30,** 1375 (1959).
87. Nielsen, J. R., Liang, C. Y., and Smith, R. M., *J. Chem. Phys.*, **21,** 383 (1953).
88. Dininny, R. E., and Pace, E. L., *J. Chem. Phys.*, **31,** 1630 (1959).
89. Redington, R. L., *J. Mol. Spect.*, **9,** 460 (1962).
90. Sanborn, R. H., Symposium on Molecular Structure and Molecular Spectroscopy, Ohio State University, June, 1963.
91. Randle, R. R., and Whiffen, D. H., "Molecular Spectroscopy," pp. 111–128, London, The Institute of Petroleum, 1954.
92. Wilcox, W. S., Stephenson, C. V., and Coburn, W. C., Jr., *WADD Tech. Report*, **60,** 333, September, 1960.
93. Jakobsen, R. J., *WADD Tech. Report*, **60,** 204, September, 1960.
94. Jakobsen, R. J., Wright-Patterson Air Force Base Tech. Report, Tech. Documentary Report No. ASD-TDR-62-895, October, 1962. *Appl. Spect.*, **18,** 88 (1964).
95. Liang, C. Y., and Krimm, S., *J. Poly. Sci.*, **27,** 241 (1958).
96. Stewart, J. E., and Hellman, M., *J. Research, NBS*, **60,** 125 (1958).
97. Dale, J., *Acta. Chem. Scand.*, **11,** 640 (1957).
98. Person, W. B., Pimentel, G. C., and Schnepp, O., *J. Chem. Phys.*, **23,** 230 (1955).
99. Pimentel, G. C., McClellan, A. L., Person, W. B., and Schnepp, O., *J. Chem. Phys.*, **23,** 234 (1955).
100. Lippincott, E. R., and O'Reilly, E. J., Jr., *J. Chem. Phys.*, **23,** 238 (1955).
101. McClellan, A. L., and Pimentel, G. C., *J. Chem. Phys.*, **23,** 245 (1955).
102. Califano, S., *J. Chem. Phys.*, **36,** 903 (1962).
103. Jakobsen, R. J., and Brewer, E. J., *Appl. Spect.*, **16,** 32 (1962).
104. Nielsen, J. R., Liang, C. Y., and Smith, D. C., *Disc. Faraday Soc.*, **9,** 177 (1950).
105. Ferguson, E. E., *J. Chem. Phys.*, **21,** 886 (1953).
106. Ferguson, E. E., Hudson, R. L., Nielsen, J. R., and Smith, D. C., *J. Chem. Phys.*, **21,** 1457, 1464, 1727 (1953).
107. Ferguson, E. E., Collins, R. L., Nielsen, J. R., and Smith, D. C., *J. Chem. Phys.*, **21,** 1470 (1953).
108. Smith, D. C., Ferguson, E. E., Hudson, R. L., and Nielsen, J. R., *J. Chem. Phys.*, **21,** 1475 (1953).
109. Ferguson, E. E., Mikkelsen, L., Nielsen, J. R., and Smith, D. C., *J. Chem. Phys.*, **21,** 1731 (1953).
110. Narasimham, N. A., El-Sabban, M. E., and Nielsen, J. R., *J. Chem. Phys.*, **24,** 420 (1956).
111. Narasimham, N. A., and Nielsen, J. R., *J. Chem. Phys.*, **24,** 433 (1956).
112. Harris, F. W., Narasimham, N. A., and Nielsen, J. R., *J. Chem. Phys.*, **24,** 1232 (1956).
113. Stojikjkovic, A., and Whiffen, D. H., *Spectrochim. Acta*, **12,** 47, 57 (1958).
114. Isaac, R., Bentley, F. F., Sternglanz, H., Coburn, W. C., Stephenson, C. V., and Wilcox, W. S., *Appl. Spect.*, **17,** 90 (1963).
115. Hochgesang, F. P., in Thiophene and its Derivatives, H. D. Hartough, ed., Chapter IV, New York, Interscience Publishers, Inc., 1952.
116. Hidalgo, A., *J. Phys. Rad.*, **16,** 366 (1955).

117. Chumaevskii, N. A., Tatevskii, V. M., and Iurev, Iu. K., *Opt. i. Spect.*, **6,** No. 1, 25 (1959).
118. Sverdlov, L. M., and Krainov, E. N., *Opt. i. Spekt.*, **6,** 214 (1959).
119. Lauer, J. L., Jones, W. H., Jr., and Beachell, H. C., *J. Chem. Phys.*, **30,** 1489 (1959).
120. Jakobsen, R. J., and Wyant, R. E., *Appl. Spect.*, **14,** 61 (1960).
121. Tipson, R. S., and Isbell, H. S., *J. Research NBS*, **64A,** 239 (1960).
122. Tipson, R. S., and Isbell, H. S., *J. Research NBS*, **64A,** 405 (1960).
123. Tipson, R. S., and Isbell, H. S., *J. Research NBS*, **65A,** 31 (1961).
124. Tipson, R. S., and Isbell, H. S., *J. Research NBS*, **65A,** 249 (1961).
125. Tipson, R. S., Isbell, H. S., and Stewart, J. E., *J. Research NBS*, **62,** 257 (1959).
126. Isaac, R., International Symposium on Far Infrared Spectroscopy, Cincinnati, Ohio, August 21–24, 1962.
127. Ulrich, W. F., The Fourth Australian Spectroscopy Conference, Canberra, August 20–23, 1963.
128. Stewart, J. E., *J. Chem. Phys.*, **30,** 1259 (1959).
129. Kohlrausch, K. W. F., *Monatschr. Chem.*, **68,** 349 (1936).
130. Hadni, A., *J. Phys. Radium*, **15,** 375 (1954).
131. Evans, J. C., *Spectrochim. Acta*, **16,** 428 (1960).
132. Miyazawa, T., Shimanouchi, T., and Mizushima, S., *J. Chem. Phys.*, **24,** 408 (1956).
133. Beer, M., Kessler, H. B., and Sutherland, G. B. B. M., *J. Chem. Phys.*, **29,** 1097 (1958).
134. Cannon, C. G., *Spectrochim. Acta*, **16,** 302 (1960).
135. Miyazawa, T., Shimanouchi, T., and Mizushima, S., *J. Chem. Phys.*, **29,** 611 (1958).
136. DeGraaf, D. E., and Sutherland, G. B. B. M., *J. Chem. Phys.*, **26,** 716 (1957).
137. Miyazawa, T., *Bull. Chem. Soc. Japan,* **34,** 691 (1961).
138. Smith, D. C., Pan, C., and Nielsen, J. R., *J. Chem. Phys.*, **18,** 706 (1950).
139. Jonathan, N., *J. Mol. Spec.*, **7,** 105 (1961).
140. Lindenmeyer, P. H., and Harris, P. M., *J. Chem. Phys.*, **21,** 408 (1953).
141. Jakobsen, R. J., Private Communication.
142. Brand, J. C. D., and Cawthon, T. M., *J. Am. Chem. Soc.*, **77,** 319 (1955).
143. Krimm, S., *J. Appl. Phys.*, **29,** 1407 (1958).
144. Wilmshurst, K. J., *J. Mol. Spec.*, **1,** 201 (1957).
145. Wilmshurst, K. J., *J. Chem. Phys.*, **23,** 2463 (19·5).
146. Liang, C. Y., and Krimm, S., *J. Mol. Spect.*, **3.** 554 (1959).
147. Lucier, J. J., and Bentley, F. F., 14th Annual Mid-America Spectroscopy Symposium, Chicago, Illinois, May 20–23, 1963, *Spectrochim. Acta*, **20,** 1 (1964).
148. Crisler, R. O., and Fenton, A. J., Tenth Annual Symposium on Spectroscopy, American Association of Spectrographers, Chicago, Illinois, June 1–4 (1959).
149. Miyazawa, T., and Pitzer, K. S., *J. Am. Chem. Soc.*, **81,** 74 (1959).
150. Katon, J. E., and Bentley, F. F., *Spectrochim. Acta*, **19,** 639 (1963).
151. Hadni, A., *Compt. rend.*, **239,** 349 (1954).
152. Miyazawa, T., *J. Chem. Phys.*, **35,** 693 (1961).
153. Miyazawa, T., Fukushima, K., and Ideguchi, Y., *J. Chem. Phys.*, **37,** 2764 (1962).
154. Tadokoro, H., *J. Chem. Phys.*, **33,** 1558 (1960).
155. Tadokoro, H., Kobayashi, M., Kawaguchi, Y., and Murahashi, S., *J. Chem. Phys.*, **38,** 703 (1963).
156. Ferraro, J. R., Peppard, D. F., and Mason, G. W., *Spectrochim. Acta*, **19,** 811 (1963).
157. Meyrick, C. I., and Thompson, H. W., *J. Chem. Soc.*, 225 (1950).
158. Stewart, J. E., Tenth Annual Symposium on Spectroscopy, American Association of Spectrographers, Chicago, Illinois, June 1–4, 1959.
159. Rockett, J., *Appl. Spect.*, **16,** 39 (1962).
160. Hooge, F. N., and Christen, P. J., *Rec. Trav. Chim.*, **77,** 911 (1958).
161. McIvor, R. A., Grant, G. A., and Hubley, C. E., *Can. J. Chem.*, **34,** 1611 (1956); McIvor, R. A., and Hubley, C. E., *Can. J. Chem.*, **37,** 869 (1959).
162. Nyquist, R. A., *Appl. Spect.*, **11,** 161 (1957).
163. Thomas, L. C., and Chittenden, R. A., *Chem. and Ind.*, 1913 (1961).
164. Corbridge, D. E. C., *J. Appl. Chem.*, **6,** 456 (1956).

165. Maiants, L. S., Popov, E. M., and Kabachnik, M. I., *Opt. i Speckt.*, **7**, 108 (1959).

166. Mortimer, F. S., *Spectrochim. Acta*, **9**, 270 (1957).

167. Trotter, I. F., and Thompson, H. W., *J. Chem. Soc.*, 481 (1946).

168. Cymerman, J., and Willis, J. B., *J. Chem. Soc.*, 1332 (1951).

169. Sheppard, N., *Trans Faraday Soc.*, **46**, 429 (1950).

170. Hayashi, M., Shimanouchi, T., and Mizushima, S., *J. Chem. Phys.*, **26**, 608 (1957).

171. Scott, D. W., Good, W. D., Todd, S. S., Messerly, J. F., Berg, W. T., Hossenlopp, I. A., Lacina, J. L., Osborn, A., and McCullough, J. P., *J. Chem. Phys.*, **36**, 406 (1962).

172. Nyquist, R. A., and Potts, W. J., *Spectrochim. Acta*, **17**, 679 (1961).

173. Malewski, G., and Weigmann, H. J., *Spectrochim. Acta*, **18**, 725 (1962).

174. Geisiler, G., and Bindernagel, K. O., *Z. Elektrochem.*, **63**, 1140 (1959), **64**, 421 (1960).

175. Zingaro, R. A., McGlothin, R. E., and Hedges, R. M., *Trans Faraday Soc.*, **59**, 798 (1963).

176. Gillespie, R. J., and Robinson, E. A., *Spectrochim. Acta*, **19**, 741 (1963).

177. Fritz, H. P., Lüttke, W., Stammereich, H., and Forneris, R., *Spectrochim. Acta,* **17**, 1068 (1961).

178. Snyder, R. G., *Spectrochim. Acta*, **15**, 807 (1959).

179. Fritz, H. P., and Mauchot, J., *Spectrochim. Acta,* **18**, 171 (1962).

180. Lippincott, E. R., and Nelson, R. D., *Spectrochim. Acta*, **10**, 307 (1958).

181. Lippincott, E. R., and Nelson, R. D., *J. Chem. Phys.,* **21**, 1307 (1953).

182. Winter, W. K., Curnette, B., Jr., and Whitcomb, S. E., *Spectrochim. Acta*, **15**, 1085 (1959).

183. Mayants, L. S., Lokshin, B. V., and Shaltuper, G. B., *Opt. i. Spekt.*, **13**, 177 (1962).

184. Sidorov, A. N., and Kotlyar, I. P., *Opt. i. Spect.*, **11**, 92 (1961).

185. Fateley, W. G., and Miller, F. A., *Spectrochim. Acta*, **17**, 857 (1961).

186. Fateley, W. G., and Miller, F. A., *Spectrochim. Acta*, **18**, 977 (1962).

187. Fateley, W. G., and Miller, F. A., *Spectrochim. Acta*, **19**, 611 (1963).

188. Lawson, J. R., and Randall, H. M., quoted by Koehler and Dennison, *Phys. Rev.*, **57**, 1006 (1940).

189. Lucier, J. J. and Bentley, F. F., *Spectrochim. Acta*, **20**, 1 (1964).

190. Smith, A. L., *Spectrochim. Acta*, **16**, 87 (1960).

191. Miller, F. A., Carlson, G. L., Bentley, F. F., and Jones, W. H., *Spectrochim. Acta*, **16**, 135 (1960).

4

MASS SPECTROMETRY

Henry A. Bondarovich* and Stanley K. Freeman
Research Department
International Flavors & Fragrances, Inc.
Union Beach, New Jersey

1. Introduction

During the past several years the organic chemist has gained appreciation of the power of mass spectrometry in the identification and structural elucidation of organic compounds. Ample demonstration can be found in the excellent works of Beynon,[1] McLafferty,[2] Biemann,[3] and Djerassi.[4] Careful examination of a mass spectrum affords information which is complementary to that derived from other spectral techniques, i.e., molecular weight, presence or absence of hetero atoms, structure of side chains, etc. It is the purpose of this chapter to acquaint the organic chemist with those features and principles of mass spectrometry which will best serve him in spectral interpretation. Since space limitations necessarily militate against elaboration upon many of the subjects discussed below, the reader is referred to the general bibliography for more expanded presentations.

2. Advantages and Limitations Compared with Other Spectral Methods

Although throughout this chapter the specific superiority and drawbacks of mass spectrometry will be stressed, a few topics will be briefly covered at this point.

2.1. Sample Size. Interpretable spectra can be obtained from as little as 0.1 μg. of sample. Infrared (IR) and nuclear magnetic resonance (NMR) recordings in particular require substantially larger quantities. Since the mass spectrometer is a "destructive" tool, other spectral data are generally compiled first when only a limited quantity of material is available. The recent years have seen burgeoning efforts to combine the powerful tools of gas liquid chromatography (GLC) and mass spectrometry.[5] Minute quantities of complex mixtures may be chromatographed and the separated components fed directly into the spectrometer, providing spectra in a matter of a few seconds. Commercial instruments are now available which are capable of directly recording the mass spectra of substances as they elute from a gas liquid chromatograph. In fact, one can purchase a combined mass spectrometer-gas liquid chromatograph apparatus. This marriage of the two units, however, affords less flexibility than one might desire.

Mass spectra have been obtained on compounds isolated by thin layer chromatography,[6] a technique requiring only minuscule amounts of sample. The mass spectrometer's high sensitivity sometimes serves as a disadvantage, viz., often samples sufficiently pure for IR, UV and NMR examination (*ca.* 85 to 90 per cent) give mass spectra which are difficult to interpret owing to the presence of peaks arising from the impurity.

*Present address: Fundamental Research Department, The Coca Cola Company, Linden, N. J.

2.2. Sample Volatility. Since the compound under investigation must first be vaporized before ionization can occur, the spectra of some very high boiling liquids as well as many solids cannot be recorded in the usual way. However, this disadvantage can be circumvented in many instances by introducing the sample directly into the ionizing region or by derivatizing the product.

2.3. Sample Stability. Dehydration, cyclization, decomposition, etc., may occur upon sample volatilization. Here again, derivatization often serves to eliminate these problems. In the case of long chain alcohols, catalytic decomposition which occurs on the hot metal surface of the spectrometer's inlet system can be avoided by using a glass system.[7,8]

2.4. Fingerprint. Low energy electron bombardment (10 to 100 eV) of a material subsequent to volatilization results in the formation of molecular ions which decompose after a short time into neutral and ionized fragments. The nature of these ions and their abundance is dependent upon the structure of the sample under examination. It follows, therefore, that different substances will give different fragmentation patterns. For this reason, the mass spectrum, like its infrared counterpart, can be considered as a "fingerprint" of a particular compound. The former sometimes is more specific, i.e., differentiation, say, between cyclic C_{15} and C_{16} ketones is not feasible by infrared means while the mass spectrometer provides an unequivocal answer. On the other hand, mass spectra of certain geometric isomers are nearly indistinguishable, whereas their IR and NMR spectra frequently are significantly different.

3. Instrumentation

3.1. Ion Production and Measurement. When a sample is vaporized into the ionizing chamber of a mass spectrometer (ca. 10^{-6} mm Hg), it is exposed to low energy electron bombardment (10 to 100 eV). The lower end of the voltage range is generally important for the examination of ionization processes and the determination of appearance potentials[*,9] whereas the higher region is used to obtain spectra for both qualitative and quantitative analysis. The molecular ion formed will be registered at a mass corresponding to the molecular weight if it is stable for more than *ca.* 10^{-5} seconds, i.e., the length of time necessary for the ion to reach the recording section of the spectrometer. A Schematic diagram of a CEC 21-103C magnetically deflecting, electrical scanning spectrometer appears in Figure 1.

The sample is introduced into the reservoir through a sintered disc, septum, gas sample flask, etc. A micromanometer, primarily used for quantitative analysis, enables one to measure the pressure exerted by the material in the reservoir. The vapor is leaked into an ion-producing source and the ions formed are accelerated through the analyzer tube and collected at the end of a 180° path. The accelerated ions, under the influence of a uniform magnetic field, follow curved paths whose radii are dependent upon their mass, electric charge, and velocity. Only ions traveling the path of one specific radius can traverse the circular route provided by the analyzer tube and strike the collector. Therefore, by varying the ion accelerating voltage, it is possible to bring ions of different mass and electric charge into register on the face of the collector at different times.† Upon electron impact, negative as well as positive ions are produced in the ionizing chamber. Repellers act both to push the positive ions toward the accelerating region and to attract and ground the negative ions.

---

*The ionization potential of a molecule is the energy required for the removal of an electron to form the molecular (parent) ion. The appearance potential of an ion fragment A^+ is equal to, or, in some instances, greater than, the sum of the dissociation energy of the bond A—X and the ionization potential of $A \rightarrow A^+$.

†This can also be accomplished in other types of instruments by mainting a constant ion accelerating voltage and varying the strength of the magnetic field.

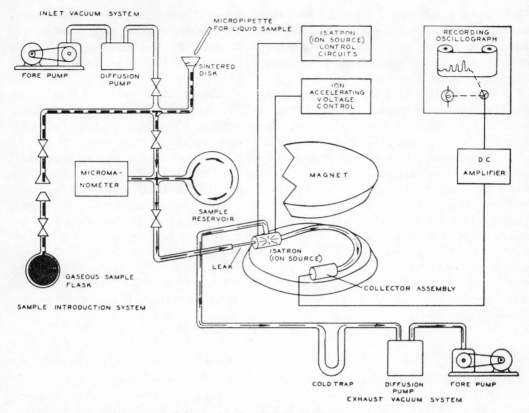

FIGURE 1. Schematic of a CEC 21-103C mass spectrometer.

The Bendix Time of Flight mass spectrometer operates on quite a different principle, i.e., a short burst of electrons creates a bundle of ions which are then accelerated down a field-free drift tube which separates them according to their weight—the lightest ions reaching the detector first, followed in succession by ions of heavier mass.

The recording of ions subsequent to proper amplification can be adequately accomplished by any one of several different types of recorders, i.e., pen-and-ink, digitizers and oscillographs. To the latter group belong the photographic and direct read-out devices. The major advantage of the recording oscillograph is that the strong and weak peaks are recognized immediately, thereby minimizing the necessity of interpreting peak sensitivities.

3.2. Sample Size and Vapor Pressure.   In order to obtain an adequate spectrum, the quantity of material introduced into the reservoir must be sufficiently large to pass through the leak and produce a pressure of approximately 10^{-6} mm in the ion source. The relatively low vapor pressure of high molecular weight organic compounds often poses a serious problem, especially when a limited supply of sample is on hand. The vapor pressure can be increased by raising the temperature of the inlet system. For stainless steel systems, the maximum temperature obtainable is about 150°, but it should be noted that catalytic decomposition can occur in the presence of metals. This problem can be avoided by using a glass system in which temperatures as high as 350 to 400° can be reached. However, in view of the inherent thermal instability of many organic substances at these elevated temperatures, it is generally best not exceed *ca.* 200°.

If the volume of the introduction reservoir is reduced by a factor of 10, the intensity of the recorded spectrum will be tenfold stronger. This is particularly useful for very small quantities of higher molecular weight materials, but the results are only qualitative in nature due to rapid sample depletion in the reservoir during the time required for a spectral recording.

The signal reaching the recorder can be increased by raising the ionizing current or by using an electron multiplier. Since the limit of signal strength increase is determined, in part, by the background or contaminants present in the system or sample, the smaller the sample quantity the greater is the danger that the spectrum will be obscured.

3.3. Resolution. The upper mass limit to which an instrument can scan and is capable of clearly resolving (see Ref. 3, page 13) adjacent peaks depends upon the ability of the instrument to separate adjacent ion beams. This resolution decreases with increasing mass weights and, therefore, a spectrometer which may be able to resolve mass 99 from mass 100 may not resolve mass 499 from mass 500. For the CEC Model 21-103C spectrometer, the ions of weight 100 have a path radius of 1.005 times that of weight 99, and the ions of weight 500 follow a path radius of only 1.001 times that of ions of weight 499. Since the larger ions have very similar radii, their separation becomes difficult. The upper mass limit to which the ion beam can be brought into focus depends on the radius of the path of deflection, accelerating potential and magnetic field strength and, as a result, a practical limit is dictated by the size of the spectrometer.

The low resolution, single-focusing, magnetic-deflecting instruments are able to give the exact integral mass of the fragments up to the spectrometer's upper mass limit. A distinct advantage of high resolution instruments is their ability to resolve not only molecular weights in the thousands, but also to separate fragments displaying the same integral weight but differing by a small fraction of a mass unit. For example, Beynon[1,p.493] lists 18 possible combinations of C, H, N and O at mass 100 ranging from 100.0354 to 100.1446, and all are distinguishable with the aid of a high resolution spectrometer. Resolution of the molecular ions of 1-methoxy- and 1,4-diaminoanthraquinone, obtained on an AEI Model MS 9 spectrometer, is depicted in Figure 2. Resolution is defined as $M/\Delta M$. In this example it is 22,200.

3.4. Spectral Presentation. There are several ways in which mass spectra can be presented for study. A mass spectrum "as recorded" (see Figure 3—the five lines represent different intensity levels) is used only to a limited extent and usually in special cases, i.e., to demonstrate the presence of metastable ions (see Section 3.6), resolution of masses, etc. It should be noted that although good reproducibility of mass spectra is obtained with instruments of the same type, fragmentation patterns are seen to vary when comparing those derived from, say, Time-of-Flight and magnetic deflecting spectrometers.

A tabular method is most commonly employed to portray fragmentations; a value of 100 per cent is assigned to the most intense peak in the spectrum—the base peak—and the others are given as percentages of the base peak. Another form of mass spectral presentation, favored by many and generally used in this chapter, is the bar graph. In effect, it is a graphical representation of the aforementioned tabular procedure and conveys to the reader the characteristics of a spectrum at a glance (see Figure 6).

When it is necessary only to illustrate certain gross spectral characteristics, it is usually sufficient to depict a bar graph representing fragment intensities as they actually appear in the mass spectrum itself (see Figure 4).

3.5. Low Voltage Spectra. A mass spectrum produced by impinging electrons of energies equal to, or slightly above, a compound's ionization potential—*ca.* 1 to 5 eV—is significantly different from that obtained under normal conditions, i.e., 50 to 100 eV. A marked reduction in the number and intensity of fragment peaks occurs in the former

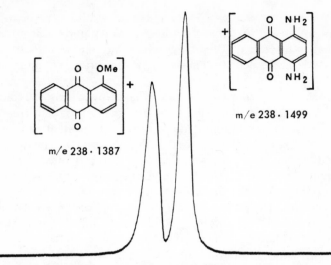

FIGURE 2. Molecular ion spectrum of 1-methoxy and 1,4-diamino-anthraquinone. (*Courtesy British Associated Electrical Industries*)

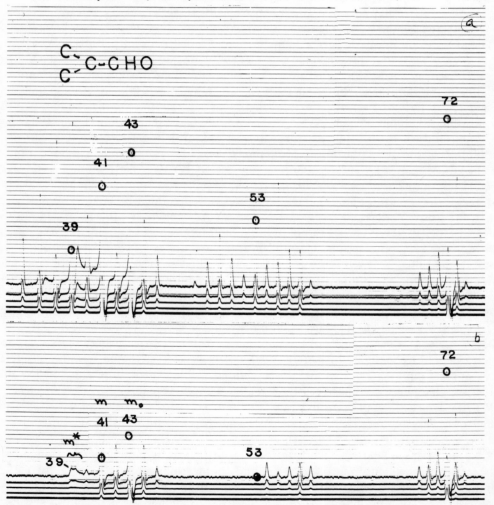

FIGURE 3. (a) High voltage (70 eV) spectrum of isobutyraldehyde. (b) Low voltage (13 eV) spectrum of isobutyraldehyde.

instance and often only the molecular ion will be present, as observed in the case of benzene, pyridine, etc.[10,11,12] It should be noted that if a material does not show a molecular ion under standard voltages, it will usually not display one at low voltages.† The value of recording a low voltage spectrum when examining unknown substances lies in the fact that the relative intensity of the molecular ion peak increases compared with the fragment ions. As a result, the task of selecting a peak attributable to the molecular ion often is considerably simplified, especially when there are present higher molecular weight fragments originating from impurities. In addition, the problem of relating fragments with the aid of metastable ions (see Section 3.6) sometimes is resolved by comparison of high and low voltage spectra.

3.6. Metastable Ions. Molecular and fragment ions of varying degrees of stability are produced under electron impact of sample vapors. Stable, positively charged ions will be formed and accelerated in the ion source (see Figure 1) and arrive at the collector with only little attendant decomposition. On the other hand, relatively unstable molecular ions will possess sufficient energy to fragment before reaching the accelerating region and the spectrum will not contain a peak corresponding to the molecular weight.

Those ions of intermediate energy, which decompose after acceleration but prior to magnetic deflection, are usually focused at a peak of nonintegral mass. These metastable ions usually appear in the spectrum as broad, low intensity peaks. The apparent mass of a metastable ion, m^*, is related to the mass of the "parent" ion, m_0, and the mass of the fragment ion, m, by the expression

$$m^* = m^2/m_0$$

Tentatively postulated molecular formulas or fragmentation processes can be supported or denied with the aid of metastable peaks; however, the failure to observe a sought-for metastable ion is not evidence that the corresponding reaction did not occur. Rather than resorting to a time consuming series of trial and error calculations, the use of Beynon's nomograms[1, p. 546] enables one to readily correlate the values of m_0, m and m^*. For example, in the 70 eV spectrum of isobutyraldehyde (Figure 3a), a metastable peak is discernible between m/e 39‡ and 40, part of which is obscured by a normal fragment of mass 39. A much clearer picture is obtained under low voltage conditions. (Figure 3b.) The related peaks m/e 43 (m_0) and 41 (m) give a metastable peak at 39.1 (m^*) attributable to the loss of two hydrogen atoms from the isopropyl moiety

$$(C_3H_7)^+ \longrightarrow (C_3H_5)^+ + 2H$$

It is difficult to accurately establish from the spectral presentation the fractional mass position of a metastable peak because of its shape. Therefore, one should be on guard for all possible ion combinations which yield a metastable ion appearing in the region of interest. One such combination in this case involves the peaks m/e 71 and 53—a loss of 18 mass units—which give a calculated metastable ion of m/e 39.6. However, this pathway is shown to be incorrect upon examining the low voltage spectrum (Figure 3b),

---

†Using a field emission ion source rather than an electron bombardment one, almost fractionless molecular ion spectra of hydrocarbons can be obtained. This indicates that the former will be valuable for the mass spectral recording of compounds whose molecular ions are very weak or nonexistent under the conditions of the latter ionizing source. (Beckey, H. D., and Wagner, G., Eleventh Ann. Meeting, ASTM Comm. E 14, Conf. on Mass Spectrometry and Related Topics, San Francisco, Calif., 1963).

‡The term "m/e" refers to the mass-to-charge ratio and is commonly employed to locate the position of a spectral peak. It has been reported [Muccini, G. A., Hamill, W. H., and Barker, R. J., *J. Phys. Chem.*, **68**, 261 (1964)] that the metastable ion, m/e 39.1 appearing in *n*-alkane spectra is pressure dependent and therefore not a collision-induced dissociation.

i.e., the peak of mass 53 is not present, but the metastable, m/e 43, and m/e 41 ion fragments remain.

4. Molecular Weight Determination

4.1. Molecular Ion Stability. It is apparent that the molecular weight of an unknown material is a valuable clue in the search for its identity. During the course of investigations performed in this laboratory, well over half the samples examined were found to display good to strong molecular ion peaks. However, when confronted with a weak series of peaks, any one of which could represent the molecular ion, some difficulty attends its selection with certainty. Obviously, then, one is on surer ground when a spectrum contains a strong parent ion peak. The intensity of the molecular ion is dependent upon the molecule's stability under electron bombardment. The mass spectra of aromatics and heteroaromatics generally evidence intense molecular ions (stabilized by resonance) while these ions are usually absent in the spectra of some tertiary alcohols and many polybasic esters. Spectra of unsaturated compounds will usually exhibit increased molecular ion abundance compared with their saturated analogues. The parent ions of saturated cyclic substances are more intense than their straight chain counterparts—all atoms are retained in the rupture of one bond in the case of the former while lower mass fragments result from the latter. Since chain branching is a favorable point of cleavage, branched compounds display weaker molecular ions than those with straight chains. The absence of a molecular ion does not necessarily imply that a molecular weight cannot be ascertained, because specific fragments stemming from the ion can often be used to good advantage (see Section 8.3).

Some acetates ionize and rearrange to eliminate "acetic acid" without displaying a molecular ion. The $(M - 60)$ peak might at first be considered to be the molecular weight, but the presence of fragments located at m/e 60 or 61 would give indication that the molecular ion, if it had been sufficiently stable, would have appeared 60 mass units higher. (Figure 4.) On some occasions an eliminated acetate ion appears at m/e 59 as the unprotonated fragment. Here infrared or NMR data would greatly simplify the interpretation.

Biemann recently reported the combined use of a high resolution spectrometer and a computer for ascertaining molecular weights of compounds where there is a high tendency for fragmentation and/or where there are present impurities of masses higher than the molecular ion. The spectrum obtained with a spectrometer of a resolving power that permits the determination of the elemental composition of all ions makes it possible to set a number of criteria which uniquely determine the molecular ion.[98]

4.2. Use of an Internal Standard. At infrequent occasions the molecular ion peak is some distance removed from the nearest fragment, complicating the task of ascertaining the true molecular weight. This difficulty is encountered because lower mass fragments must be "counted" when working with some spectrometers in order to arrive at a mass value for the molecular ion. The mass spectra are not linearly presented and, as a result, the peaks cannot be interpolated accurately. In cases such as these, perflorokerosine is employed as an internal calibration standard and can be added to the sample already present in the instrument and on which a spectrum has been previously recorded. It is an excellent standard owing to its volatility, evenly spaced peaks, and high molecular weight.

4.3. (M + 1) Peak Method. It is sometimes possible to determine the molecular weight of a compound which does not exhibit a strong molecular ion by the $(M + 1)$ technique. Many different types of organic compounds containing hydrogen will display a large peak

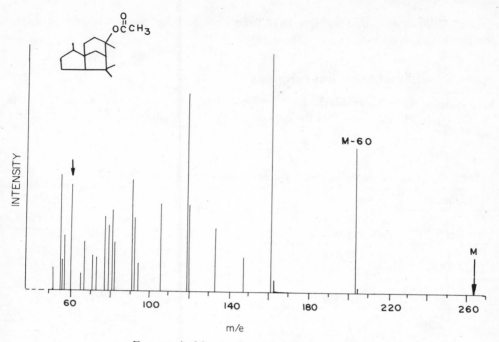

FIGURE 4. Mass spectrum of cedryl acetate.

one mass unit above their molecular weight when a large sample is introduced into the reservoir, thereby substantially increasing its pressure. The possibility of using this method was proposed by McLafferty[17] for alcohols, ethers, glycols and nitriles. It also can be employed for sulphones,[18] carbonates,[19] and esters.[20] The intensity of the (M + 1) peak is proportional to the square of the sample pressure[21] which indicates that it is formed by an ion-molecule reaction. The formation of this peak is also effected by lowering the ion repeller voltage, allowing the ions to spend a longer time in the source and thereby increasing the statistical probability of such a reaction to occur. This can be readily accomplished in a CEC 21-103C mass spectrometer by merely switching from the focused to the nonfocused position. The decrease in sensitivity accompanying this change can be at least partially compensated by increasing the ion current. Although the most intense peak arising from ion-molecule reactions is usually found at (M + 1), small fragments are at times observed at (M + base peak),[22] lending additional corroboration to the assignment of the molecular ion.

4.4. Application of Graham's Law. A leak in the mass spectrometer (see Figure 1) allows a stream of gaseous sample to flow from the reservoir into the ionization chamber. At sufficiently small leaks the gas will obey Graham's Law and the intensity of the spectral peaks can then be correlated with the depletion and thus with the molecular weight.

$$K_a(M_a)^{1/2} = K_x(M_x)^{1/2}$$

where

K_a = rate of decay for a unicomponent peak of the known in the mixture
K_x = rate of decay for a unicomponent peak of the unknown in the mixture
M_a = molecular weight of the known compound
M_x = molecular weight of the unknown compound.

Reasonably good molecular weights have been obtained for benzene, acetone, cyclopentanone and tetrachloroethane using this method.[13, 14]

5. Determination of Empirical Formulas

5.1. Isotope Abundance Method.

The known isotopic compositions of the elements C, H, O, N, S, etc., are sufficiently constant to permit utilization of this technique (see Table 1[3]).

TABLE 1.   Commonly Encountered Elements and Their Natural Abundance

Element	Abundance (%)	Element	Abundance (%)
^{1}H	99.985	^{31}P	100.000
^{2}H	0.015		
^{12}C	98.893	^{32}S	95.0
^{13}C	1.107	^{33}S	0.76
		^{34}S	4.22
^{14}N	99.634	^{36}S	0.14
^{15}N	0.366		
		^{35}Cl	75.77
^{16}O	99.759	^{37}Cl	24.23
^{17}O	0.037		
^{18}O	0.204	^{79}Br	50.537
		^{81}Br	49.463
^{19}F	100.000	^{127}I	100.000
^{28}Si	92.21		
^{29}Si	4.70		
^{30}Si	3.09		

It is readily apparent from the data presented that the bulk of the listed elements have two or more isotopes and, therefore, most of the fragment and molecular ions appearing in mass spectra will not merely exhibit single peaks—due to the lightest isotope of the elements—but, in addition, other peaks will appear in their vicinity due to the heavier isotopes.

Empirical formulas generally are best determined employing high resolution spectrometers with the aid of internal standards, but isotope abundance ratios are extremely helpful when only low resolution instruments are available. It has been shown[16] that the natural abundance of ^{13}C varies, so that it is nearly impossible to obtain highly accurate calculated values of abundance ratios. In spite of this fact, one can arrive at reasonably close approximations which often permit the investigator to determine an empirical formula. As an illustration, the following information was derived upon examination of the pertinent spectral regions of an unknown material of molecular weight 136.

The peak intensity ratios of the molecular ion (M) and its two associated isotopes (M + 1 and M + 2), were found to be

$$(M + 1/M) \times 100 = 11.1$$
$$(M + 2/M) \times 100 = 0.57$$
$$(M + 1/M + 2) = 19.45$$

Referring to Beynon's tables,[15] several possibilities are seen.

No.	Possible Empirical Formulas	$\dfrac{M + 1}{M} \times 100$	$\dfrac{M + 2}{M} \times 100$	$\dfrac{M + 1}{M + 2}$
1	$C_{11}H_4$	11.95	.65	18.39
2	$C_{10}H_{16}$	11.06	.55	19.99
3	$C_{10}H_2N$	11.22	.57	19.67
4	$C_{10}O$	10.84	.73	14.85
5	$C_9H_{14}N$	10.33	.48	21.51
6	$C_9H_{12}O$	9.96	.64	15.47

Formulas 3 and 5 can be immediately eliminated on the basis of the "Nitrogen Rule," which states, in part, that a substance containing an odd number of nitrogen atoms will have an uneven molecular weight. Since 3 and 5 represent an even mass, they are fragment ions rather than molecular ions. The absence of peaks occurring, at m/e 31 and (M − 18), indicative of oxygen-containing fragments, essentially rules out 4 and 6. This leaves us with a choice between two hydrocarbons; 1 and 2. The former corresponds to a highly unsaturated (possibly cyclic) compound which would be expected to exhibit a strong molecular ion. Since the unknown's parent peak is relatively weak, its molecular formula is probably represented by 2.

Owing to the difficulties inherent in measurements of this sort, abundance ratios calculated from a mass spectrum will differ somewhat from the theoretical values and the best fit must be taken from the available literature data after eliminating as many closely lying empirical formulas as possible. Biemann[3, p. 62] has described a simplified method which can be applied to give acceptable intensity ratios of the peaks M, (M + 1) and (M + 2) for molecules containing C, H, O and N.

A mass spectrum under study must possess certain features in order for one to utilize the isotope abundance procedure for determining an empirical formula. The first requirement is that the compound should display a fairly intense molecular ion peak—which therefore limits the number of materials amenable to this technique. Secondly, the presence of impurity peaks occurring at M, (M + 1) and (M + 2) obviously can introduce large errors in abundance ratio calculations. Also, a peak at (M − 1), large enough to significantly contribute its isotopes to the M peak, would adversely affect the accuracy of the intensity measurements, but the theoretical contribution of the former to the latter can be taken into account by the use of Beynon's tables.[15] Elimination of both the impurity and (M − 1) peaks sometimes can be effected by recording the spectrum under low voltage conditions (see Section 3.5). However, in so doing, the intensity of the parent peak usually decreases. Finally, it should be borne in mind that some compounds undergo an ion-molecule reaction (see Section 4.3), ion, making it impossible to obtain a correct value for the (M + 1) peak. The total hydrogen count, derivable from an NMR spectrum, often can play an important role in corroborating or denying the validity of a postulated empirical formula which has been obtained from mass spectral data.

6. Cis-Trans Isomerism

The differentiation between *cis* and *trans* isomers often can be accomplished by mass spectrometry. In the ionized state, the *cis* isomers of 1,2-disubstituted cyclopropanes,[23] cyclobutanes,[24] cyclopentanes[25] and cyclohexanes[26,27] are less stable than the corresponding *trans* isomers. This is evidenced by a lower relative abundance of the *cis* isomer's molecular ion. However, the ratios of the molecular ions (in per cent total ionization of *trans/cis* forms) of many substituted ethylenes; 2-butene, 2-pentene, 4-methyl-2-pentene and 3-hexene, indicate no stability difference between the isomers. Introduction of alkyl groups results in increased steric hindrance and differences in these ratios have been reported, viz., 1.22 and 7 for 5,5-dimethyl-3-hexene and 2,2,5,5-tetramethyl-3-hexene, respectively.[28] It is likely that ionization occurs by removal of one of the nonbonding pi electrons of the double bond. Therefore, isomerism will disappear in the ionized molecule and the energy provided by steric hindrance is released and used for bond rupture. The ionization potentials of *cis* and *trans* decalin were found to be equivalent, but the appearance potentials of two selected fragments (m/e 96 and 82) were significantly different, the values in both cases being smaller for the *cis* isomer.[29] This fact indicates that the removal of an electron from the two isomers requires the same energy and that geometrical isomerism is retained in the ionized molecule in the fundamental state.

The double-bond isomers of seven hexen-1-ols are easily recognized by their different base peaks.[30] As one might expect, the mass spectra of their *cis* and *trans* isomers are generally very similar. Although differences in the abundance of the molecular ions of these isomers are small in comparison with experimental error, the parent ion peak is somewhat more intense for the *trans* and the dehydration fragment is stronger in the case of the *cis* form. Loss of water from the molecular ion would be sterically favored in the case of the *cis* isomer.

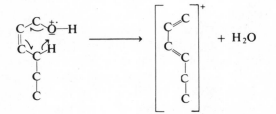

7. Fragmentation and Rearrangement

Since almost every compound will have its own distinct and specific fragmentation pattern, the chemist has at his disposal an excellent method for the qualitative analysis of unknown organic compounds. Although the spectra of some geometrical and substituted aromatic isomers[31] are quite similar, the small differences that do exist can be used in some instances for differentiation. Theoretical aspects of fragmentation will not be explored in this chapter but it should be noted that an attempt has been made to explain mass spectra via the quasi-equilibrium theory.[32,33] Equations developed from this theory have been applied with some success to the calculation of mass spectra of several simple molecules[34,35,36] but Friedman, *et al.*[37] have shown that inconsistencies exist in the area of the threshold energy. A recent review of the current status of the statistical theory of mass spectra is given by Rosenstock and Kraus.[38]

In order to illustrate the fragmentation process, a hypothetical sequence is presented on p. 181. It is initiated by the ion bombardment (*ca.* 50 to 100 eV) of a gaseous molecule at low pressure which results first in the elimination of an electron to form a molecular ion. Molecular ions usually exist in highly excited states and degrade rapidly to produce ionized and neutral fragments in varying nature and abundance. The ionized fragments are recorded as the mass spectrum.

Reactions (1) through (4) represent the simple cleavage of one bond. Further decomposition of fragment ions is shown in reactions (5) and (6), and reaction (7) depicts a rearrangement of the molecular ion. In practice, it will be found that fragmentation pathways

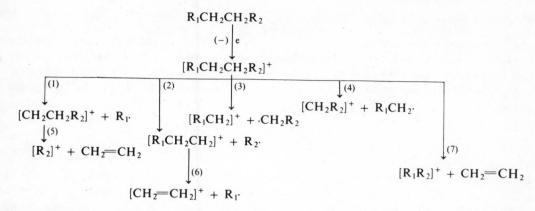

are considerably more complex than shown above, i.e., actually many more fragments occur of the general type formed in reactions (5) and (6).

The illustrated fragment $(R_1R_2)^+$ of reaction (7) is obviously not a result of simple bond cleavage but arises through a rearrangement process. Interpretation of mass spectra representing only simple bond cleavages would be no simple task in itself, but with seemingly random rearrangements also occurring, the diagnostic problems become very complex. It seems that when there is random rearrangement in a molecule, an exchange of two atoms or groups of the starting ion probably occurs to yield a new ion of very similar structure.[39] Using deuterobutane isomers, fragments were found that indicated exchange of hydrogen and deuterium in all possible positions of the molecule.[40] In order to simplify spectral determinations which are hampered by relatively unpredictable possibilities of molecular rearrangements, McLafferty[41] has classified such anomalies as "more random" or "more specific." The former appear to involve a higher energy reshuffling process in which various atoms or groups are equilibrated in the molecule and are found particularly in the mass spectra of hydrocarbons. The latter can yield either specific ions of high abundance through formation of a sterically favored transition state or more stable product. McLafferty also proposed further classifications according to whether or not the ions or neutral species involved contained an odd or even number of electrons. This has been particularly useful in correlating rearrangements, because ion stabilities are usually greater for those ions containing an even number of electrons.[42] A limited categorization has been made of the specific rearrangements based on whether the decomposing ion or its products contain odd (O.E.) or even (E.E.) number of electrons.

(1) O.E. ion $\longrightarrow$ O.E. ion + E.E. molecule
(single rearrangement)

(2) O.E. ion $\longrightarrow$ E.E. ion + O.E. radical
(double rearrangement)

(3) Cyclic O.E. ion $\longrightarrow$ E.E. ion + O.E. radical
(single rearrangement)

(4) E.E. ion $\longrightarrow$ E.E. ion + O.E. molecule
(single rearrangement)

(5) Ion $\longrightarrow$ E.E. ion + E.E. molecule + others
(multiple rearrangements in bond cleavages)

It is assumed that in reactions (1) through (4) the only products formed are a positive ion and a neutral fragment. The rearranging unit(s) is either an atom (mainly hydrogen) or a group such as CH_3. Specific examples of rearrangements will be presented in Section 8.

8. Group Fragmentations*

8.1. Acetals. The molecular ion is either missing or extremely weak and cannot be used with assurance to establish the molecular weight. $(M - 1)$ peaks are often present and they usually are somewhat stronger than the molecular ion. The predominant fragmentation process is α-cleavage with the loss of R_1 or one of the OR_2 groups from the parent ion.

The remaining fragments can be characterized as to whether or not they contain one or two oxygen atoms because of the mass difference between C and O. Loss of OR_2 would produce peaks of m/e 59 or 73 or 87, etc., and elimination of R_1 yields fragments at m/e 75 or 89 or 103, etc., depending on the type of substituent. These peaks will stand out above the rest in the upper half of the mass spectrum.[43] Preference of loss seems to be based on the length of the alkyl groups. When $R_1 > R_2$, the $(M - R_1)$ peaks are generally stronger, and when $R_2 \geq R_1$, the $(M—OR_2)$ peaks tend to be more intense.

The probable mechanism of fragmentation for dipropoxy ethane is as follows:

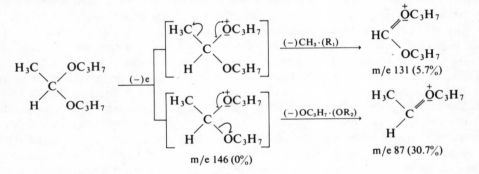

A limited number of mixed acetals have been examined in this laboratory and loss of the larger alkoxy group appears to predominate:†

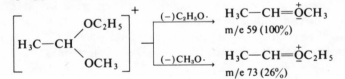

8.2. Acids. 8.2.1. Aliphatic. The molecular ion abundance of monocarboxylic acids ·decreases with increasing molecular weight[44,45] and the introduction of unsaturation in conjugation with the carboxyl group increases the relative intensity of the ion.

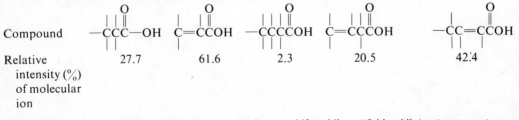

Compound	$-\overset{\mid}{\underset{\mid}{C}}\overset{\mid}{\underset{\mid}{C}}\overset{O}{\overset{\|}{C}}-OH$	$\overset{}{\underset{\mid}{C}}=\overset{}{\underset{}{C}}\overset{O}{\overset{\|}{C}}OH$	$-\overset{\mid}{\underset{\mid}{C}}\overset{\mid}{\underset{\mid}{C}}\overset{\mid}{\underset{\mid}{C}}\overset{O}{\overset{\|}{C}}OH$	$\overset{}{\underset{}{C}}=\overset{}{\underset{\mid}{C}}\overset{\mid}{\underset{\mid}{C}}\overset{O}{\overset{\|}{C}}OH$	$-\overset{\mid}{\underset{\mid}{C}}\overset{}{\underset{}{C}}=\overset{}{\underset{}{C}}\overset{O}{\overset{\|}{C}}OH$
Relative intensity (%) of molecular ion	27.7	61.6	2.3	20.5	42.4

. * A full arrow ($\longrightarrow$) will be used to indicate a two-electron shift, while a "fishhook" ($\frown$) represents a one-electron transfer.[4]

†This has been confirmed recently by McFadden [McFadden, W. H., Wasserman, J., Lundin, R. E., and Teranishi, R., *Anal. Chem.*, **36**, 1031 (1964)].

Almost all compounds containing carboxyl groups display a peak at m/e 60. This characteristic rearrangement ion varies in abundance from <1 per cent in propionic and acrylic acids to 100 per cent in butyric, valeric and isovaleric acids. It has been shown by ^{13}C labeling that the carboxyl group is retained in the rearranged m/e 60 ion.[44] The probable mechanism is therefore one which requires a cleavage of the β-bond accompanied by γ-hydrogen rearrangement and the elimination of a neutral olefin.

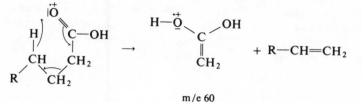

m/e 60

The m/e 45 ion $(COOH)^+$ usually is present in the spectra of low and high molecular weight acids but the (M − 17), (M − 18) and (M − 45) peaks, occurring in varying abundance for the lower weight acids, are missing for the higher members.

8.2.2. Aromatic. Monocarboxylic acids display very intense molecular ions due to the high resonance stability of the aromatic ring. Proximity of methyl substituents and increasing molecular weight adversely affect the stability of the molecular ion.[46,47] The two major fragments of benzoic acid result from α-cleavage on either side of the C=O group. This is paralleled in the case of toluic acid, but here the position of methyl substitution influences the cleavage and causes a relatively strong (M − 18) peak in the ortho isomer —possibly arising by way of a cyclic transition state.

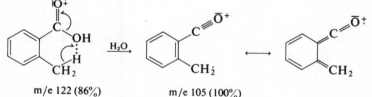

m/e 122 (86%)   m/e 105 (100%)

RELATIVE INTENSITY (%)

Ion	Benzoic Acid	o-Toluic Acid	m-Toluic Acid	p-Toluic Acid
M	86	84	87	97
M-17 (OH)	100	32	49	76
M-18 (H_2O)	1	100	4	2
M-45 (COOH)	64	86*	100*	100*

* Stability is probably due to the formation of the tropylium ion.[48]

For dicarboxylic acids, the molecular ion intensity is related to the respective positions of the two carboxyl groups, the abundance decreasing with the proximity of these moieties. The peaks present in the spectra of monoacids also appear for the diacids (M − 17, M − 18, M − 45) and, in addition, one observes the fragment (M − 90), attributable to the α-cleavage loss of both carboxyl groups. It should be mentioned that the (M − 45) peak is less important in the case of the diacids than it is for the monoacids and also that the (M − 17) peak decreases with the proximity of methyl substituents.[47]

Benzenic compounds substituted with three or more carboxylic acid groups are difficult to volatilize and are not stable, making it difficult to obtain a representative spectrum.

8.3. Alcohols. 8.3.1. Aliphatic. *8.3.1.1. Primary.* The molecular ions of both straight chain and branched primary alcohols decrease with increasing molecular weight, in fact, the parent ions for those containing more than *ca.* five carbon atoms are usually so small as to be insignificant.[43] The (M − 1) peaks, which also decrease in abundance with increasing molecular weight, are very often more intense than the molecular ion, the former being the most intense fragment ions arising in the spectral region above the dehydration peak (M − 18). The (M − 1) peak has been shown to be formed by loss of an α-hydrogen,[50,51,52] probably forming the following ion:

$$R\!-\!\overset{\overset{\displaystyle H}{|}}{C}H\!\!-\!\!\overset{+\cdot}{\underset{\cdot\cdot}{O}}H \;\rightarrow\; R\!-\!CH\!=\!\overset{+}{\underset{\cdot\cdot}{O}}H + H\cdot$$

Fragments in the same order of intensity as the molecular ion are sometimes also observed at (M − 2), (M − 3) and sometimes (M − 4), etc. For long chain alcohols, this decomposition has been shown to be accelerated in mass spectrometers employing stainless steel systems and reduced when using a glass system.[7]

The ion formed by loss of H_2O is always significant and can easily be mistaken for a molecular ion. The following elimination mechanism, yielding a cyclic ion, has been postulated by McLafferty.[14 Gen. Ref., p. 334]

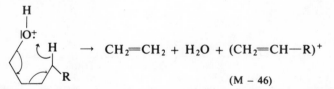

Following the (M − 18) peak there are usually two more important ones located at (M − 33) and (M − 46).[43] The (M − 33) fragment corresponds to the loss of either H_2O and CH_3 or CH_2OH and 2H. The (M − 46) fragment is probably due to a double elimination[4 p. 33] of H_2O and $CH_2\!\!=\!\!CH_2$.

$$\text{(structure)} \;\rightarrow\; CH_2\!\!=\!\!CH_2 + H_2O + (CH_2\!\!=\!\!CH\!-\!R)^+$$

$$(M - 46)$$

Spectra of primary alcohols which do not contain molecular ions often could be mistaken for olefinic-type spectra. However, peaks of masses 31, 45, 59, etc., arise from the fragmentation of an alcohol, and their presence would indicate that one is dealing with an oxygen-containing substance and not an olefin. It should be noted that their absence is not proof that the compound does not, in actuality, contain oxygen, i.e., furan.

The base peak, located at m/e 31, is observed in the spectra of C_1–C_4 straight chain primary alcohols, and its abundance decreases sharply in the heavier alcohols. This fragment ion probably has the following resonance stabilized form.

$$CH_2\!\!=\!\!\overset{+}{\underset{\cdot\cdot}{O}}\!-\!H$$

Branching on the γ-carbon and beyond causes no marked change from the fragmentation process of straight chain alcohols. However, branching at the end of a chain (especially when an isopropyl or tertiary butyl group is present) will result in stronger peaks at m/e 43 and 57, respectively, than those found in the analogous straight chain alcohols.

Alcohols branched on the α-carbon will generally evidence the same spectral profiles as their straight-chain isomers and, in addition, there will appear intense fragment ions arising from α-cleavage. This cleavage results in the formation of either a secondary or tertiary carbonium ion, depending on the number of branches. In lower molecular weight alcohols, this peak is very often the base peak, but its intensity drastically diminishes for the heavier ones.[43]

8.3.1.2. Secondary and Tertiary Alcohols. The molecular ions appear to be somewhat more abundant in the spectra of secondary than in those of primary or tertiary alcohols, but the former are still very weak. In a series examined by Friedel, *et al.*[43] they were less than 2 per cent of the base peak. The (M − 1) peaks sometimes appear in secondary and tertiary alcohol spectra, but not as consistently as in the primary alcohols and are therefore less reliable for molecular weight determinations. In branched compounds, especially those with methyl substituents, there will be found (M − 15) peaks due to loss of methyl.

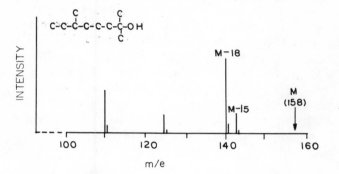

FIGURE 5. Mass spectrum of 1,1,5-trimethyl-1-heptanol.

Many lower molecular weight secondary, and especially tertiary, alcohols exhibit no (M − 18) peaks. When these fragments are present they are less intense than those arising from primary alcohols. However, the higher molecular weight alcohols (greater than C_8) display (M − 18) peaks which are of comparable intensity for all three types. That part of a fragmentation pattern which has two peaks separated by three mass units—due to (M − 15) and (M − 18) cleavages—can be used to advantage in ascertaining a molecular weight when no molecular ion is visible. The (M − 46) peak, due to loss of H_2O and C_2H_4, is prevalent for primary alcohols but usually is missing in secondary and tertiary compounds. A methyl substituent located on the α-carbon of a secondary alcohol will result in an abundant fragment ion (m/e 45) which is often the base peak. Dimethyl substituents present on the α-carbon atom in tertiary alcohols will yield a very intense peak at m/e 59.

$$R-\overset{\overset{+\!\!\cdot}{O}H}{\underset{\underset{Me}{|}}{C}}H \longrightarrow \overset{\overset{+}{O}H}{\underset{\underset{Me}{|}}{C}}H + R$$

m/e 45

In the unsymmetrical substituted secondary and tertiary alcohols, the most intense fragment ions result from the loss of the largest alkyl group.

8.3.2. Aromatic. Phenol exhibits a resonance stabilized molecular ion which is the base peak.[53] Strong fragments also appear at m/e 66 and 65 due to the loss of CO and COH, respectively.[4 p. 54]

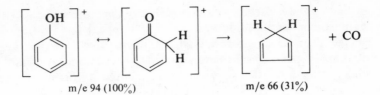

$$m/e\ 94\ (100\%) \qquad\qquad m/e\ 66\ (31\%)$$

Cresols display abundant (M − 1) ions which are attributable to the loss of a hydrogen atom to form the hydroxy tropylium ion. The proximity of methyl substituents to the hydroxyl group causes an increased loss of water from the molecular ion: ortho > meta > para. The spectra of methyl substituted benzyl alcohols also show an ortho effect, i.e., the ortho isomer's base peak appearing at m/e 104 (M—H₂O).

The fragment ion resulting from dehydration can also be seen in hydroxybenzenes: catechol > resorcinol > hydroquinone.

8.4. Aldehydes. 8.4.1. Aliphatic. Both branched and straight chain aldehydes exhibit molecular ion peaks, but there is a rapid decrease in their intensity above C_4 compounds. α-Cleavage to yield the alkyl ion fragments is insignificant, but α-cleavage resulting in the formation of the formyl ion, CHO^+ (m/e 29) predominates in the C_1 to C_3 aldehydes. The peak of mass 29 in C_4 aldehydes contains a minor amount of CHO^+ and a major quantity of $C_2H_5^+$, but in aldehydes $>C_4$ this peak is due mainly to $C_2H_5^{+}$.[55]

β-Cleavage predominates in n-C_4 and higher aldehydes resulting in an m/e 44 ion. This ion originates by transfer of a γ-hydrogen, probably through a 6-membered ring intermediate[55] by a homolytic process,[4p.4] for example:

$$R{-}CH{-}\overset{H}{\underset{\underset{CH_2}{CH_2}}{}}\!\!\overset{\cdot\cdot{+}}{O}\!\!\underset{C-H}{} \longrightarrow R{-}CH{=}CH_2 + CH_2{=}CH{-}\overset{\cdot{+}}{O}H$$

$$m/e\ 44$$
$$(100\%\ in\ C_4{-}C_7)$$

α-Methyl and α-ethyl substitution results in rearranged ions of m/e 58 and 72, respectively, and these ions can be used to locate the position of substitution as well as the nature of the substituent. There is a preferential loss of the larger alkyl fragments.

Straight chain and non-α-branched aldehydes show a strong (M − 44) peak which is due to the loss of $C_2H_4O(CH_2{=}CH{-}OH)$ and results in an olefinic ion $(C_nH_{2n})^+$. However, the spectra of α-branched aldehydes sometimes contain very weak (M − 44) peaks.

Aldehyde spectra also contain dehydration ions (M − 18) which are stronger in straight chain than in branched compounds. In addition, there is also found an (M − 28) peak due to the elimination of ethylene arising from β, γ, δ, etc., cleavage in C_4, C_5, C_6, etc., respectively, with a hydrogen rearrangement to the oxygen-containing fragment.

8.4.2. Aromatic. Because of resonance stabilization, aromatic aldehydes give rise to very stable molecular ions. In addition, the (M − 1) peak, due to the loss of the aldehydic hydrogen,[56] is important, for it is of the same order of intensity as the molecular ion. The spectra contain a limited number of strong peaks and are correlatable with the major fragmentations of the compound. α-Cleavage, accompanied by the loss of the CHO group (M − 29), produces intense peaks that sometimes form the base peak in the spectrum. The abundance of these fragments decreases with the number of ring methyl substituents.[47] (See Figure 6, p. 187).

$$\overset{\text{O}}{\overset{\|}{}}$$

8.5. Esters. 8.5.1. Aliphatic ($R_1C{-}O{-}R_2$). The molecular ion abundance varies over a wide range, i.e., it is negligible in tertiary butyl acetate and is the base peak for

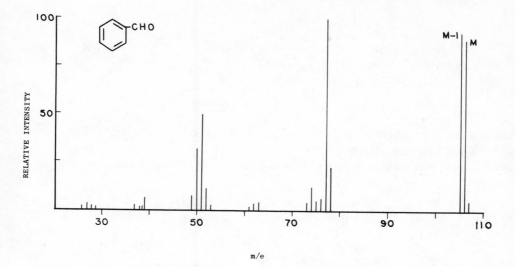

FIGURE 6. Mass spectrum of benzaldehyde.

ethyl stearate,[57] however, the latter is the exception rather than the rule. In general, a sharp decrease in intensity occurs with increasing chain length of R_2.[58] The molecular ion intensity is minimal in spectra of C_5 or C_6 methyl esters and increases as R_1 becomes larger.[18]

Fragments attributable to $R_1, R_1\overset{\text{O}}{\overset{\|}{C}}, R_1\overset{\text{O}}{\overset{\|}{C}}O, \overset{\text{O}}{\overset{\|}{C}}OR_2, OR_2, R_2$ and rearrangement ions[58,59] are frequently encountered in ester spectra:

(a) R_1 and $R_1\overset{\text{O}}{\overset{\|}{C}}$ often form the base peak and display "paraffin type" peaks at masses 29, 43, 57, 71, etc.

(b) $\overset{\text{O}}{\overset{\|}{C}}OR_2$ are usually intense and exhibit peaks at masses 59, 73, 87, etc.; $R_1=C_1$, C_2, C_3, etc., respectively.

(c) OR_2 show peaks of only moderate intensity at masses 31, 45, 59, etc., and then only when R_2 contains no unsaturation.

(d) R_2 appears as $(R - H)$ when R_2 is $\geqslant C_2$, sometimes producing an olefin-type fragmentation pattern.

(e) $R_1\overset{\text{O}}{\overset{\|}{C}}{-}O$ are relatively weak. However, when $R_2 \geqslant C_2$ peaks are observed equivalent in mass to this fragment plus two hydrogen atoms arising from R_2.[57] These rearrangement ions, appearing at m/e 47, 61, 75, 89, etc., are usually associated with a particular ester type, i.e., formate, acetate, propionate, butyrate, etc., respectively.

It should be noted that a peak at m/e 61 sometimes occurs in the spectra of esters higher than acetates, e.g., n-propyl propionate, so that its presence is not certain indication of an acetate. Rearrangement peaks are also found at masses 60, 74, 88, etc.

The m/e 74 rearrangement ion forms the base peak in methyl-n-pentanoate and the higher methyl esters studied by Ryhage, et al.[18] The rearrangement pathway may be represented as follows:

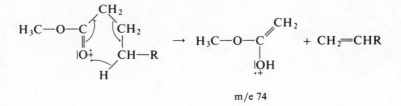

m/e 74

Analogous rearrangement peaks were found in the spectra of ethyl and butyl esters at masses 88 and 116, respectively.[57]

Branching on the carbon chain will produce changes in the fragmentation patterns:

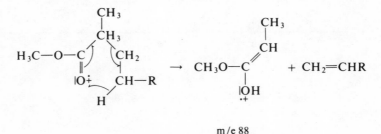

m/e 88

Substitution of an alkyl group further along the chain will produce preferential cleavage at the point of branching.[61]

8.5.2. Aromatic. The molecular ions vary in abundance and depend upon the ester type.[62,46]

(a) Benzyl esters (Ar—CH$_2$—O—C(=O)—R) exhibit relatively intense molecular ions. Ion fragments are observed that correspond to Ar—CH$_2$, Ar—CH$_2$O, C(=O)—R and R. The base peak is often m/e 91 and, in addition, the m/e 108 peak is quite strong. The latter is a rearrangement ion (Ar—CH$_2$OH)$^+$ and is a base peak for benzyl acetate.

(b) β-Phenylethyl esters (Ar—CH$_2$—CH$_2$—O—C(=O)—R) display no molecular ions, the major fragments corresponding to Ar—CH$_2$CH$_2$, Ar—CH=CH$_2$, Ar—CH$_2$, C(=O)—R and R. The base peak (m/e 104) is rearranged Ar—CH=CH$_2$ ion.

(c) Cinnamyl esters (Ar—CH=CH—CH$_2$—O—C(=O)—R) show strong molecular ions. Fragments are found that are correlatable with Ar—CH=CH—CH$_2$, Ar—CH=CH—CH$_2$O, C(=O)—R and R, but the base peak in the case of cinnamyl formate is m/e 115 (M − 47), a rearranged ion.

(d) Benzoate esters (Ar—C(=O)—O—R) have variable molecular ion intensities. When R is less than C$_4$ they are abundant and when R is C$_4$ or greater the compounds display very weak or no molecular ions. The base peak is m/e 105 (Ar—C=O)$^+$. Fragment ions are observed that correspond to Ar, ArC, $ArC-O$ + 2H and R or R − H. (with the two C's bearing =O groups shown above)

(e) Salicylate esters (HO—Ar—COOR) evidence strong molecular ion peaks but their strength decreases somewhat with increasing R groups. The base peak (m/e 120) is a rearranged ion:

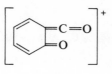

The fragmentations found correspond to OH, HO—Ar—$\overset{O}{\overset{\|}{C}}$, HO—Ar—$\overset{O}{\underset{\|}{\overset{\|}{C}}}$—OH, and R or R − H.

(f) Phthalate esters' [ortho Ar(COOR)$_2$] molecular ions decrease in intensity rapidly with increasing R groups. The base peak of dimethylphthalate is m/e 163; the remaining phthalates show a base peak at m/e 149 which probably corresponds to the rearranged ion:

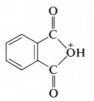

Di-2-ethylhexylphthalate (Octoil) is used as a diffusion pump oil in some instruments and there is a possibility that it will contaminate the mass spectrometer's system. Also, Octoil finds use as a plasticizer and can occur as an artifact in a sample which has been in contact with Tygon tubing. The presence of a possible phthalate ester contaminant can be seen by an m/e 149 peak.

(g) Cinnamate esters (Ar—CH=CH—COOR) show molecular ions of variable strength. Intense peaks are found which correspond to Ar, Ar—CH=CH and Ar—CH=CH—C=O (base peak, m/e 131).

8.6. Ethers. 8.6.1. Aliphatic. The spectra are quite similar to those of other compounds containing electron donating functional groups, i.e., alcohols and amines. The molecular ion abundance decreases rapidly with increasing molecular weight and branching but is significant (*ca.* 3 per cent) through C_{10} straight chain ethers and is sufficiently strong (*ca.* 0.1 per cent) for molecular weight determinations through n-C_{16}.[17] The molecular ion peak is usually absent in the spectra of tertiary ethers.

Symmetrical ethers undergo cleavages α to the oxygen atom, possibly because of the lowered electron density which weakens the C—O bond. Mixed, unbranched ethers also undergo a favored cleavage α to the oxygen atom, preferentially losing the more highly substituted fragment; β-cleavage plays a less important role. Note the relative intensities of the α- and β-cleavage fragments in the following example: (This is a simplified picture; actually other mechanistic pathways could give rise to fragments contributing to the intensity of the postulated ions.)

$$\underset{\substack{m/e\ 73\ (24\%)}}{C_3H_7\overset{+}{-}\underset{}{\overset{\cdot}{O}}=CH_2} \xleftarrow{(-)C_3H_7^{\cdot}} \quad \underset{m/e\ 43\ (100\%)}{\xrightarrow{(-)\cdot OC_4H_9} (C_3H_7)^+}$$

$$\underset{}{\overset{\beta}{\ }} C_3H_7\overset{\cdot+}{-}\underset{}{\overset{}{O}}-C_4H_9 \ \overset{\alpha}{\ }$$

$$\underset{\substack{m/e\ 87\ (13\%)}}{CH_2=\overset{+}{O}-C_4H_9} \xleftarrow{(-)C_2H_5\cdot} \quad \underset{m/e\ 57\ (85\%)}{\xrightarrow{(-)C_3H_7O\cdot} (C_4H_7)^+}$$

In mixed straight chain and β-branched ethers, β-cleavage becomes more pronounced:

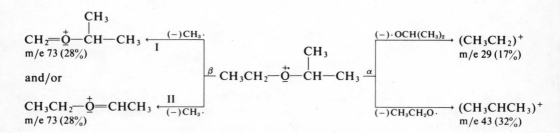

The spectrum of the following α-branched ether contains fairly strong peaks attributable to both α- and β-cleavage.

$$\underset{\substack{m/e\ 73\ (28\%)}}{CH_2=\overset{+}{O}-\overset{\overset{\displaystyle CH_3}{|}}{CH}-CH_3} \underset{I}{\xleftarrow{(-)CH_3\cdot}}$$

and/or

$$\overset{\beta}{\ } CH_3CH_2-\overset{\cdot+}{O}-\overset{\overset{\displaystyle CH_3}{|}}{CH}-CH_3 \ \overset{\alpha}{\ }$$

$$\underset{\substack{m/e\ 73\ (28\%)}}{CH_3CH_2-\overset{+}{O}=CHCH_3} \underset{II}{\xleftarrow{(-)CH_3\cdot}}$$

$$\xrightarrow{(-)\cdot OCH(CH_3)_2} \underset{m/e\ 29\ (17\%)}{(CH_3CH_2)^+}$$

$$\xrightarrow{(-)CH_3CH_2O\cdot} \underset{m/e\ 43\ (32\%)}{(CH_3CHCH_3)^+}$$

However, the strongest peak in the spectrum, m/e 45, is due to a rearrangement and most likely results from further decomposition of the fragment formed via path II_β. This step is aided by the elimination of a neutral olefin.

$$\overset{\overset{\displaystyle H}{|}}{CH_2}\!\!-\!\!CH_2\!\!-\!\!\overset{+}{O}\!=\!CHCH_3 \ \rightarrow \ \underset{m/e\ 45\ (100\%)}{H\overset{+}{O}=CHCH_3} + CH_2=CH_2$$

8.6.2. Cyclic.[33 p. 348]   High resolution spectra of several cyclic ethers of the type

$$\underset{\diagdown O \diagup}{CH_2-(CH_2)_n}$$

where n = 1, 2, 3 or 4, contain large fragments resulting from the loss of CH_2O and CHO as well as CH_2O^+ and CHO^+ ions themselves. Cleavage of the carbon-oxygen bond, accompanied by a hydrogen radical migration, would result in ion a, and further bond rupture leads to the fragments arising from the loss of CH_3 and CHO.

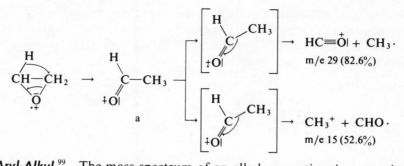

8.6.3. Aryl-Alkyl.[99]   The mass spectrum of an alkyl aromatic ether contains a limited number of strong peaks representing ions of the principal groups contained in the compound. Under the driving force of stabilization, these moieties rearrange during the fragmentation process.

8.6.4. Aryl-Aryl (Symmetrical and Unsymmetrical).   The molecular ion is usually the base peak.[63] Diphenyl ether exhibits fragment ions that are due to the elimination of CO, phenyl and phenyloxy groups from the molecular ion. A generalization can be made that "fission of the ether ion occurs . . . with the production of aryl ions in significant abundance, but with little production of the corresponding aryloxy ion."[63]

8.7. Furans.   These compounds are resonance stabilized. Furan itself displays a molecular ion that is the second most intense peak and is 25 per cent of the total ion current.[64] It has been theorized that the following fragmentation mechanism takes place to form the very stable cyclopropenyl ion at m/e 39, the base peak in the spectrum.[4 p. 226; 64, 65]

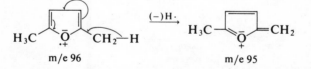

The spectrum of 2,5-dimethylfuran contains an intense $(M - 1)$ peak which has been attributed to the presence of a conjugated, stabilized cation.[4 p. 227]

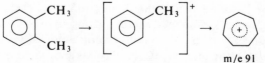

8.8. Hydrocarbons.[66, 67, 68, 69, 70, 81]   **8.8.1. Aromatic.**   The molecular ion is the most abundant one in the spectra of pure aromatics and heteroaromatics. In such conjugated systems the ionization is not localized in any one particular area, and diffusion of the charge prevents a strongly directed cleavage mechanism from predominating.

8.8.2. Alkyl Benzenes.   Aromatic isomers differing in the position of substitution give spectra that are very similar, i.e., those of o-, m-, and p-xylene are almost identical. This similarity has been explained on the basis of the formation of a symmetrical tropylium ion.[48]

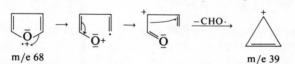

However, the appearance of a strong m/e 91 peak is merely indicative of an alkyl benzene compound and should not be taken as incontrovertible evidence for its presence. These aromatics yield spectra that contain much stronger parent ion peaks than those exhibited by *n*-paraffins of comparable molecular weight. In addition, spectra of the former are much simpler than those of the alkyl hydrocarbons. Substituted alkyl benzenes containing substituents on the α-carbon atom undergo α,β-cleavage.

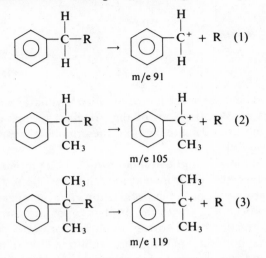

Compounds of the type shown in (3) often give a peak at mass 91 also, which occurs via a secondary transition process.

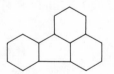

$$119^+ \;\rightarrow\; 91^+ + 28$$

A metastable ion at m/e 69.6 confirms this pathway. Aromatic spectra also contain peaks at masses 39, 50, 51, 52, 63, and 65. It must be emphasized that these are not entirely specific for aromatic compounds and, therefore, should be used as supporting evidence for structural assignment. For example, the spectrum of perhydrofluoranthene:

is quite similar at lower masses to that of an aromatic substance, i.e., m/e 91 is 27 per cent of the base peak.[1 p. 344]

Alkyl benzene spectra also exhibit fragment ions at m/e 77 $(C_6H_5)^+$, m/e 78 $(C_6H_6)^+$, and m/e 79 $(C_6H_7)^+$. The latter indicates that hydrogen migration accompanied by α-bond rupture has occurred. A combination of α- and β-bond cleavage produces peaks at m/e 91, 92, 93 and 105, 106, 107. Major fragments sometimes arise from alkyl ions, but attempts to relate them to specific structural features have met·with little success.

8.8.3. Alkanes. The straight chain members display a molecular ion, the intensity of which decreases with increasing molecular weight. Loss of a methyl group (M − 15) is not favored. The first fragment found below the parent ion is at (M − 29) which is due to loss of C_2H_5. However, when a branched methyl group is present, for example, in isoalkanes, an (M − 15) fragment will be observed. Compounds of C_4 and higher evidence a base peak at m/e 43 $(C_3H_7)^+$ or m/e 57, $(C_4H_9)^+$. Alkanes yield a series of peaks differing by 14 mass units (CH_2) with empirical formulas of C_nH_{2n+1}.

Fragmentation is favored at the point of branching, due to the greater stability of the secondary and tertiary carbonium ions formed, and the more branches present at a carbon the greater is the probability of cleavage at that carbon. It follows, then, that the molecular ion abundance decreases with increased branching. Hydrocarbons containing one substituent on the chain cleave about the substituted carbon atom. Each cleavage of a branch produces a pair of adjacent peaks at odd and even masses. The odd mass is equal to the remaining fragment and the even mass is due to the loss of a hydrogen from this fragment.

8.8.4. Alkenes. These unsaturated hydrocarbons present spectra that are more difficult to correlate with structure than do the saturated hydrocarbons or compounds possessing functional groups. The molecular ions are usually present, decreasing with increasing molecular weight, but isomers are often almost indistinguishable and rearrangement peaks are present in great number. Allylic cleavage predominates with the charge remaining on the unsaturated portion, resulting in intense peaks which are very often the base peaks. A series of fragments are formed at masses 41, 55, 69, 83, etc.; two mass units below those found in the alkane series.

8.8.5. Alkynes. Rearrangements occur to a smaller extent than for the corresponding alkanes and fragments at m/e 27 and 39 occur in approximately the same intensity range. The spectra of heavier 1-alkynes contain a series of peaks at masses 67, 81, 95, etc. Alkyne isomers appear to be more readily distinguishable than the corresponding alkene isomers.

8.8.6. Cycloparaffins. The molecular ion is more abundant in cycloparaffins than in straight chain paraffins containing the same number of carbon atoms owing to the added stabilization of the ring system. Compounds containing cyclohexyl rings give fragments at m/e 83, 82, and 81 and correspond to the ring fragment and ring fragment less 1 and 2 hydrogens, respectively.

8.9. Ketones. 8.9.1. Aliphatic. The molecular weight of nearly any ketone through 2-undecanone can be determined from its relatively prominent molecular ion.[71] The intensity of this ion varies with the molecular weight and is found generally to be greater for the lower (C_3–C_8) than for the higher (C_9–C_{11}) ketones.

Unsymmetrical aliphatic ketones (R_1—CO—R_2) usually yield four major fragmentation peaks arising from α-cleavage on either side of the carbonyl group—R_1^+, R_1CO^+, R_2^+ and R_2CO^+. Loss of the larger alkyl group is favored. All reported methyl ketones (R_1=CH_3) evidence base peaks at m/e 43.[71] The isotope peak at m/e 44 indicates that m/e 43 cannot be due entirely to $(C_3H_7)^+$ but may be mainly the fragment ion $(CH_3CO)^+$. Aliphatic ketone spectra contain rearrangement peaks of varying strength—the most intense rearrangement ions are found at m/e 58, 72, or 86 and are correlatable with methyl, ethyl, or isopropyl ketones, respectively. The strongest rearrangement peak for *n*-propyl and the butyl to hexyl ketones is at m/e 58.

Many ketones display two or more ions which probably arise from a double rearrangement process involving β-cleavage with transfer of a γ-hydrogen.

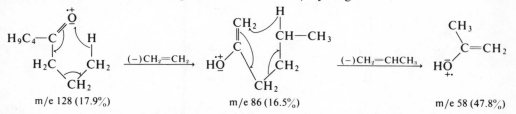

The order of γ-hydrogen migration is tertiary > secondary > primary.[4]

8.9.2. Cyclic. A high resolution spectrum of cyclopentanone shows that the base peak (m/e 55) is composed of the fragments $(C_3H_3O)^+$ and $(C_4H_7)^+$ in a 17:1 ratio[72] and deuterium labeling has indicated the following type of fragmentation mechanism:[4 p. 18, 73]

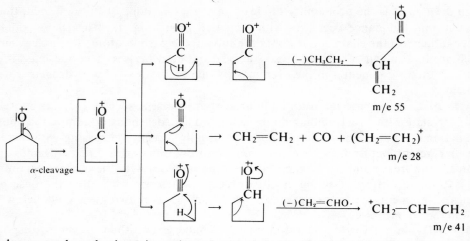

Cyclohexanone has also been investigated with the aid of a high resolution spectrometer[72] and deuterium labeling. A mechanism similar to that postulated for cyclopentanone has been proposed.[74] The first step again involves α-cleavage to produce an intermediate ion from which a fragment m/e 55 can form:

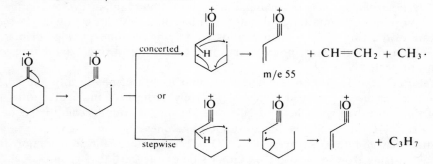

Molecular ions of polycyclic ketones give significantly intense peaks and, therefore, molecular weights can be readily determined.

8.9.3. Aromatic. The spectra of aromatic ketones generally contain a limited number of strong peaks which are correlatable with the major cleavages in the compounds. Deuterium labeling of acetophenone[75] indicates that the first major cleavage to occur takes place α to the carbonyl group with attendant loss of a methyl radical. This produces the base peak at m/e 105. The presence of a metastable peak at 56.6 gives evidence that the fragment of m/e 105 loses CO to form the phenyl ion. α-Cleavage also yields $(CH_3CO)^+$—seen by a peak at m/e 43.

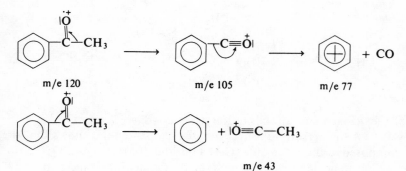

8.10. Lactones. The intensity of the molecular ion depends on the lactone type and number of substituents present on the ring. No parent ion is observed in the spectra of β-propiolactone due no doubt to the instability of the strained four-membered ring. γ-Butyrolactone has a relative molecular ion intensity of 20.6 per cent, and the base peak at m/e 28 consists of $(C_2H_4)^+$ and $(CO)^+$ in a ratio of approximately 5:1.[76] γ-Crotono-lactone

displays a fairly abundant molecular ion (51.3 per cent) and the base peak at m/e 55 consists of $C_3H_3O^+$. The stability of the molecular ion is greater for the unsaturated lactones and their spectra are characterized by a larger number of rearrangement peaks.[77] γ-Lactones containing a side chain

cleave at the ring, giving an intense m/e 85 ion

which is often the base spectral peak. Similarly substituted δ-lactones also fragment at the point of ring substitution, but in this case an m/e 99

fragment is formed which often will be the most abundant ion. The molecular ions of both γ- and δ-lactones decrease with increasing molecular weight. An attached ring, especially one containing unsaturation, adds stability to the molecular ion, as for example, in coumarin (Figure 7).

8.11. Nitriles, Aliphatic. Nitriles containing one nitrogen display their molecular ions at uneven mass numbers. Aliphatic nitriles higher than C_2 have very weak parent ions. These compounds undergo ion-molecule reactions which gives an (M + 1) peak that is often more intense than the molecular ion itself. Nitriles also exhibit an (M − 1) peak that is usually more abundant than the molecular ion[78] and may be represented as a hybrid of two resonance forms.

$$R-\overset{\cdot}{C}H-C\equiv\overset{\cdot}{N}^+ \quad \leftrightarrow \quad R-CH=C=\underset{=}{N}^+$$

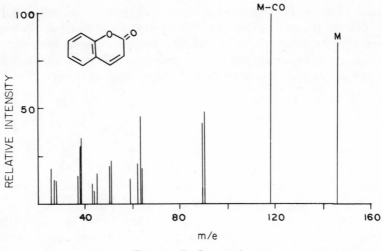

FIGURE 7. Coumarin.

Straight chain nitriles (C_3–C_{10}) show a base peak at m/e 41 which is formed by β-cleavage accompanied by a hydrogen atom rearrangement. There is evidence that the γ-hydrogen is the one which is involved.[80]

$$R-CH=CH_2 + H-\overset{\cdot+}{N}=C=CH_2$$
$$m/e\,41$$

β-cleavage of α-methyl nitriles occurs to yield an m/e 55 ion in place of the m/e 41.

9. Spectral Approach

9.1. Preliminary. Before recording a mass spectrum, one should acquaint himself with the background of the sample under investigation. Spectral information culled from IR, NMR, and UV data, e.g., the general type of compound (aliphatic, benzenic, etc.), the nature of its functional groups, the presence or absence of conjugation, etc., are of invaluable assistance in simplifying the diagnostic task. If the preparative route leading to the substance is known, the reaction conditions, mechanism, yields, purity of intermediates, etc., often will prove helpful.

Since a knowledge of the sample's purity is important, a rule has been established in this laboratory that a two-column GLC analysis be performed on submitted materials and that their purity must exceed 95 per cent. This is especially important if the substance is derived from natural sources. It has been our experience that many products of this type appear to be homogeneous on a single, packed chromatographic column but are actually seen to be grossly impure when examined on another column of different polarity. For this reason we routinely employ 10 foot by ¼ inch columns of 25 per cent SE 30 (nonpolar) and 25 per cent "Carbowax" 20M (polar) to "screen" and purify natural products.

In view of the fact that materials isolated by GLC at relatively high temperatures may be contaminated with column coatings, one should familiarize himself with the salient spectral features of these substrates in order to avoid interpretive errors. In addition to determining that one is dealing with a single chemical entity, the dual column technique can yield even more valuable information. Concidence of the retention values of an "unknown" with one or more of those in a reference file is of considerable interpretive aid.[82] Obviously, noncongruency of these values eliminates a large number of chemicals from consideration. Also, the difference in retention values for a particular material between the polar and nonpolar columns gives some indication of its functionality, viz., alcohols exhibit large negative differences, whereas these differences are of approximately equal value but opposite in sign for aliphatic hydrocarbons and border on zero for aliphatic esters.

One is sometimes confronted with a mixture whose components are poorly resolved when employing the GLC columns described above. In these instances capillary columns or long, lightly loaded $\frac{1}{8}$-inch packed columns must be used in order to obtain materials of high purity.

A distinct advantage of the GLC-mass spectrometric coupled technique is that it requires only very small samples. A Bendix time-of-flight mass spectrometer has proven eminently satisfactory for "on the fly" examination of natural products.[97] Ryhage[83] and Biemann[84] have described relatively simple apparatus which "concentrate" GLC isolated substances prior to their direct passage into a mass spectrometer. Finally, it should be mentioned that, since it is rather difficult to differentiate between many geometrical isomers by means of mass spectrometry, the general ability of GLC to resolve them materially aids the interpreter.

Immediately subsequent to recording a mass spectrum, it should be examined for the presence of interfering impurities, the possible existence of mixtures, general spectral intensity, etc. Chemical, additional GLC or TLC purification may be necessary to eliminate the impurities or to separate the components of a mixture before proceeding further.

9.2. Interpretation. The following step-wise approach is a general one and does not necessarily apply in its entirety, nor in the exact order presented, for all spectral interpretations.

(a) Establish the molecular ion subsequent to ascertaining the individual fragmentation masses. The former is usually the highest mass spectral peak, discounting the heavy isotope contribution. If required, the molecular weight sometimes can be verified by examining a low voltage spectrum and by using the (M + 1) and effusion techniques. The latter procedure, however, is limited to molecular weights lower than *ca.* 200. A low voltage spectrum offers the additional advantage of presenting a simplified spectrum containing ion fragments produced only by the most energetically favored bond ruptures. In addition, seek to correlate the molecular ion location with peaks attributable to loss of H_2O (M − 18), loss of methyl (M − 15), etc.

(b) Tabulate the five to ten most intense peaks in decreasing order of abundance and employ them when conducting a search through laboratory reference files and published compendia.[85,86] Not infrequently, the peak intensity order does not coincide exactly with that of a particular reference spectrum, in spite of the fact that both spectra represent the same substance. There are several possible explanations for this anomaly, i.e., presence of impurities, variations in instrumental parameters, use of different type spectrometers, etc. Therefore, one should not summarily reject a reference spectrum for this reason.

A search according to molecular weight[66,87,49] often unearths the mate to an unknown's spectrum. In addition, one sometimes can identify the components of a mixture by this approach if the individual molecular weights have been ascertained.

(c) The empirical formula next should be calculated if one fails to identify the material under investigation by means of reference files or literature data. This may be readily derived from the exact molecular weight as presented in high resolution spectra or approximated from isotopic ratios obtained from low resolution spectra. It should be called to the reader's attention that the isotopic ratio differences decrease with increasing molecular weight, and the attainment of reasonably accurate formulas, therefore, becomes less likely for high molecular weight compounds. The presence of Cl and Br may be deduced from the isotope ratio values, *ca.* 3/1 and 1/1 (Table 1, page 178). For a compound containing one atom of Cl or Br, the (M + 2) peak will be approximately one-third of, or about equal to, the intensity of the molecular ion respectively. However, the isotopic contributions are of general utility only for the more stable aromatics because of the low molecular ion abundance of aliphatic halogens. In like manner, sulfur may be recognized from contribution of ^{34}S to the (M + 2) peak.

(d) Attempt to correlate fragment pairs that total to the molecular weight. A clearer picture of the fragmentation process sometimes is obtained when this approach is successful.

(e) Gain as much information as possible regarding the possible nature of the more abundant fragment ions. Valuable clues may be found in the literature.[88,89,90] If one is apprised of the type of "unknown" which confronts him, i.e., aliphatic ester, hydrocarbon, etc., application of the fragmentations peculiar to the particular class is often very fruitful.

(f) Carefully examine the spectrum for the presence of metastable ions. Keep in mind that they are sometimes partially obscured by other spectral peaks. Use them to tie together fragment ions to aid in the postulation of mechanistic pathways.

(g) Be aware of the fact that various rearrangements often occur which easily could lead to erroneous assignments. For instance, the mass spectrum of ethyl nicotinate contains an intense peak at m/e 123 which could not arise by simple bond cleavage, but must be due to a rearrangement process which is supported by a metastable peak of mass 100.2, viz.:

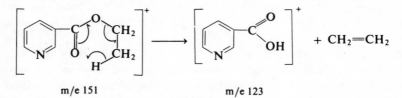

m/e 151   m/e 123

The ability to lose a stable, neutral fragment will often promote a rearrangement, and this type of driving force should be borne in mind when interpreting fragmentation processes.

(h) When interpreting spectra recorded on low resolution spectrometers it should be realized that any particular peak might represent any of a number of fragment ions. As a corollary, the loss of a neutral or radical fragment, i.e., CO (mass 28), could be mistaken for C_2H_4. A partial list of some of the more common isobaric fragments is presented below:

Mass	Fragment
28	N_2, CO, C_2H_4
29	CHO, C_2H_5
30	NO, CH_2NH_2
41	$(CH_2CN + H)$, C_3H_5
43	CH_3CO, C_3H_7
44	CO_2, $C_2H_4O(CH_2CHO + H$, etc.$)$, CH_3CHNH_2
45	CO_2H, C_2H_5O $(C_2H_4OH, CH_3CHO + H$, etc.$)$
57	C_3H_5O $(C_2H_5CO$, etc.$)$, C_4H_9
58	$C_3H_6O(CH_3COCH_2 + H$, etc.$)$, $C_3H_8N(C_2H_5NHCH_2$, etc.$)$
59	$C_3H_7O[(CH_3)_2COH$, etc.$]$, $C_2H_3O_2(COOCH_3$, etc.$)$, $C_2H_5NO(NH_2COCH_2 + H$, etc.$)$
60	$C_2H_4O_2(CH_2COOH + H$, etc.$)$, CH_2NO_2
61	$C_2H_5O_2(COOCH_3 + 2H$, etc.$)$, $C_2H_5S(CH_2CH_2SH$, etc.$)$

69	C_3H_5CO, C_5H_9
70	C_4H_6O ($C_3H_5CO + H$, etc.), C_5H_{10}
71	C_4H_7O (C_3H_7CO, etc.), C_5H_{11}
73	C_4H_9O ($C_3H_7OCH_2$, etc.), $C_3H_5O_2$ ($CH_3CO_2CH_2$, etc.)
85	C_5H_9O (C_4H_9CO, etc.), C_6H_{13}, $C_4H_5O_2$($C_3H_5CO_2$, etc.)

(i) Record the spectra of selected derivatives. For example, trimethylsilyl ethers[91] of alcohols, glycols and phenols are more volatile than the original materials and they give characteristic (M − CH_3) peaks which can be used to establish molecular weights. Methyl esters of acids have greater stability and volatility than the acids themselves. Substitution of $-CD_3$ for $-CH_3$ can give information concerning the number of methyl groups in the fragment ions—a shift of three mass units is observed for each one.

(j) After postulating a structure, attempt to predict the probable fragmentation processes in order to correlate them with the ions actually present in the spectrum. Compounds of similar structure also should be studied in this manner until one is selected which best fits the spectral data. It is sometimes difficult or impossible to narrow the choice to only one substance, i.e., in the case of certain geometrical isomers. Finally, obtain a sample of the proposed compound(s) and compare its spectrum with that of the unknown.

(k) An intriguing new development,[96] employs a technique which takes into consideration all the ions that are formed in a high resolution mass spectrometer. Using a double-focusing instrument, the ions are simultaneously focused in one plane and a photographic plate, placed in the focal plane, obtains a sharp line for each mass. The masses are semi-automatically measured and fed into a computer, The resulting "element map" depicts the distribution of elements within the molecule and, in addition, illustrates the combination of elements and the relative abundance. These data provide some primary structural information without requiring detailed mechanisms to support conclusions.

PROBLEMS

The reader will gain appreciation of the fact from the following problems that identification of relatively simple molecules by mass spectrometry indeed is not difficult if the interpreter is armed with a few pertinent bits of information derived from other spectral sources, GLC retention values, etc. Understandably, the diagnostic task becomes somewhat more demanding as the molecular intricacy increases. The successful application of mass spectrometry to structural elucidation of highly complex materials involves obtaining and interpreting spectra of molecules of related structures.[92,93] Similarities and differences between the spectrum of an unknown compound and that of a known can then be used to arrive at a structural assignment.

1. The bar spectrum depicted in Figure 8 is that of an ultraviolet transparent substance. Its very weak infrared spectrum displayed only three absorptions—all in the 8.5 to 9.5 μ range. These data suggest an acetal, thus, the peak at m/e 173 (ca. 0.3 per cent relative intensity) is not the molecular ion. It is possible that the molecular weight is 174 and that the m/e 173 ion fragment is due to (M − 1), a not unusual occurrence for aldehydes, ethers, acetals, nitriles, and alcohols. The peak at m/e 159 is attributable to loss of methyl (M − 15). Assuming an acetal of molecular weight 174,

one interprets the m/e 129 (M − 45) peak as arising from loss of OR_2, and this is confirmed by the second most intense ion fragment of mass 45 $(OC_2H_5)^+$. It is now necessary to establish whether $R_2 = R_3$. It was noted previously (Section 8.1) that, in mixed acetals, the larger alkoxy group is lost preferentially. The base peak at m/e 73 can be ascribed to loss of OR_3, i.e.,

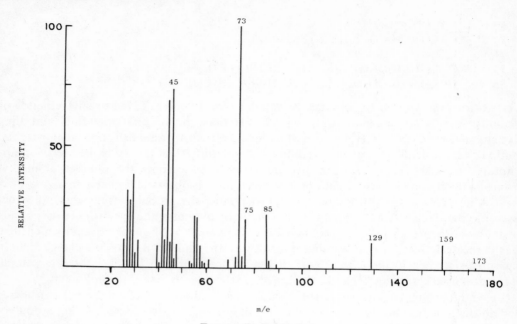

FIGURE 8. Problem 1.

$(R_1CHOC_2H_5)^+$, and R_3, then, is C_6H_{13}. The latter fragment appears at m/e 85. It is apparent that R_1 is CH_3, and the acetal in question is:

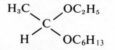

2. Information gleaned from the NMR spectrum of a homogenous material indicated it to be either A or B:

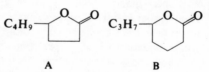

How does its mass spectrum (Figure 9) establish the correct structure with certainty?   (see Section 8.10)

3. The infrared spectrum of a material submitted for mass spectral identification indicated that it was an ortho disubstituted benzene containing a carbonyl grouping. A low voltage recording displayed a probable molecular ion base peak at m/e 146, and it is the second most abundant fragment in the bar graph presentation of the 70 eV spectrum (Figure 10). The presence of oxygen is inferred from the m/e 129 (M − OH) and 128 (M − H_2O) and, although there is no observable fragment at m/e 31, one of low intensity at m/e 45 $(C_2H_5O)^+$ further confirms this belief. In addition, the m/e 118 peak may be due to loss of CO. In further corroboration of the infrared spectral interpretation, the substance appears to be aromatic in nature, viz., the stability of the molecular ion and peaks at m/e 39, 50, 51, 63, 65, 77, 78, and 91.

The peak intensity ratios for M, (M + 1) and (M + 2) are:

$$(M + 1/M) \times 100 = 11.20$$
$$(M + 2/M) \times 100 = 0.77$$
$$(M + 1/M + 2) = 14.54$$

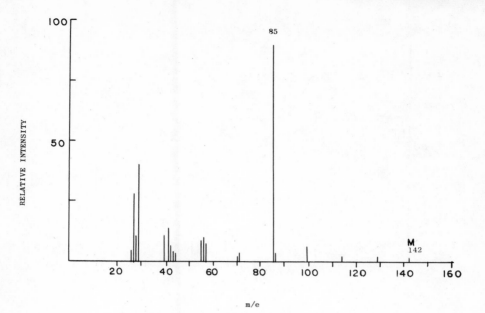

FIGURE 9. Problem 2.

and applying Beynon's tables[15]:

No.	Possible Empirical Formulas	$\frac{M + 1}{M} \times 100$	$\frac{M + 2}{M} \times 100$	$\frac{M + 1}{M + 2}$
1	$C_9H_6O_2$	9.90	0.84	11.81
2	C_9H_8NO	10.27	0.68	15.22
3	$C_{10}H_{10}O$	11.00	0.75	14.72
4	$C_{10}H_{12}N$	11.38	0.59	19.34
5	$C_{11}N$	12.27	0.69	17.84
6	$C_{11}H_{14}$	12.11	0.67	18.10

Formulas 2, 4, and 5 obviously are fragments rather than molecular ions (Nitrogen Rule), and we may eliminate Formula 6 since it does not contain oxygen. Formula 1 does not fit the data because the infrared spectrum showed only a single carbonyl absorption the intensity of which was in the right order of magnitude for a monocarbonyl of molecular weight *ca.* 150. It follows, then, that the empirical formula most likely is 3. Using the formula $C_{10}H_{10}O$, the "points of unsaturation" next are determined (see page 66).

$$R = 2(10) + 2 - 10/2 = 6$$

Four of the six calculated points are accounted for by the benzene ring (one ring and three double bonds), and the fifth arises from the C=O group. There remains then another double bond or a ring. The following structures are the most plausible ones from the mass spectral evidence:

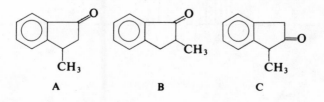

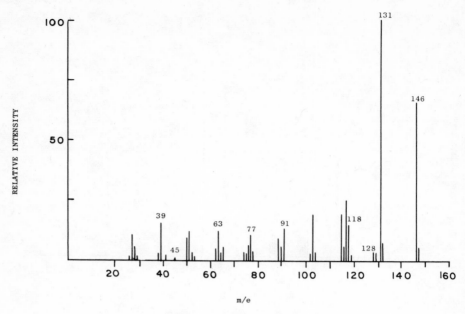

FIGURE 10. Problem 3.

It is very difficult to ascertain the correct one from mass spectrometry. NMR readily eliminates compound C but is of little assistance in differentiating between A and B. The distinctly different ultraviolet absorption spectra of the latter two, however,[94,95] show that the unknown under examination is 3-methylindanone (A).

4. The molecular ion of a 1,2,3-trisubstituted benzenic hydrocarbon contaning no methyl group is m/e 158 and represents 34 per cent of the base peak which appears at m/e 130. An em-

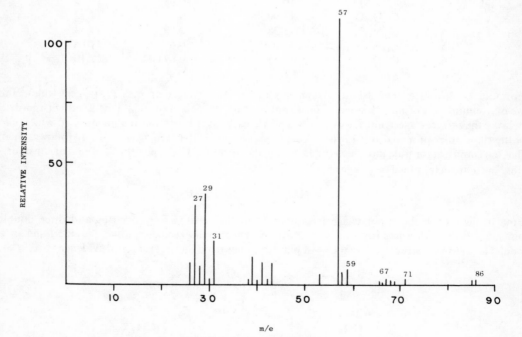

FIGURE 11. Problem 4.

pirical formula of $C_{12}H_{14}$ was obtained from its mass spectrum. Supplied with the additional information that the most intense peak of tetralin falls at (M − 28), determine the structure of the material (see Ref. 81).

5. A sample of unknown origin was GLC isolated (polar and non-polar columns) in quantity sufficient only to record its mass spectrum (Figure 11). A metastable ion appears under the leading edge of the m/e 66 peak. The retention value difference between the two chromatographic liquid phases indicated that it might be an alcohol or aromatic ester. Location of the molecular ion at m/e 86 is corroborated by a peak at mass 71 (M − CH_3) and weak fragment ions at masses 69 (M − OH) and 68 (M − H_2O). Minor impurities were observed in the molecular ion region, in spite of the fact that the substance had been "doubly GLC trapped," which militated against determining an empirical formula.

The m/e 85 peak (M − 1), nearly as intense as the parent ion, places the compound in the group comprising acetals, alcohols, aldehydes, ethers, etc. A reasonably intense ion at m/e 31 is additional evidence that the compound contains oxygen. Lack of aromaticity is inferred from the absence of peaks at m/e 63, 77, and 78. The base peak, m/e 57, might be $(C_4H_9)^+$, $(C_3H_5O)^+$, etc. If the fragment ion were $(C_4H_9)^+$, the remaining mass of 29 would be CHO, unlikely in light of the retention time difference value. The $(C_3H_5O)^+$ peak can be either $(HO-CH-CH=CH_2)^+$ or $(HO-\underset{\diagdown_{C}\diagup}{C-C})^+$, location of the hydroxyl moiety on either of the doubly bonded carbon atoms

would represent a highly unstable compound. Taking into account the preceding data, two probable structures are:

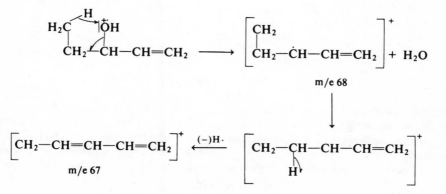

Cleavage α to the vinyl group will form the fragment ion at m/e 59 which may be ascribed to $(C-C-C-OH)^+$, and this would indicate that structure A is the most likely one. Allylic bond rupture would readily occur in the following manner to produce a very stable fragment ion at m/e 57, the base peak:

m/e 57

The second most intense ion, m/e 29, is attributable to $(C_2H_5)^+$.

The metastable ion at m/e 66.01 ties together the m/e 67 and 68 fragments, and a possible route is represented as follows:

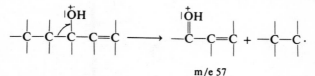

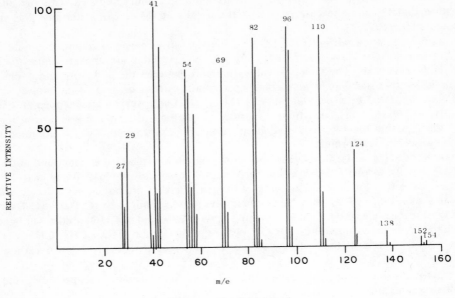

FIGURE 12. Problem 6.

6. What is the identity of the compound whose bar graph spectrum appears in Figure 12? Hint: The m/e 154 peak intensity is pressure sensitive. (See Ref. 78.)

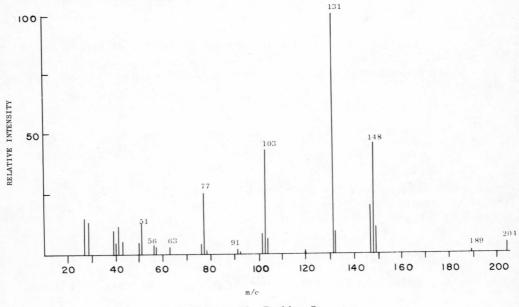

FIGURE 13. Problem 7.

7. The mass spectrum of a monosubstituted aromatic ester (IR) is depicted in Figure 13. The fact that it is neither an acetate nor a formate is evident from the infared spectrum. The compound is assigned a molecular weight of 204, corroborated by the m/e 189 peak (M − CH$_3$). Aromaticity is confirmed by fragment ions at m/e 50, 51, 63, 76, 77, and 78. The m/e 91 peak is of low intensity. Since the rather abundant m/e 103 ion is 26 mass units higher than the m/e 77 one (C$_6$H$_5$)$^+$, the former might signify a conjugated aromatic system, e.g.,

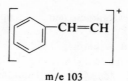

m/e 103

β-Ring cleavage difinitely would not be favored in this fragment, the required location of bond rupture—in addition to hydrogen migration—to produce an m/e 91 peak. The mass difference between the m/e 131 and 103 fragment ions can be attributed to the $-\overset{O}{\overset{\|}{C}}-$ part of an ester. If this difference were due to $-CH_2-CH_2-$ one would have expected to find a peak at m/e 117 also. The m/e 131 base peak obviously denotes a highly stable ion:

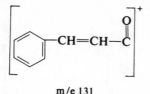

m/e 131

The last intense peak is located 17 mass units higher at m/e 148, and might be due to:

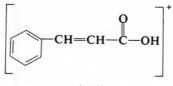

m/e 148

but, since IR shows no carboxyl group, this fragment may arise by a rearrangement process of the ester. Similar to acetate ester cleavage (see Figure 4), the R group in

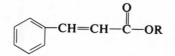

is seen to have a mass of 57 and, therefore, is C_4H_9. The peak at m/e 57 then may be assigned to $(C_4H_9)^+$. From the mass spectrum alone, it is impossible to establish which one of the three isomers is present. Little can be gleaned from the IR gem-dimethyl group region (*ca.* 7.25 μ) but the NMR spectrum of the ester clearly shows that the group in question is *i*-butyl:

$$\text{C}_6\text{H}_5-CH=CH-\overset{O}{\overset{\|}{C}}-O-CH_2CH-(CH_3)_2$$

REFERENCES

1. Beynon, J. H., "Mass Spectrometry and its Application to Organic Chemistry," Amsterdam, Elsevier Publishing Co., 1960.
2. McLafferty, F. W., "Mass Spectrometry" in Nachod and Phillips, eds., "Determination of Organic structures by Physical Methods," Vol. 2, pp. 63–179, New York, Academic Press, Inc., 1962.

3. Biemann, K., "Mass Spectrometry Organic Chemical Applications," New York, McGraw-Hill Publishing Co., Inc., 1962.
4. Budzikiewicz, H., Djerassi, C., and Williams, D. H., "Interpretation of Mass Spectra of Organic Compounds," San Francisco, Holden-Day, Inc., 1964.
5. Teranishi, R., Schultz, T. H., McFadden, W. H., Lundin, R. E., and Black, D. R., *J. Food Sci.*, **28**, 541 (1963).
6. Fétizon, M., in "Thin Layer Chromatography," Marini-Bettolo, Ed., p. 69, Amsterdam, Elsevier Publishing Co., 1964.
7. Brown, R. A., Young, W. S., and Nicolaides, N., *Anal. Chem.*, **26**, 1653 (1954).
8. Ryhage, R., and Stenhagen, E., *J. Lipid Research*, **1**, 361 (1960).
9. Field, F. H., and Franklin, J. L., "Electron Impact Phenomena and the Properties of Gaseous Ions," in Massey, H. S. W., Ed., "Pure and Applied Physics," Vol. I, New York, Academic Press, Inc., 1959.
10. Honig, R. E., *Anal. Chem.*, **22**, 1474 (1950).
11. Field, F. H., and Hastings, S. H., *Anal. Chem.*, **28**, 1248 (1946).
12. Lumpkin, H. E., *Anal. Chem.*, **30**, 321 (1958).
13. Eden, M., Burr, B. E., and Pratt, A. W., *Anal. Chem.*, **23**, 1735 (1951).
14. Zemany, P. D., *J. Appl. Phys.*, **23**, 924 (1952).
15. Beynon, J. H., and Williams, A. E., "Mass and Abundance Tables for Use in Mass Spectrometry," Amsterdam, Elsevier Publishing Co., 1963.
16. Park, R., and Dunning, H. N., *Geochim. Cosmochim. Acta*, **22**, 99 (1961).
17. McLafferty, F. W., *Anal. Chem.*, **29**, 1782 (1957).
18. Ryhage, R., and Stenhagen, E., *Arkiv Kemi*, **13**, 523 (1959).
19. Quayle, A., 8th International Spectroscopic Colloquium, Lucern (1959).
20. Biemann, K., Gopp, F., and Seibl, J., *J. Am. Chem. Soc.*, **81**, 2274 (1959).
21. Wertzler, R., and Kinder, J. F., Group Report 54, July 1948, Consolidated Engineering Corp., Pasadena, California.
22. Beynon, J. H., Lester, G. R., Saunders, R. A., and Williams, A. E., *Trans. Faraday Soc.*, **57**, 1259 (1961).
23. D'Or, L., Momigny, J., and Natalis, P., Symp. Mass Spectrometry, Oxford, Sept. 1961.
24. Laune, J., Thesis, University of Liege, 1961.
25. Natalis, P., *Bull. Soc. Chim. Belges*, **66**, 5 (1957).
26. Natalis, P., *Bull. Soc. Chim. Belges*, **79**, 519 (1960).
27. Natalis, P., *Nature*, **195**, 380 (1962).
28. Natalis, P., *Nature*, **197**, 73 (1963).
29. Natalis, P., *Nature*, **197**, 284 (1963).
30. Honkanen, E., Moisio, T., Ohno, M., Hatanaka, A., *Acta Chem. Scand.*, **17**, 2051 (1963).
31. Momigny, J., and Natalis, P., *Bull. Soc. Chim. Belges*, **66**, 26 (1957).
32. Rosenstock, H. M., Wallenstein, M. B., Wahrhaftig, A. L., and Eyring, H., *Proc. Nat. Acad. Sci. U.S.*, **38**, 667 (1952).
33. Wahrhaftig, A. L., in "Advances in Mass Spectrometry," J. D. Waldron, Ed., p. 274, London, Pergamon Press, 1959.
34. Kropf, A., Ph.D. Thesis, University of Utah, 1954.
35. Collins, J., *Bull. Soc. Roy. Sci. Liege*, **25**, 520 (1956).
36. Friedman, L., Long, F. A., and Wolfberg, M., *J. Chem. Phys.*, **26**, 613 (1957).
37. *Ibid.*, **30**, 1605 (1959).
38. Rosenstock, H. M., and Krauss, M., in "Advances in Mass Spectrometry," Vol. II, R. M. Elliott, Ed., p. 251, London, Pergamon Press, 1963.
39. McLafferty, F. W., *App. Spect.*, **11**, 148 (1957).
40. McFadden, W. H., and Wahrhaftig, A. L., *J. Am. Chem. Soc.*, **78**, 1572 (1956).
41. McLafferty, F. W., *Anal. Chem.*, **31**, 82 (1959).
42. Friedman, L., and Long, F. A., *J. Am. Chem. Soc.*, **75**, 2832 (1953).
43. Friedel, R. A., Schultz, J. L., and Sharkey, A. G., *Anal. Chem.*, **28**, 926 (1956).
44. Happ, G. P., and Stewart, D. W., *J. Am. Chem. Soc.*, **74**, 4404 (1952).

45. Trent, F. M., Miller, F. D., and Brown, G. H., *Appl. Spectr.*, **15**, 64 (1961).
46. McLafferty, F. W., and Gohlke, R. S., *Anal. Chem.*, **31**, 2076 (1959).
47. Aczel, T., and Lumpkin, H. E., *Anal. Chem.*, **33**, 386 (1961).
48. Rylander, R. N., Meyerson, S., and Grubb, H., *J. Am. Chem. Soc.*, **79**, 842 (1957).
49. Gohlke, R. S., ed., "Uncertified Mass Spectral Data," pub. by Dow Chemical Co., Framingham, Mass., in cooperation with ASTM Committee E14 on Mass Spectrometry (1963).
50. Burr, J. G., *J. Am. Chem. Soc.*, **79**, 751 (1957).
51. Condon, F. E., *J. Am. Chem. Soc.*, **73**, 4675 (1951).
52. Eliel, E. L., and Prosser, T. J., *J. Am. Chem. Soc.*, **78**, 4045 (1956).
53. Aczel, T., and Lumpkin, H. E., *Anal. Chem.*, **32**, 1819 (1960).
54. Beynon, J. H., Lester, G. R., and Williams, A. E., *J. Phys. Chem.*, **63**, 1861 (1959).
55. Gilpin, J. A., and McLafferty, F. W., *Anal. Chem.*, **29**, 990 (1957).
56. McCollum, J. D., and Meyerson, S., *J. Am. Chem. Soc.*, **85**, 1739 (1963).
57. Ryhage, R., and Stenhagen, E., *Arkiv Kemi*, **14**, 483 (1959).
58. Sharkey, A. G., Shultz, J. L., and Friedel, R. A., *Anal. Chem.*, **31**, 87 (1959).
59. Beynon, J. H., Saunders, R. A., and Williams, A. E., *Anal Chem.*, **33**, 221 (1961).
60. Dinh-Nguyen, Ng., Ryhage, R., Ställberg-Stenhagen, S., and Stenhagen, E., *Arkiv Kemi*, **18**, 393 (1961).
61. Ryhage, R., and Stenhagen, E., *Arkiv Kemi*, **15**, 333 (1960).
62. Emery, E. M., *Anal. Chem.*, **32**, 1495 (1960).
63. Wilson, J. M., *Experientia*, **15**, 403 (1960).
64. Collin, J., *Bull. Soc. Chim. Belges*, **69**, 449 (1960).
65. Collin, J., *Bull. Soc. Chim. Belges*, **69**, 575 (1960).
66. "Catalogue of Mass Spectral Data," American Petroleum Institute Res. Proj. No. 44, Pittsburgh, Penn., Carnegie Institute of Technology.
67. Mohler, F. L., Bloom, E. G., Williamson, L., Wise, C. E., and Wells, E. J., *J. Res. Nat. Bur. Std.*, **43**, 533 (1949).
68. Bloom, E. G., Mohler, F. L. H., Tengel, J. H., and Wise, C. E., *J. Res. Nat. Bur. Std.*, **41**, 129 (1948).
69. O'Neal, M. J., and Wier, T. P., Jr., *Anal. Chem.*, **23**, 830 (1951).
70. Kinney, I. W., and Cook, A. L., *Anal. Chem.*, **24**, 1391 (1952).
71. Sharkey, A. G., Jr., Shultz, J. L., and Friedel, R. A., *Anal. Chem.*, **28**, 934 (1956).
72. Beynon, J. H., Saunders, R. A., and Williams, A. E., *Appl. Spect.*, **14**, 95 (1960).
73. Natalis, P., *Bull. Soc. Chim. Belges*, **67**, 599 (1958).
74. Seibl, J., and Gaumann, T. Z., *Anal. Chem.*, **197**, 33 (1963).
75. Meyerson, S., and Rylander, P. N., *J. Am. Chem. Soc.*, **79**, 1058 (1957).
76. Beynon, J. H., Personal communication.
77. Friedman, L., and Long, F. A., *J. Am. Chem. Soc.*, **75**, 2832 (1953).
78. McLafferty, F. W., *Anal. Chem.*, **34**, 26 (1962).
79. Beugelmans, R., Williams, D. H., Budzikiewez, H., and Djerassi, C., *J. Am. Chem. Soc.*, **86**, 1386 (1964).
80. Pottei, R. F., and Lossing, F. P., *J. Am. Chem. Soc.*, **83**, 4737 (1961).
81. Meyerson, S., *Appl. Spect.*, **9**, 120 (1955).
82. Van den Dool, H. and Kratz, P., *J. Chrom.*, **11**, 463 (1963).
83. Ryhage, R., *Anal. Chem.*, **36**, 759 (1964).
84. Watson, J. T. and Biemann, K., *Anal. Chem.*, **36**, 1135 (1964).
85. "Index of Mass Spectral Data," Published by American Society for Testing Materials, ASTM Special Technical Publication No. 356.
86. Von Hoene, J. and Loeffler, M., "Indexed Catalogue of Mass Spectral Data," Published by Westinghouse Research Laboratories, Pittsburgh, Pa., 1958.
87. "Mass Spectral Data," Manufacturing Chemists Association Research Project, Published by Chem. and Petroleum Research Lab., Carnegie Institute of Technology, Pittsburgh, Pa., 1959.
88. McLafferty, F. W., "Mass Spectral Correlations," American Chemical Society, Washington, D. C., 1963.

89. Nishino, Y., *Japan Analyst*, **10,** 591 (1961).
90. Silverstein, R. M. and Bassler, G. C., "Spectrometric Identification of Organic Compounds," New York, London, John Wiley & Sons, Inc., 1963.
91. Zahn, C., Mass Spectrometric Determination of Alcohols by Their Trimethylsalyl Ethers, U.S. Bureau of Mines Report No. 5976 (1962).
92. Djerassi, "Chemistry of Natural Products, 2" p. 575, Int'l. Union of Pure and Applied Chemistry, Intern. Symposium, Prague, 1962.
93. McLafferty, F. W., and Gohlke, R. S., *Chem. Eng. News*, **42,** 96 (1964).
94. Heddon, G. D., and Brown, W. G., *J. Am. Chem. Soc.*, **75,** 3744 (1953).
95. Baddeley, G., Rasburn, J. W. and Rose, R., *J. Chem. Soc.*, 3168 (1958).
96. Biemann, K., Bommer, P., and Desiderio, D. M., Tetrahedron Letters, No. 26, 1725 (1964).
97. Schultz, T. H., Teranishi, R., McFadden, W. H., Kilpatrick, P. W., and Corse, J., *J. Food Sci.*, **29,** 790 (1964).
98. Biemann, K., and McMurray, W., Tetrahedron Letters, 647 (1965).
99. Barnes, C. S., and Ocolowitz, J. J., *Aust. J. Chem.*, **16,** 219 (1963).

GENERAL REFERENCES

1. Aston, F. W., "Mass Spectra and Isotopes," London, Edward Arnold Ltd., 1960.
2. Beynon, J. H., "Mass Spectrometry and Its Applications to Organic Chemistry," Amsterdam, Elsevier Publishing Co., 1960.
3. Beynon, J. H., and Williams, A. E., "Mass and Abundance Tables for Use in Mass Spectrometry," Amsterdam, Elsevier Publishing Co., 1963.
4. Biemann, K., "Mass Spectrometry—Organic Chemical Applications," New York, McGraw-Hill Publishing Co., Inc., 1962.
5. Biemann, K., "Applications of Mass Spectrometry" in Bentley, K. W., Ed., "Elucidation of Structures by Physical and Chemical Methods," Vol. XI, Part I, New York, Interscience Publishers, Inc., p. 259, 1963.
6. Budzikiewicz, H., Djerassi, C., and Williams, D. H., "Interpretation of Mass Spectra of Organic Compounds," San Francisco, Holden-Day, Inc., 1964.
7. Budzikiewicz, H., Djerassi, C., and Williams, D. H., "Structure Elucidation of Natural Products by Mass Spectrometry, Vol. I, Alkaloids," San Francisco, Holden-Day, Inc., 1964.
8. Duckworth, H. E., "Mass Spectroscopy," London, Cambridge University Press, 1960.
9. Elliott, R. M., Ed., "Advances in Mass Spectrometry," (Proceedings of a Conference Held in Oxford, Sept. 1961), Vol. II, New York, The MacMillan Co., 1963.
10. Ewald, H., and Hintenberg, H., "Methods and Uses of Mass Spectroscopy," Translated from a publication of Verlag Chemie, GmbH, Weinheim/Bergstrasse, Germany, 1963—United States Atomic Energy Commission Division of Technical Information, Issued 1962.
11. Field, F. H., and Franklin, J. L., "Electron Impact Phenomena and the Properties of Gaseous Ions" in H. S. W. Massey, Ed., "Pure and Applied Physics," Vol. 1, New York, Academic Press, Inc., 1957.
12. Lederberg, J., "Computation of Molecular Formulas for Mass Spectrometry," San Francisco, Holden-Day, Inc., 1964.
13. McLafferty, F. W., "Mass Spectrometry" in Nachod, F. C., and Phillips, W. D., Eds., "Determination of Organic Structures by Physical Methods," Vol. 2, New York, Academic Press, Inc., p. 93, 1962.
14. McLafferty, F. W., Ed., "Mass Spectrometry of Organic Ions," New York and London, Academic Press, 1963.
15. McLafferty, F. W., "Mass Spectral Correlations," Washington, D.C., American Chemical Society, 1963.
16. Reed, R. I., "Ion Production by Electron Impact," London and New York, Academic Press, Inc., 1962.
17. Reed, R. I., "Mass Spectrometry as a Structural Tool" in Raphael, R. A., Taylor, E. C., and

Wynberg, H., Eds., "Advances in Organic Chemistry Methods and Results," Vol. 3, New York, Interscience Publishers, Inc., p. 1, 1963.

18. Robertson, A. J. B., "Mass Spectrometry," London, Methueun & Co., Ltd., 1954.
19. Silverstein, R. M. and Bassler, G. C., "Spectrometric Identification of Organic Compounds," p. 4, New York, John Wiley & Sons, Inc., 1963.
20. Stewart, D. W., "Mass Spectrometry" in Weissberger, A., Ed., "Physical Methods of Organic Chemistry," Vol. I, Part 4, New York, Interscience Publishers, Inc., p. 3449, 1960.
21. Waldron, J. D., Ed., "Advances in Mass Spectrometry" (Proceedings of the 1958 Conference of the Hydrocarbon Research Group, The Institute of Petroleum, London), London and New York, Pergamon Press, 1959.

5

PROTON NUCLEAR MAGNETIC RESONANCE SPECTROSCOPY

Ajay K. Bose
Department of Chemistry and Chemical Engineering
Stevens Institute of Technology
Hoboken, New Jersey

1. The Empirical Approach

1.1. Introduction. A remarkable feature of organic chemistry in the last two decades has been the widespread acceptance of complex new tools for physical measurements on molecules. Such measurements have often preceded the development of adequate theories correlating chemical structure and molecular parameters. Nevertheless, many chemists have used these new tools relying on a pragmatic and empirical approach and contributed to a notable advance in the art of organic chemistry. Important factors in the rapid introduction of these new instruments have been their commercial availability and the relative ease with which academic laboratories in the United States and some other countries have been able to obtain generous government funds for expensive research "hardware." For any laboratory engaged in meaningful organic research today, a nuclear magnetic resonance spectrometer is a high priority item in spite of its price, which may range from $25,000 to $100,000 depending on the model, the type, and the accessories selected.

The history of nuclear magnetic resonance spectroscopy is short but fascinating. What was originally planned to be a specialized tool for physicists developed to be an instrument of unusual power for chemists for probing into the structural features of molecules.

The present generation of graduate students in chemistry and even the undergraduate students in some universities are being taught NMR spectroscopy taking advantage of their background in quantum mechanics. For the organic chemist of an earlier vintage, however, or the biochemist with his lack of familiarity with chemical physics and electronics, NMR spectroscopy has assumed the proportions of a dilemma; either he has to do without it or he has to rely for the interpretation of the spectra on an expert—often a physical chemist without an intimate knowledge of organic chemistry. There is a partial solution to this dilemma which an increasing number of practicing organic chemists are discovering—it is to utilize the NMR spectrometer as a "black-box" and to interpret the spectra on an empirical basis reserving the privilege of assistance from an expert as the need arises. Most of this chapter is addressed to organic chemists and biochemists of this category. We shall, therefore, equate the preparation of a solution of the sample in a suitable solvent with the production of a spectrum without any comments regarding the intermediate steps. Our attention will be focused on proton magnetic resonance spectroscopy. The commercial units at the lower price range, such as Varian's A-60 spectrometer, are restricted to this type of spectra alone. For obtaining NMR spectra of other nuclei, more elaborate equipment (such as Varian's DP-60 or HR-100) has to be used.

Each field of science gives rise to a new terminology. In this respect NMR spectroscopy has been no exception. In keeping with the empirical approach mentioned earlier, discussions of the theory of nuclear magnetic resonance have been omitted. Several of the books and chapters listed in the general reference have dealt at length with the theoretical background. A brief description of the phenomenon of nuclear magnetic resonance is provided in the Appendix.

1.2. Empirical Interpretation. In NMR spectrometry, a liquid or a solution is placed in a strong magnetic field and irradiated with radio frequency waves—the spectrum is a graph (see Figure 1)* that records an increasing magnetic field along the abscissa and the corresponding intensity of energy absorption along the ordinate. The "chromophore" in proton NMR spectra is the proton, and such a spectrum of a compound will show signals for *nothing* but protons (not even deuterium or tritium) but it will show *every* proton in the molecule. Furthermore, there is a quantitative aspect of NMR spectra—the area under a peak or peaks is strictly proportional to the number of protons responsible for the signal.

A specific proton in a molecule might give rise to a single peak, a doublet, a triplet or a multiplet of greater complexity. A single peak would result if the particular proton was not interacting with (i.e., was not "coupled" with) another proton or other appropriate nuclei; the exact nature and extent of coupling will decide the multiplicity of the peak (see below).

The position of a peak (or the center of gravity of a multiple peak) in the spectrum is characteristic of the electronic and magnetic environment of the proton corresponding to it. Equivalent protons, i.e., those situated in identical environments, will generate signals that will coincide in position. On the other hand, protons differing in their surroundings will, in general, be non-equivalent and produce signals that are separated from one another in the spectrum. The proton that resonates at a higher magnetic field is considered more "shielded" than one resonating at a lower field. It is the convention that in recording the spectrum the field increases from left to right (see Figure 1). The location of a peak is described by its distance from the signal of a standard compound, usually tetramethylsilane (TMS; $(CH_3)_4Si$), which is added to a sample before recording the spectrum.

Since all the protons in TMS are equivalent, the resonance signal is a single sharp peak corresponding to the twelve protons. From experience it has been found that very few protons have their signal to the right of (that is, at higher magnetic field than) the TMS resonance. It is therefore convenient to use TMS as an internal standard to define the high field end of the spectrum.

The distance of a peak from the TMS signal—or the "chemical shift"—can be measured in cycles per second (cps) or in parts per million (ppm). The former unit depends on the oscillator frequency of the spectrometer—currently 60 Mc/sec for most instruments. The other unit, which is defined by the relationship in Eq. 1-1, is independent of this frequency and permits the direct comparison of spectra recorded on spectrometers of different field strength.

$$ppm = \frac{cps}{Mc} \tag{1-1}$$

The τ scale introduced by Tiers assigns the value of 10.00 τ to the TMS signal and uses the ppm unit. A lower τ value for a peak signifies a signal at a lower field and greater "deshielding." An alternative scale (δ scale) employs the same ppm unit but assigns the value of 0.00 δ to the TMS signal; a signal at a higher field has a lower δ value. These two scales are easily inter-converted since $10 - \tau = \delta$. If a chemical shift is measured in the

---

*Unless mentioned otherwise, the τ scale will be used in the Figures for reporting chemical shifts.

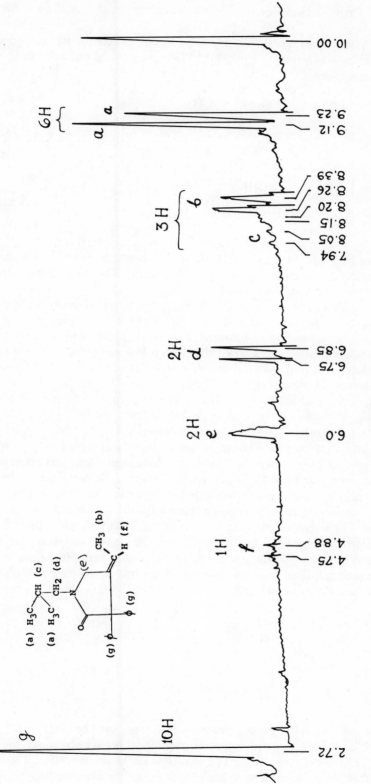

FIGURE 1.

cps unit, it is of course essential to state the standard used and the oscillator frequency employed.

A typical NMR spectrum is shown in Figure 1. This spectrum was recorded on a 60 Mc spectrometer using a solution of compound (I) in deuterated chloroform to which a trace of TMS had been added.

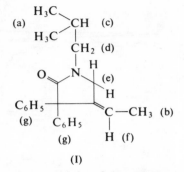

(I)

The sharp single peak at the extreme right of the spectrum is the TMS signal. The chemical shifts of the different peaks are shown on the τ scale. The relative areas under the peaks (hence the number of protons responsible for the signals) are also indicated. This information, together with symmetry considerations, permits us to make assignments for the groups of equivalent protons marked "a," "b" and "g" (aromatic protons). The other assignments can be made by taking note of the $n + 1$ rule which states that the multiplicity of a proton signal is $n + 1$ when the proton has n equivalent protons on the α-carbon atoms. The interaction between protons or other nuclei is called spin-spin coupling and is characterized by coupling constants (J) that determine the contour of the proton signal (see Section 2). Thus, the coupling of the two equivalent methyl groups with the neighboring single proton in the isobutyl side chain produces a doublet ($n = 1$). The methyl group on the other side-chain also produces a doublet because of coupling with the single olefinic proton. The olefinic proton in turn is expected to give a signal that is a quartet owing to the spin interaction with the three equivalent methyl protons. On this basis the assignment for peak f can be made although the quartet here is not clearly discernible. The peaks d and e each correspond to two protons. The doublet nature of the former is an indication that it belongs to the methylene on the side chain which has one vicinal proton. The signal of the proton marked c is split into a multiplet by the adjacent methyl and methylene protons and is superimposed on the doublet due to the methyl group of the ethylidene side chain. Most of these assignments can be made independently from a scrutiny of published data on the chemical shift for protons in different environments (see Table 1 and Charts 1 and 2).

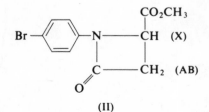

(II)

A spectrum of somewhat greater complexity is that for compound (II) (see Figure 2). The tall peak at 6.19 τ, corresponding to three protons, is obviously the signal for the methyl group of the ester function. The chemical shift and the lack of splitting are consistent with this assignment. The symmetrical pattern corresponding to four protons at

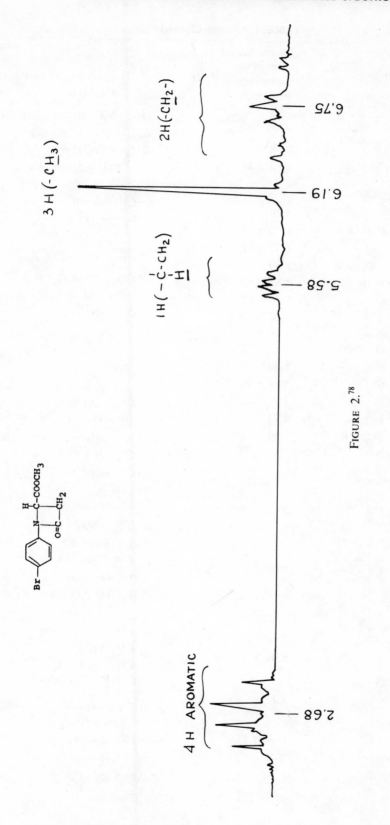

FIGURE 2.[78]

TABLE 1. Proton Chemical Shifts (τ)

Group	Resonance Lines of the Underlined Protons, τ	Group	Resonance Lines of the Underlined Protons, τ
Alkane		(R=H, Alkyl, Aryl, OH, OR or NH$_2$)	
		C$\underline{H}_3$—CO—Cl (or Br)	7.19–7.34
◁—C$\underline{H}_2$	9.78	C$\underline{H}_3$—CO—C=C—	
—C$\underline{H}_2$—	8.52–8.75	or C$\underline{H}_3$—CO—Ar	7.32–8.17
		C$\underline{H}_3$—CO—SR	7.46–7.67
β-functional groups		—C$\underline{H}_2$—S—R	7.47–7.61
—C$\underline{H}_2$—C—N	8.38–8.80	—N◁—C—	
—C$\underline{H}_2$—C—CO—R	8.10–8.37	(C$\underline{H}_2$)	8.52
C$\underline{H}_3$—C—N	8.92–9.12	—C$\underline{H}_2$—N	6.88–7.72
C$\underline{H}_3$—C—N—CO—R	8.80	—C$\underline{H}_2$—N—CO—R	
C$\underline{H}_3$—C—CO—R	8.88–9.07	(or N—SO$_2$R or N—Ar)	6.63–6.72
—C$\underline{H}_2$—C—C=C—	8.40–8.82	—C$\underline{H}_2$—N$^+$—	6.60
—C$\underline{H}_2$—C—Ar	8.22–8.40	C$\underline{H}_3$—N—N—	7.67
—C$\underline{H}_2$—C—O—R	8.19–8.79	—C◁—O	
—C$\underline{H}_2$—C—O—COR		(C$\underline{H}_2$)	7.71
and —C$\underline{H}_2$—C—O—Ar	8.50	—C$\underline{H}_2$—O—R	6.42–7.69
—C$\underline{H}_2$—C—Cl	8.04–8.40	—C$\underline{H}_2$—O—CO—R	
—C$\underline{H}_2$—C—Br	7.97–8.32	or —C$\underline{H}_2$—O—Ar	5.71–6.08
—C$\underline{H}_2$—C—I	8.14–8.35	—C$\underline{H}_2$—Cl	6.43–6.65
—C$\underline{H}_2$—C—SO$_2$—R	7.84	—C$\underline{H}_2$—Br	6.42–6.75
—C$\underline{H}_2$—C—NO$_2$	7.93	—C$\underline{H}_2$—I	6.80–6.97
		C$\underline{H}_3$—SO—R	7.50
α-functional groups		—C$\underline{H}_2$—SO$_2$—R	7.08
—C$\underline{H}_2$—C=C—	7.69–8.17	C$\underline{H}_3$—SO$_2$—Cl	6.36
C$\underline{H}_3$—C=C—CO—R	7.94–8.07	—C$\underline{H}_2$—SO$_2$F	6.72
—C$\underline{H}_2$—C=C—O—R	8.07	C$\underline{H}_3$—O—SO—OR	6.42
C$\underline{H}_3$—C=C—	7.97–8.06	C$\underline{H}_3$—O—SO$_2$—OR	6.06
COOR or CN		C$\underline{H}_3$—S—C≡N	7.37
C$\underline{H}_3$—C=C—	8.09–8.13	—C$\underline{H}_2$—N=C=S	6.39
O—CO—R		—C$\underline{H}_2$—NO$_2$	5.62
C$\underline{H}_3$—C=C—	8.17	—C$\underline{H}_2$(C=C—)$_2$	6.95–7.10
—C=C—		Ar—C$\underline{H}_2$—C=C—	6.62
—C$\underline{H}_2$—Ar	6.94–7.47		
—C$\underline{H}_2$—C≡N	7.42	*Alkyl Groups α to Two or More Functional Groups*	
C$\underline{H}_3$—C=NOH	8.19	Ar—C$\underline{H}_2$—Ar	6.08–6.19
—C$\underline{H}_2$—CO—R	7.61–7.98	Ar—C$\underline{H}_2$—N	6.68
		Ar—C$\underline{H}_2$—OR	5.51–5.64
		Ar—C$\underline{H}_2$—Cl	5.50

TABLE 1. (*Continued*)

Group	Resonance Lines of the Underlined Protons, τ	Group	Resonance Lines of the Underlined Protons, τ
Ar—C$\underline{H}_2$—Br	5.57–5.59	—CH=C—O—R	4.45–5.46
Ar—C$\underline{H}_2$—O—CO—R	4.74	C=C$\underline{H}$—O—CO—CH$_3$	2.75
—C=C—C$\underline{H}_2$—O—R	6.03–6.10	$\underline{H}_2$C=C—O—CH$_2$—C=C	5.87–6.17
—C=C—C$\underline{H}_2$—Cl	5.96–6.04	R—CO—C$\underline{H}$=C—CO—R	3.87–3.97
—C=C—C$\underline{H}_2$—OR	5.82	Br—C$\underline{H}$=C—	3.00–3.38
—C≡C—C$\underline{H}_2$—Cl	5.84–5.91	—C$\underline{H}$=C—C≡N	4.25
—C≡C—C$\underline{H}_2$—Br	6.18	Ar—C=C$\underline{H}$—	4.60–4.72
Cl—C$\underline{H}_2$—C≡N	5.93	Ar—C$\underline{H}$=C—	3.72–3.77
Br—C$\underline{H}_2$—C≡N	6.30	H—C=C—	
—C$\underline{H}$(OR)$_2$	4.80–5.20	$\underline{H}$ CO—R	3.60–3.70
		Ar—C$\underline{H}$—C—CO—R	2.28–2.62
Acetylenic and Olefinic Protons			
—C≡C—$\underline{H}$	7.07–7.67	*Aldehydes*	
—C=C—C≡C—$\underline{H}$	7.13	R—C$\underline{H}$O	0.20–0.43
Ar—C≡C—$\underline{H}$	6.95	>C=C—C$\underline{H}$O	0.32–0.57
—C=C$\underline{H}$—	4.87	Ar—C$\underline{H}$O	−0.08 to +0.35
—C=C$\underline{H}_2$	5.37		
—C=C$\underline{H}$—CO—R	3.95–4.32	*Carboxylic Acids*	
—C$\underline{H}$=C—CO—R	2.96–4.53	R—COO$\underline{H}$	−0.97 to −1.52
—C=C$\underline{H}$—O—R	3.55–3.78	>C=C—COO$\underline{H}$	−1.57 to −2.18

Hydroxyl Groups. The position of the hydroxyl proton is very dependent on concentration, temperature, and the presence of other easily exchanged protons (H$_2$O!). It is displaced strongly to lower τ values by intramolecular hydrogen bonding (in some stable planar systems to $\tau = -5.0$) and to higher values by increased shielding.

Amine Protons. The position of —N$\underline{H}_2$ and —N$\underline{H}$ protons is dependent above all on the basicity of the nitrogen atom. Strongly basic amines show NH— absorption in the C-methyl region.

R—N$\underline{H}_2$ and R—N$\underline{H}$—	7.88–8.90
R—CO—N$\underline{H}$—	2.3 –3.9
	2.6 –2.7

2.68 τ is due to the symmetrically placed aromatic protons; this assignment is justified on the basis of the chemical shift as well as the known patterns for *p*-disubstituted benzene derivatives (see Section 2). Area measurements indicate that the quartet around 5.58 τ is a one proton signal. The multiplet centered at 6.75 τ must account for the remaining two protons. The first degree approximation of the $n + 1$ rule is not applicable here. The three protons on the heterocyclic ring constitute a special grouping (ABX) and lead to a characteristic pattern which is considered later (see Section 2.3).

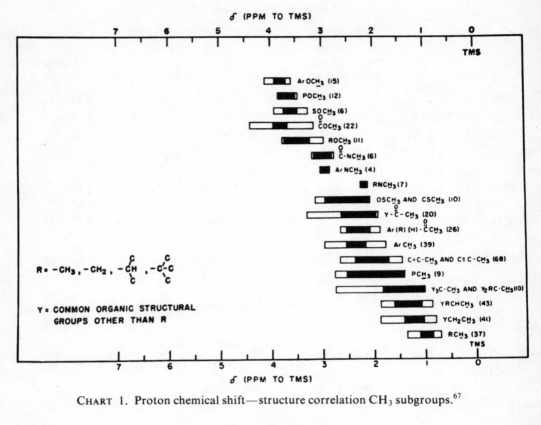

CHART 1. Proton chemical shift—structure correlation CH_3 subgroups.[67]

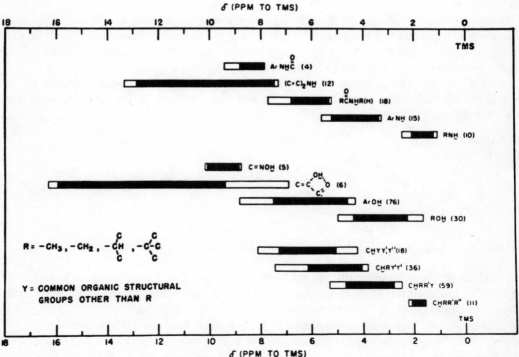

CHART 2. Proton chemical shift—structure correlation CH, OH and NH subgroups.[67]

It should be noted that the $n + 1$ rule is satisfactory for dealing with coupled protons differing considerably in their chemical shift. When protons that have nearly the same chemical shift value are coupled, the resulting pattern shows a marked departure from predictions based on the simple $n + 1$ rule.

1.3. Chemical Shift. During the last decade the NMR spectra of several thousand organic compounds have been studied. A few hundred spectra have become available in recent compilations.[1] Many spectra are reported every year as part of research publications. An extensive table of "shielding values" for protons in a variety of organic compounds has been assembled by Tiers.[2] In this table compounds are arranged in the increasing order of τ-value so that one can easily look for a clue to the assignment of a peak of known chemical shift. A rearrangement of this table and some additional data by functional groups has been made.[3] An abbreviated and slightly modified version of this is reported in Table 1. In general, the methine proton in $Z\!-\!\overset{\displaystyle |}{\underset{\displaystyle |}{C}}\!-\!H$ appears at a lower field (by 0.1 to 0.5 ppm) than the corresponding methylene protons in $Z\!-\!CH_2\!-$ which in turn are at a lower field (by 0.1 to 0.5 ppm) than the methyl protons in $Z\!-\!CH_3$. We have therefore shortened Table 1 by recording the chemical shift of only methylene protons as far as feasible.

Yet another convenient correlation of the spectral positions for protons in different environments is in the form of bar graphs shown in Charts 1 and 2. The first graph is devoted exclusively to methyl groups. For the study of the corresponding methylene and methine protons, extrapolation to somewhat lower (by 0.1 to 1.0 ppm) τ-values is required.

1.4. Protons on Three-membered Rings. The protons of cyclopropane absorb at an unusually high field—their signal appears at 9.78 τ. This is in sharp contrast with the range (8.5 to 8.8 τ) for the ring protons of other cyclic systems. The substitution of electronegative groups on the ring causes deshielding and may even completely counteract the shielding effect of the cyclopropyl ring in some cases (see Chart 3).

The olefinic protons in cyclopropene (III) resonate at a very low field (2.99 τ in contrast to 4.41 τ in cyclohexene) and the signals for the allylic protons are found at a very high field[4] (9.08 τ in contrast to 8.04 τ in cyclohexene, IIIA).

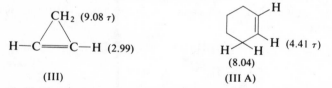

(III)   (III A)

Even in heterocyclic three-membered ring systems, upfield shift of the protons bonded to the ring carbon is noticeable. This special effect could provide evidence for the presence of epoxide, episulfide and other three-membered cyclic structures. Thus, in the aziridinium derivative IV, the $-\!N\!-\!CH_2$ signal (6.98 τ) appears at a *higher* field than the $-\!N\!-\!CH_3$ peak (6.84 τ).[5] Ordinarily the N-methylene protons resonate at lower field than the N-methyl protons; see, for example, the assignments for V.

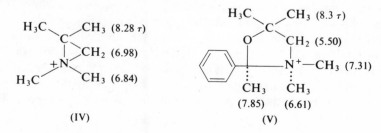

(IV)   (V)

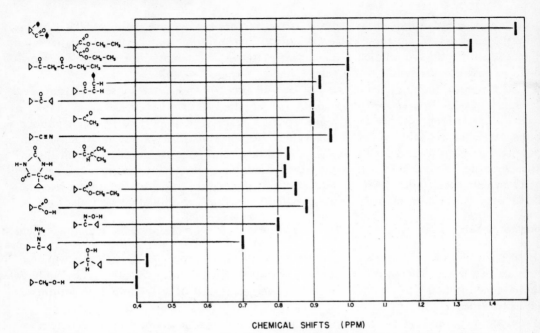

CHART 3. Substituents on cyclopropane shown in order of increasing electron withdrawing ability based upon decreased magnetic screening of the cyclo-proprane protons that remain, as indicated by increasing chemical shifts in values.[69]

The methylene protons adjacent to the ether oxygen resonate at 5.27 τ in trimethylene oxide, at 6.37 τ in tetrahydrofuran, and at 6.44 τ in tetrahydropyran.

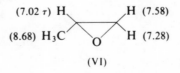

In the epoxide VI, however, the signal of the methylene protons absorb at consider-ably higher field, namely 7.28 and 7.58 τ.[1]

(7.02 τ) H．．．．．．．．．．H (7.58)

(8.68) H_3C．．．．．．．．．O．．．．．．．．H (7.28)

(VI)

2. Spin-Spin Interaction

2.1. Nomenclature. A study of the chemical shift provides valuable information about the structure of a compound. But much additional information can be obtained by an examination of the interaction or spin coupling of the different protons (see Table 2). In discussing the spectra involving protons coupled with one another, a convenient nomen-clature has been proposed[6]; the protons that have quite similar chemical shift are described as A, B, C, whereas another group of protons with similar chemical shifts but of a different order of magnitude are described by the letters X, Y, Z. The ethyl group in $-O-CH_2-CH_3$ can thus be described as an A_3X_2 system whereas the ethyl group at the end of a long aliphatic chain becomes an A_3B_2 system. A methylene group without any α-protons can constitute either an A_2 system or an AB or AX system. Two vicinal

TABLE 2.[60]   Proton Spin-spin Coupling Constants (cps)

Structural type		J_{ab}
		12-15
CH_a---CH_b		2-9
CH_a—$(C)_n$—CH_b; $n > 0$		0.0
		0–3.5
		6–14
		11-18
		4-10
		0.5-2.0
$C=CH_a$—$CH_b=C$		10-13
CH_a—$CH_b=O$		1-3
CH_a—$C\equiv CH_b$		2-3
	o	7–10
	m	2–3
	p	1

protons, such as in —$\overset{\displaystyle H}{\underset{\displaystyle |}{C}}$—$\overset{\displaystyle H}{\underset{\displaystyle |}{C}}$—, would be an AB system or an AX system depending on the environment. More complex systems such as ABX, A_2B_2, or ABC also are found often. Most of these systems have received adequate quantum mechanical treatment and are described in detail elsewhere.[7,8,9] In keeping with our empirical approach we shall refrain from quantum mechanical analyses of the coupling patterns but discuss the main findings from an utility point of view.

2.2. Two Proton Patterns.   The spectrum of the compound VII recorded on a 60 Mc spectrometer is shown in Figure 21 (see Section 3.6).

$$(H_3C—CH=CH—O—)_2CH_2$$
(VII)

The protons of the methylene group are equivalent. Since they are not vicinal to any other protons, there is no spin interaction and therefore no splitting of the signal produced by the methylene protons. The sharp peak at 5.12 τ, corresponding to 2H in area, can be assigned to these two protons constituting an A_2 system.

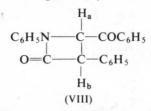

(VIII)

The protons H_a and H_b in VIII are non-equivalent because of the difference in their environment. Since they are vicinal, they are coupled to each other. Application of the $n + 1$ rule leads to the prediction that the signal of each proton should be a doublet. The spectrum (CDCl$_3$ 60 Mc) of VIII (Figure 3) displays two doublets (4.60 and 4.65 τ; 5.72 and 5.77 τ). The center of gravity of each doublet, namely 4.625 and 5.745 τ, corresponds to the chemical shift of H_a and H_b. The separation of each doublet (0.05 ppm = 60 × 0.05 = 3.0 cps) in cps unit measures the coupling constant, hence J_{ab} = 3.0 cps. It is of great importance to note that the value of the coupling constant in cps is not altered when a spectrometer of a different oscillator frequency is used. The coupling constant may be modified, however, by changing the solvent.

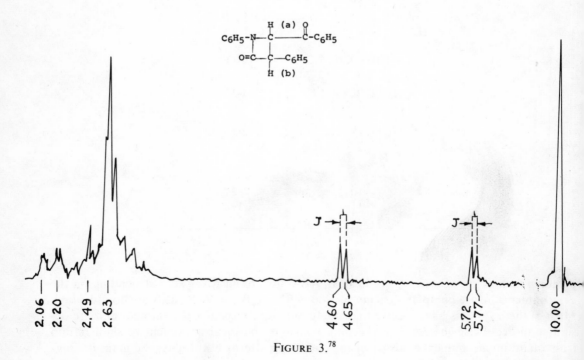

FIGURE 3.[78]

It has been established from theoretical considerations that the AX pattern should consist of four signals of equal intensity (Figure 3A). Two coupled protons having chemical shifts of the same order of magnitude constitute an AB system. Two factors influence the AB pattern: the coupling constant J_{AB} and the difference in the chemical shift of the two protons, δ_{AB}. When δ_{AB}/J_{AB} ratio is large (i.e., the protons tend to the AX system), the spectrum consists of four signals of nearly equal intensity (Figure 3A) but as the δ_{AB}/J_{AB} ratio gets smaller, the inner and outer pair of signals become increasingly unequal in intensity and the inner peaks move closer to each other (Figure 4A). In some cases the quartet even may give the appearance of a triplet due to the proximity of the two inner peaks. In identifying an AB pattern consisting of lines 1, 2, 3 and 4 it is important to remember that the separation between 1 and 2 must equal that between 3 and 4—each being the measure of J_{AB}. It is very helpful to use a pair of dividers to compare accurately the

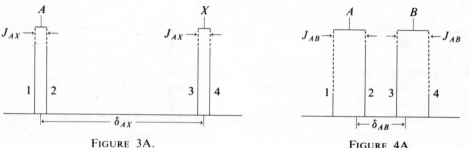

FIGURE 3A.

FIGURE 4A.

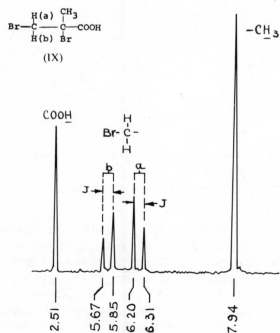

FIGURE 4.[78]

separation between different pairs of lines. By using theoretically deduced relationships[7] the chemical shifts of A and B can be calculated and shown to lie nearer to the center lines (2 and 3) than to the outer lines (1 and 4).

The methylene group in IX displays an AB spectrum (Figure 4). At first sight, the methylene protons may appear to be equivalent. However, there is a slight non-equivalence which is caused by the presence of an asymmetric center in the immediate neighborhood. An examination of the Newman projections (IXa, IXb and IXc) reveals that at no time do H_a and H_b find themselves in the same environment, in spite of free rotation around the bond C_2—C_3. They are, therefore, magnetically nonequivalent.

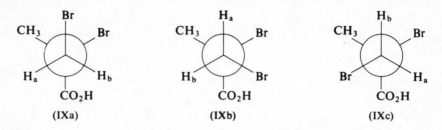

(IXa)　　　　　　(IXb)　　　　　　(IXc)

2.3. Three Proton Patterns.　Three coupled protons correspond to one of the following systems: A_2X, AB_2, ABC (all three chemical shifts are quite similar) and AMX (all three chemical shifts are quite different).

The two equivalent protons of the A_2X system will give rise to a doublet (see Figure 5), the separation of which equals J_{AX}. The X part of the spectrum will be a triplet (lines 1–3, the separation 1,2 = 2,3 = J_{AX}).

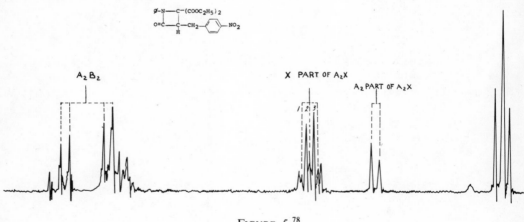

FIGURE 5.[78]

No quantum mechanical calculation is necessary to predict the signals due to three coupled protons, AMX, which are located at widely separated regions of the spectrum. A detailed and self-explanatory analysis of such a system is given in Figure 6 for the ABX system; the X band is a symmetrical quartet reflecting the effect of J_{AX} and J_{BX}. The AB part consists of eight lines (1–8) the position and intensity of which have been calculated from quantum mechanical considerations. One feature of significance is the equivalence of the following separations; 1, 2; 3, 4 and 5, 6; 7, 8. The ABC system does not show these symmetry features and is considerably more difficult to analyze (see Figure 7). The

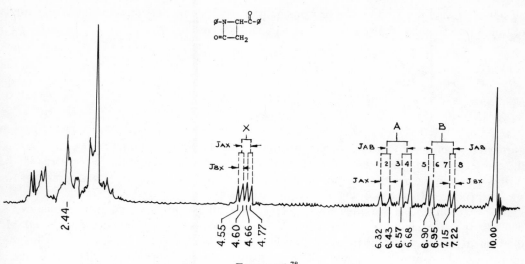

FIGURE 6.[78]

AB_2 system lends itself to detailed analysis and produces a nine line pattern. Aromatic protons often constitute an AB_2 system.

2.4. Four Proton Patterns. The simplest arrangement, A_3X, produces a spectrum that can be easily predicted from the $n + 1$ rule: a doublet (3H) and a quartet (1H).

The detailed considerations of the A_2X_2 system has revealed that a set of two triplets will occur only under special circumstances. In general, two sets of ten lines will be produced under the influence of the following coupling constants: J_{AX}, J_{AX}, J_{AA} and J_{XX}. Spectra of increasing complexity are produced by A_2B_2 and AB_3 systems. Wiberg and Nist[10] have computed the profiles of the spectra of different systems for various combinations of chemical shifts and coupling constants. An organic chemist, however, may find it wise to seek expert help at this stage. Recently, programs for computers have been developed for the complete analysis of systems involving as many as six or seven coupled nuclei.

2.5. Analysis of Complex Spectra. Often the interpretation of spectra is made difficult

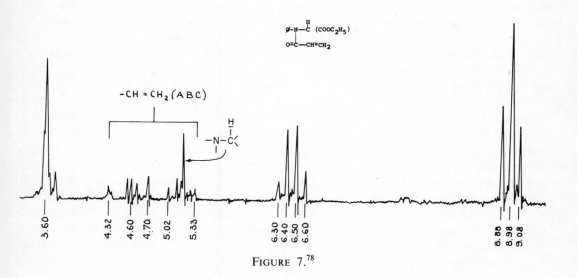

FIGURE 7.[78]

by signal overlap due to different protons with nearly the same chemical shift. An example of this is provided by Figure 5. In this spectrum of compound X,

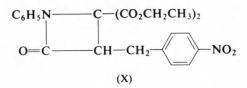

(X)

a quartet generated by the methylene protons of the two ethyl groups has nearly masked the triplet corresponding to the ring methine proton. Similarly, the symmetry of the A_2B_2 pattern in the aromatic region has been diminished by the partial overlapping of the signals produced by the two sets of aromatic protons.

Higher resolution is provided by a spectrometer using a higher oscillator frequency. A 100 Mc spectrometer gives a spectrum with much less overlapping than does a 60 Mc instrument. It is important to note, however, that if the spectrum consists of singlets due to uncoupled protons, no change will be perceived on changing the oscillator frequency because the chemical shift of a signal is independent of this frequency.

For a signal generated by a proton that is coupled to other protons, the chemical shift corresponds to the center of gravity of the signal, whatever be its multiplicity. The τ value of this center of gravity is not altered by a change from one oscillator frequency to another. Nevertheless, the contour of the spectrum does change because the separation between peaks in ppm units is altered in such a way as to keep unchanged the coupling constants involved when measured *in cps units* (see Section 2.2). Thus, for a doublet due to coupling (such as the methyl signals of an isopropyl group) with $J = 6$ cps, the separation between the two lines will be 6/60, i.e., 0.1 ppm in a 60 Mc spectrum and 6/100, i.e., 0.06 ppm in a 100 Mc spectrum (see Section 1.1). If the two spectra are drawn on the same scale, the coupled signals will appear closer together in the 100 Mc spectrum than in the 60 Mc spectrum. This will, of course, lead to much less overlapping in the spectrum recorded on the higher frequency spectrometer.

A specific illustration is given in Figure 8. The triplet (H-2) centered at 3.71 δ in the 60 Mc spectrum shows the following chemical shift: 3.84, 3.71 and 3.58 δ, $J = 8$ cps. The corresponding numbers in the 100 Mc spectrum are: 3.79, 3.71 and 3.63 δ, $J = 8$ cps. Since the center of gravity of the triplet in both spectra have the same value on the δ (or τ) scale and the same separation on the cps scale, this triplet must correspond to a set of coupled protons rather than a group of non-coupled, unsplit protons.

Both the coupling constant and the chemical shift, however, may be altered by a change of solvent. The addition of a small amount of benzene to the common solvent—carbon tetrachloride or deuterated chloroform—sometimes separates signals that are super-imposed and aids in the interpretation of a spectrum. An example is shown in Figures 9 and 9A. When carbon tetrachloride was used as the solvent, the doublet at 8.77 and 8.91 τ was partially obscured by the methyl peak at 8.73 τ. Substitution of benzene for carbon tetrachloride resulted in some relative movements of peaks and the doublet (8.70, 8.83 τ) became easy to percieve. Some organic laboratories recommend as a routine procedure the rerunning of each spectrum after the addition of some benzene; if any significant change is noticed, then the compound may be dissolved in pure benzene and the spectrum recorded again. When examining an unknown compound, it is desirable to obtain a third spectrum after the addition of a few drops of deuterated water. Exchangeable protons—for example the H of alcohols and carboxylic acids and some N—H (indole's N—H does not exchange with any reasonable speed)—are promptly revealed by this technique. Deu-

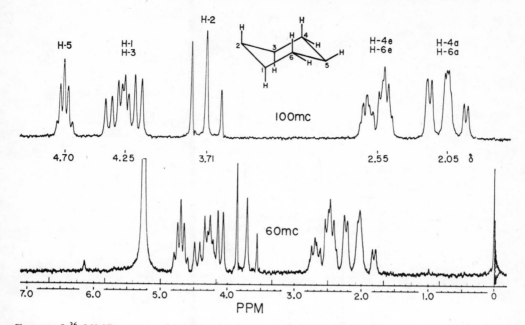

FIGURE 8.[36] NMR spectra of 1,2,3,5-cyclohexanetetrol in D_2O at 60 and 100 Mc. (Chemical shifts in δ units).

terium produces no signals in a spectrometer set up for protons, therefore the signals of replaceable protons are drastically reduced in intensity. It should be remembered that the chemical shift of a hydroxyl proton signal is very dependent on the solvent. When —OH groups are present, some signals are not only reduced in intensity but also shifted in position on the addition of D_2O. Another point to bear in mind about this spectrum is the appearance of an H—OD signal at about 5.3 τ after deuterium exchange. A comparison

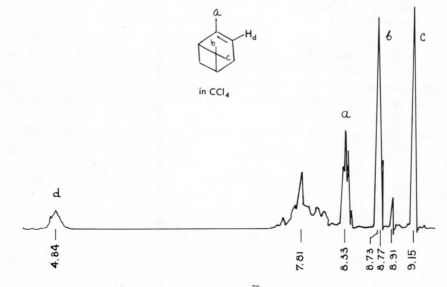

FIGURE 9.[78]

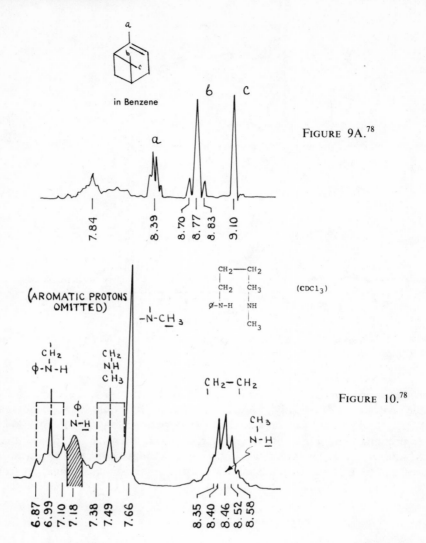

FIGURE 9A.[78]

FIGURE 10.[78]

of Figure 10 and 10A clearly shows the presence of an exchangeable proton in the molecule. Note the new band in Figure 10A—that this signal does not correspond to the compound under examination is shown by its area relative to the rest of the spectrum. For steroids it has been suggested that a comparison be made of their spectra in $CDCl_3$ and pyridine (see Section 3.2).

2.6. Special Techniques. In a recent study[22] on the conformation of D-glucal triacetate,

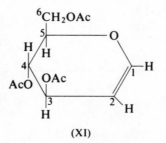

(XI)

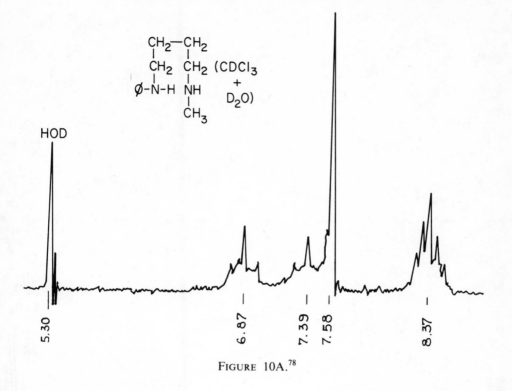

FIGURE 10A.[78]

it was found that the resolution in the spectrum (Figure 11A) in deuterated chloroform at 60 Mc was inadequate for providing much information on chemical shifts and coupling constants. From a consideration of expected chemical shits it was possible to assign individual protons to broad areas of the spectrum as shown in Figure 11A. Only one coupling constant, namely, J_{12} = 6.4 cps, could be determined from this spectrum.

Considerably more information became available from the 100 Mc spectrum ($CDCl_3$) (Figure 11B). It may be noted that although Figure 11B is on a slightly more expanded ppm scale than 11A, the coupled peaks (such as the quartet at 6.53 δ or at 4.81 δ) are closer in the former. This compression of signals generated by individual coupled protons has been discussed earlier (see Section 2.5). By using the criterion that a change in the oscillator frequency changes the contour but not the chemical shift of the signal produced by a coupled proton, it is easy to deduce that the quartets at 6.53 δ and 4.81 δ are genuine coupling patterns. The latter involves J_{12} and J_{23}. Since the value of J_{12} is known from the analysis of the other quartet, the value of J_{23} could be calculated to be 3.2 cps. The allylic coupling (see Section 4.1) J_{13} was found to be 1.3 cps.

At a first approximation, the $n + 1$ rule was applied to the analysis of the signals due to H-3 and H-4. By a process of trial and error the various peaks in the 5.34 δ region were matched with J_{13} and J_{23}, thus revealing J_{34} and the quartet pattern of H-4. Continuing with this approach, tentative assignments could be made for all the chemical shifts and coupling constants.

The spectrum of XI using benzene as the solvent (Figure 11C) showed clearly that one of the H-6 protons produces a quartet. No further information could be obtained from this spectrum. The coupled protons in XI constitute a seven spin system. It is possible to feed to a computer the first order spectral parameters discussed above and use a reiterative

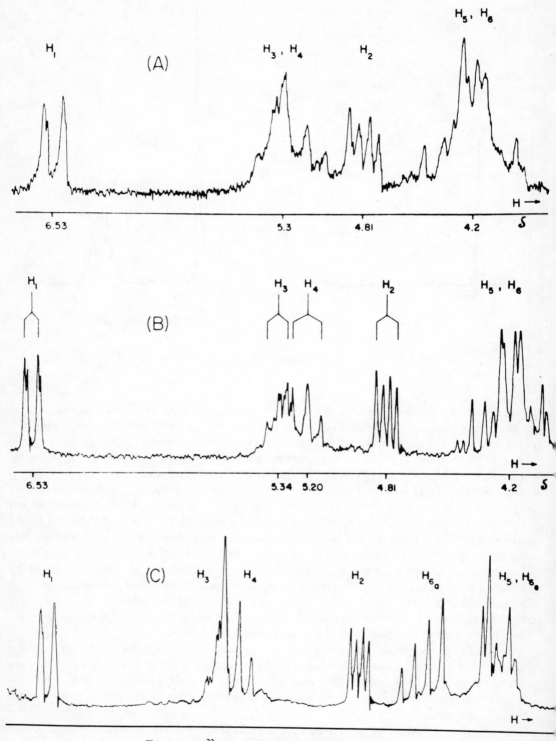

FIGURE 11.[22] NMR spectra of D-glucal triacetate.
A. In $CDCl_3$ at 60 Mc
B. In $CDCl_3$ at 100 Mc
C. In benzene at 100 Mc

process to refine these parameters for the best fit. Examples of this type of operation are cited later.

In this study recourse was taken to another very powerful technique—decoupling. Using a special device called a "decoupler," the spectrum is scanned using two radio frequencies instead of the usual single frequency. The separation between these frequencies is set equal to the measured chemical shift between two protons suspected of being coupled together. One radio frequency is of low intensity and is utilized for "seeing" the first proton, H_A; the other frequency then automatically irradiates the second proton, H_X, if nearly the correct value of chemical shift difference has been used. This latter irradiation, which has to be intense, perturbs the second proton and cancels the coupling with the first proton. The signal of H_A is now observed as a singlet instead of a doublet. After reversing the order of the two frequencies, the field is scanned again. This time H_X is "seen" and H_A is perturbed so that the signal of H_X becomes a singlet. In case H_X had been coupled with other protons, the signal pattern would have been noticeably changed because of the elimination of AX-coupling.

In a modification of this "double resonance" technique, called "tickling," the total suppression of coupling is not effected. The use of a low intensity irradiating frequency leads

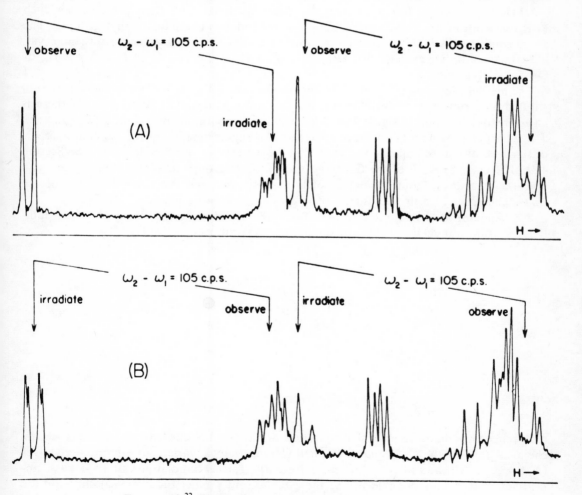

FIGURE 12.[22] Decoupling experiment on D-glucal triacetate.

to only a partial perturbation of H_X and thus merely reduces the extent of coupling experienced by H_A.

In the double resonance experiment with XI, the separation between the frequencies was set at 105 cps to approximate the chemical shift (119 cps) between H-1 and H-3. The spectra so recorded (Figure 12) displayed decoupling between these protons. Furthermore, H-4 and H-5 were also decoupled since their chemical shift (101 cps) also was matched. Confirmation was thus obtained for the assignments made previously. Further illustrations of the use of decoupling in spectral assignments are provided later (see Section 5.3).

3. Selected Functional Groups

3.1. The Methyl Group. The methyl group occupies a special position among functional groups in proton NMR spectroscopy. The free rotation of this group around the single bond C—Z— in a molecule CH_3—Z— ensures that the three methyl protons "see" exactly the same environments. They are therefore completely equivalent to one another and their signals coincide. The resonance signal of a methyl group, whether it is a singlet, doublet, or triplet, usually consists of sharp peaks with an area of three protons and therefore can be differentiated from the peaks due to other protons (see Section 3.2).

NMR spectroscopy has outmoded the classical, destructive chemical analyses such as Kuhn-Roth or the Zeisel determination or the iodoform test for methyl groups. The sharp single peaks with an area corresponding to 3H occurring at characteristic τ values give quantitative evidence for O—CH_3, N—CH_3, S—CH_3, C—CH_3, Ar—CH_3 or O=C—CH_3 groups.

The methyl group signal in alkyl chains occurs near 9.1 τ. If the methyl group is substituted on a ring such as cyclohexane, the location is at a slightly lower field. If there is an α-proton, the methyl signal is a doublet with a separation of about 0.12 ppm (i.e., $J = 7$ cps) employing a 60 Mc spectrometer. The angular methyl group, so characteristic of steroids, of course appears as a singlet in the absence of unusual features (see Section 4.3). The chemical shift of the C-19 and C-18 methyl groups in substituted steroids can reveal a great deal about the nature of the substituents and the stereochemistry of the rings. This special feature will therefore be considered in some detail.

3.2. Angular Methyl Signals in Steroids. Several investigators have observed additivity relations for chemical shifts of angular methyl protons in steroids (XII).

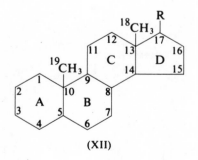

(XII)

Zürcher[11] has made an extensive collection of data on the effect of substituents on the chemical shift of the C-18 and C-19 methyl groups in a variety of steroid derivatives (A/B *cis*, A/B *trans*, 14 α-, 14β-, etc.). Recently, further tabulations of data have appeared.[12,13] It is now possible to use these tables and predict the chemical shift for the C-18 and C-19 methyl groups of many steroid structures. Thus, we can calculate the position of the C-19 methyl signal in methyl 3,7,12-triketocholanate (XIII) using the data of Zürcher. We note that this compound belongs to the 5β, 14α-class.

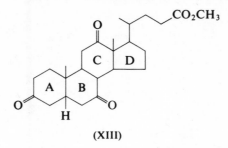

(XIII)

The parent compound, therefore, is 5β, 14α-androstane and the substituents are 17β-$C_4H_8CO_2CH_3$, 3-oxo (5β-steroid), 7-oxo, and 12-oxo groups.

	Calc.[11] 19-H (ppm)	Obsd.[14] 19-H (δ)	Diff. (ppm)
5β, 14α-androstane	0.925		
17β, $C_4H_8CO_2CH_3$	−0.008		
3-oxo (5β-)	0.117		
7-oxo	0.275		
12-oxo	0.100		
	1.409	1.36	0.05

Theories of diamagnetic bond anisotropy (see Appendix) predict that the chemical shift is, among other things, a function of bond angles and interatomic distances. The effect of a substituent group on chemical shift will be dependent upon the exact location and structural orientation of the substituent group relative to the proton in question. From symmetry considerations of the steroid molecule relative to the freely rotating protons of the C-19 methyl group, the 2- and 4-positions are equivalent to each other; in an A/B *trans* steroid (XIV), the 2-, 4- as well as 6-positions should be equivalent. These and similar equivalencies indeed are found to hold true.[11,14] Departure from such equivalence may be indicative of a distortion in the shape of the steroid rings.

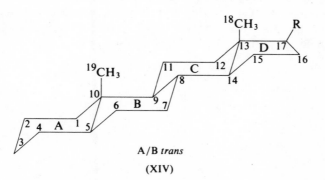

A/B *trans*

(XIV)

If the A/B ring junction is *cis* (see XV), the symmetry between rings A and B relative to C-19 is destroyed and equivalence between groups in the two rings is not to be expected. Thus, the contribution of the keto group to the chemical shift of the C-19 methyl group is almost the same (0.25 ppm) for 7-ketocholestane (A/B *trans*), 3-ketocholestane and 7-ketocholanic acid (A/B *cis*) but the corresponding contribution (0.11 ppm) of the keto group in 3-ketocoprostane (A/B *cis*) or 3-ketocholanic acid is quite different.[14]

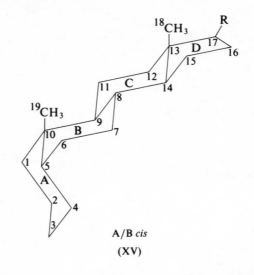

A/B *cis*

(XV)

An interesting application of the chemical shift of angular methyl groups has been made in deducing the structure of hydroxylated products obtained by microbiological transformations of steroids.[15] An hydroxyl group 1,3-diaxial to a methyl group produces strong deshielding of the methyl group. From a consideration of the conformation of the steroid ring system, it can be predicted that 8β- and 11β-hydroxy groups would produce large shifts of both C-18 and C-19 methyl signals. The C-19 methyl signal alone should undergo an appreciable shift on the introduction of a 2β-, 4β- or 6β- hydroxyl. On the other hand, a 15β- or 16β-hydroxyl group should produce a considerable shift of the C-18 methyl signal alone. The recent work of Tori and Kondo[13] on the NMR spectra of hydroxylated Δ⁴-3-ketosteroids bears out these relationships except in the case of the 2-hydroxy derivatives; a 2α-hydroxy- rather than a 2β-hydroxy-Δ⁴-3-ketosteroid is reported to have a large effect on the C-19 methyl signal. A reinvestigation of the stereochemistry of the 2-hydroxy steroids involved appears desirable.

3.3. Methyl Signals in Sapogenins. From a study of the NMR spectra of a large number of sapogenins, it has been shown that a clear distinction between the "normal" or 25L or 25S series (XVI) and the "iso" or "neo" or 25D or 25R series (XVII) can be made on the basis of the chemical shift of the 27-methyl signal.[16]

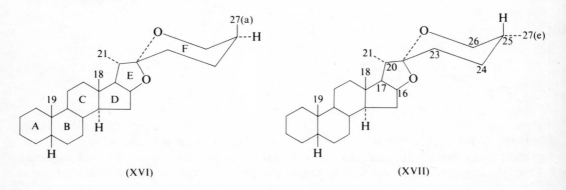

(XVI)   (XVII)

These two series are isomeric at C_{25}. When ring F is in the chair conformation, the 27-methyl is axial in 25S-sapogenins and equatorial in the 25-epimers. Even though the peaks due to the different methyl groups overlap, it is possible to locate the C_{27} methyl signal. The C_{19} and C_{18} methyl signals are, of course, singlets whereas the C_{21} and C_{27} methyl groups give rise to two doublets. It has been established[17,13] that in the 25R series the signal due to the C_{27} occurs at the highest field; usually this methyl signal appears as a low shoulder on the high field side of the tall C_{18} methyl peak. In the isomeric series, the C_{27} methyl peaks are at lower field than the C_{18} methyl signal. Use of pyridine[17] as a solvent in some cases may make the methyl signals separate from one another and easier to recognize.

Confirmatory evidence for the stereochemistry at C_{25} is available from a study of the heavily deshielded (5.8–7.0 τ) C_{26} methylene group.[17] Coupling with the axial C_{25} proton in the 25R series produces a characteristic broad multiplet with two main broad signals separated by 5 cps. (Figure 13A). An equatorial C_{25} proton, on the other hand, generates a splitting pattern that approximates a quartet (Figure 13B).

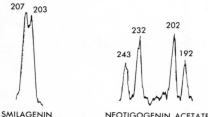

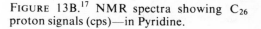

SMILAGENIN   NEOTIGOGENIN ACETATE

SMILAGENIN   NEOTIGOGENIN ACETATE

FIGURE 13A.[17] NMR spectra showing C_{26} proton signals (cps)—in $CDCl_3$.

FIGURE 13B.[17] NMR spectra showing C_{26} proton signals (cps)—in Pyridine.

3.4. The Ethyl Group.

Since the most commonly used ester is the ethyl ester, a practicing organic chemist soon becomes familiar with its A_3X_2 pattern consisting of a triplet for the methyl signal at about 8.85 τ and a quartet for the methylene protons near 5.9 τ. The coupling between the methyl and methylene protons are of the order of 7 cps. Similar spectra are obtained for ethyl groups in ethyl ethers and ethyl ketones. The methyl triplet, however, becomes distorted as the chemical shifts of methyl and methylene protons approach each other. Thus, the signal of a methyl group at the end of a moderately long aliphatic chain is hardly recognizable as a triplet (Figure 14).

The two ester groups in a substituted malonic ester are often equivalent to each other and their signals are superimposed (Figure 15). Lack of symmetry in the molecule, of course, will lead to a separation of the two sets of signals as shown in Figure 16. It is customary for organic chemists to use ethyl esters, but from the point of view of NMR spectrometry it is preferable to work with methyl esters instead. In ethyl or higher esters, the alkoxy protons produce multiple signals in the 9 τ and the 6.0 to 6.5 τ region whereas the methyl ester generates a single sharp peak near 6.3 τ and leaves the rest of the spectrum uncluttered (see Figure 2).

The geminal protons of a methylene group near an asymmetric center are magnetically non-equivalent (see Section 2.2). They may display an AB rather than an A_2 profile (see Figure 4) if the non-equivalence is sufficiently pronounced. The presence of an asymmetric atom is not a necessary condition, however. Even some symmetrical molecules such as acetaldehyde diethyl acetal (XVIII) show an AB quartet for the methylene protons.[18] In

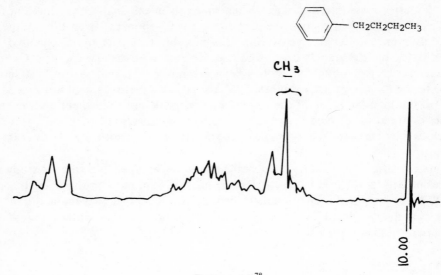

FIGURE 14.[78]

such molecules the necessary asymmetry may be provided by the conformational preference of certain rotamers.

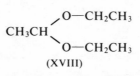

(XVIII)

It should be noted that this type of asymmetry cannot lead to isolable optical isomers.

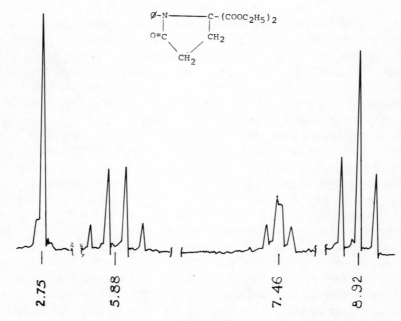

FIGURE 15.[78]

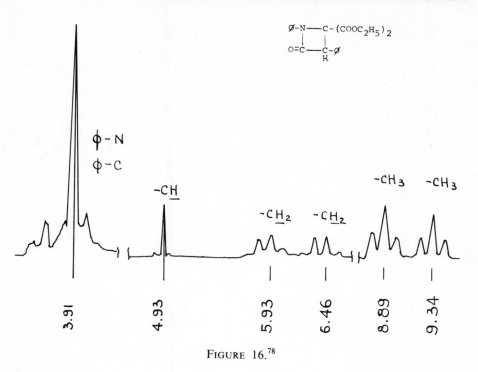

FIGURE 16.[78]

The asymmetry in a molecule may be due to the presence of a low asymmetry at atoms such as sulfur or phosphorus. In a recent publication[19] it has been reported that the methylene protons of N,N'-diethylmethanesulfinamide (XIX) give rise to a multiple line ABX_3 spectrum in place of the usual A_2X_3 quartet.

$$(CH_3CH_2)_2N—SO—CH_3$$
$$(XIX)$$

The methyl signal, however, continues to be a triplet. By using a computer program, an acceptable fit was obtained between the observed and the calculated spectra using the following parameters: $J_{AB} = 0.350$ ppm, $J_{AC} = J_{BC} = 7.0$ cps. The equivalence of J_{AC} and J_{BC} leads to the triplet for the methyl group.

A curve has been theoretically derived relating the value of J_{AB} to the bond angle between geminal protons in saturated compounds.[20] The geminal coupling constant is ~ 12 cps when the bond angle is nearly tetrahedral (e.g. in cyclohexane) but it is greatly reduced as the bond angle increases. For a cyclopropyl methylene group, J_{gem} is about 5 cps.

3.5. The Isopropyl Group. Each methyl of an isopropyl group is split into a doublet with $J \cong 7$ cps. The methine proton is a multiplet and easily obscured by other proton signals. If the two methyl groups have the same chemical shift, then the methyl signals consist of a doublet corresponding to six protons (Figure 17). If the isopropyl group is next to an asymmetric center or there is restricted rotation making the two methyl groups non-equivalent, two doublets instead of the usual one are obtained. In some cases, an overlap of these four lines may give the appearance of a triplet which can be resolved into two doublets by recording the spectrum on a 100 Mc spectrometer. The presence of other methyl groups in the same molecule may make assignment difficult because of overlap. A pair of dividers with the gap corresponding to about 7 cps is of considerable assistance in trying to match peaks belonging to an isopropyl group (see Figure 18).

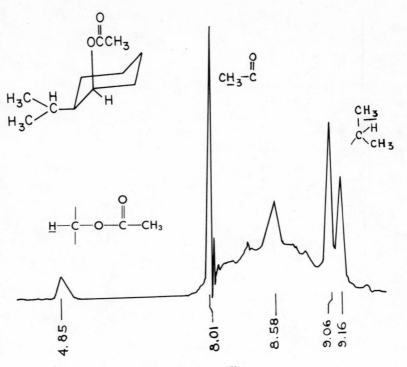

FIGURE 17.[78]

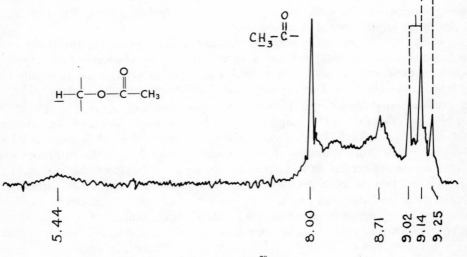

FIGURE 18.[78]

When the isopropyl group is adjacent to a center of asymmetry, the two methyl groups become nonequivalent. This non-equivalence persists when the isopropyl group in C_6H_5—CH—O—$(CH_2)_n$—$CH(CH_3)_2$ is as many as seven bonds away from the asymmet-

CH$_3$

ric center (n = 2).[21] The reason for this is not clearly understood yet.

3.6. Olefinic Protons.   A particularly useful aspect of NMR spectrometry is the recognition of olefinc protons and the determination of their environment. A tetrasubstituted ethylene can only be suspected on the basis of the chemical shifts of allylic protons ($\approx 8.0\ \tau$), but for the other ethylene derivatives tangible evidence is presented by the resonance of the olefinic protons in the 4 to 5 τ region. Conjugation of the double bond shifts the signals further down field.

Much information can be obtained from the value of the coupling constant involving the vicinal olefinic protons H_a and H_b in H_a—C=C—H_b. In substituted ethylenes, J_{ab} for the *trans* isomer (11 to 18 cps) is considerably larger than the J_{ab} for the *cis* isomer (6 to 14 cps). If the double bond is part of a ring, the olefinc protons are *cis* to each other but the coupling constant decreases with the size of the ring: cyclohexene, 8.8 to 10.5 cps; cyclopentene, 5.1 to 7.0 cps; cyclobutene, 2.5 to 4.0 cps; cyclopropene, 0.5 to 2.0 cps.

The methylene group —C=C—H protons have little interaction (J = 0.5 to 3 cps)

H

with each other and often produce a doublet pattern (Figure 19)[79] which may coalesce into a singlet in some compounds. When the coupling between these two protons is not negligible, an AB quartet is observed.

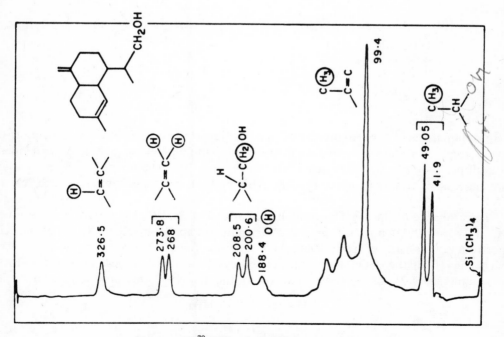

FIGURE 19.[79] (Chemical shift in cps units).

The vinyl side chain

is of common occurrence in natural products and merits detailed comments. These three protons can constitute an ABC or an ABX system (see Section 2.3.). In sandracopimaric acid XXA (Figure 20B) the four extreme downfield signals appear to constitute the X part of an ABX spectrum. It is easy to determine that J_{AX} and J_{BX} are 10 and 18 cps. The single peak at 4.83 τ obviously corresponds to the olefinc proton at C_{14}; the broadening of this signal is due to allylic coupling (see Section 4.1). The remaining eight lines in the downfield region must, therefore, belong to the AB part of the ABX pattern. By searching for lines that are 10 and 18 cps apart in this octet, one can analyze the pattern after some trial and error. The small value of the geminal coupling constant ($J_{AB} = 1.7$ cps) is expected.

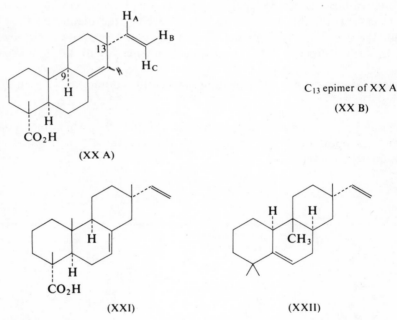

C_{13} epimer of XX A

(XX B)

(XX A)

(XXI)   (XXII)

In isopimaric acid XXI (Figure 20A)[80] the position of the double bond in the ring is different from XXA and the resonance of the corresponding olefinic proton shows evidence of multiple coupling. The stereochemistry of the vinyl side chain is the same in sandaracopimaric acid. It may be noted that the ABX patterns are quite similar in both XX and XXI.

The resonance of the vinyl protons of pimaric acid (XXB) (Figure 20C) and rimuene (XXII) (Figure 20D), however, present a very different appearance: the X part of the ABX spectrum now consists of six lines instead of the usual four.

The signals of the —O—CH=CHCH₃ group show some interesting features. In the spectrum (Figure 21) of the compound XXIII, the methyl groups produce a symmetrical

$$H_2C(O—C=CCH_3)_2$$
$$H\ \ H$$

(XXIII)

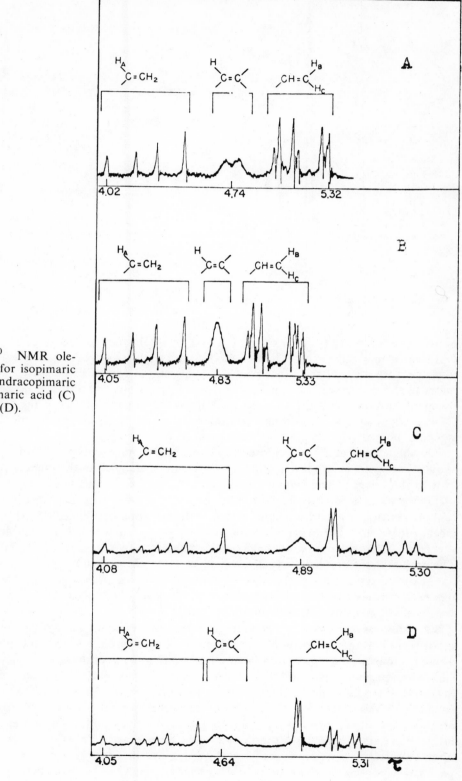

FIGURE 20.[80] NMR olefinic signals for isopimaric acid (A), sandracopimaric acid (B), pimaric acid (C) and rimuene (D).

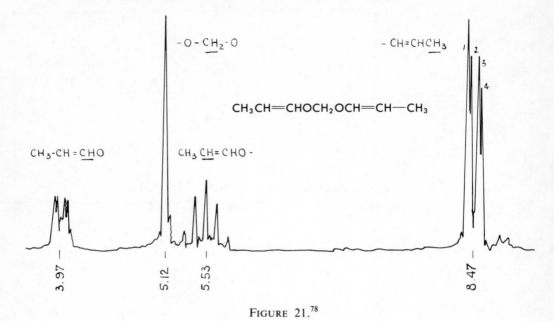

FIGURE 21.[78]

pattern of four peaks (1–4) in which 1–2 = 3–4 = 1.7 cps and 1–3 = 2–4 = 6.8 cps. At first sight it may appear that the two methyls are slightly non-equivalent. But this is unlikely because none of the other proton signals shows evidence for such a lack of symmetry in the molecule. The coupling of J = 6.8 cps is obviously due to the interaction of the methyl protons with the adjacent olefinic proton. The smallness of the other coupling (J = 1.7 cps) suggests long-range spin interaction (see Section 4) and indeed can be assigned to homoallylic coupling (see Section 4.2).

The single peak at 5.12 τ representing two protons must correspond to the methylene group. The signal at still lower field (3.97 τ) has to be assigned to the olefinic protons adjacent to the oxygen. The symmetrical pentet centered at 5.55 τ indicates that the other olefinic proton is interacting with four protons through identical coupling constants (J = 6.8 cps). The accidental equivalence of the coupling between the methyl and the adjacent proton and that between the two olefinic protons has led to a simplification of the spectrum. Normally one would have expected an octet (two quartets) instead of the pentet. The peak at the lowest field actually is such an octet ($J_{vicinal}$ = 6.8 cps, $J_{homoallylic}$ = 1.7 cps).

The allylic system, X—CH_2—CH=CH_2, also deserves attention. The five proton system here produces a complex pattern that involves geminal coupling, vicinal coupling as well as allylic coupling (see Section 4.1).

3.7. Alcohols and Esters.   The marked deshielding effect of the hydroxy group results in shifting the signal of the protons on the carbon carrying a hydroxy group to about 6τ. These protons thus are separated from most of the other protons and the pattern of their signals can provide useful information. Acetylation of the hydroxyl group causes a downfield shift of nearly 1 ppm for these protons (compare Figures 22A and 23A). A comparison of the NMR spectra of an alcohol and its acetate (or other esters), therefore, aids the identification of the protons attached to the carbinol carbon.   Furthermore, from the integration data it becomes a simple matter to determine the number of protons shifted upon acetylation.   The number of acetyl groups can be ascertained from the size of the peak corresponding to their methyl signal near 8 τ. On the basis of these data it is usu-

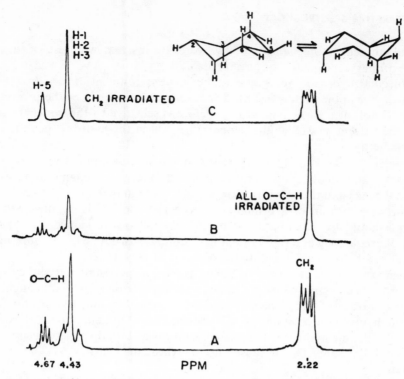

FIGURE 22.[36] NMR spectra of 1,2,3,5-cyclohexanetetrol in D_2O (100 Mc). (Chemical shift in δ units).

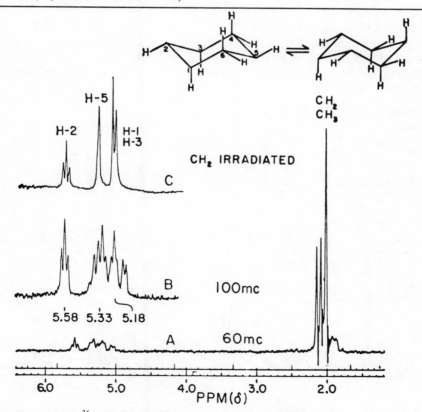

FIGURE 23.[36] NMR spectra of 1,2,3,5-cyclohexanetetrol acetate in $CDCl_3$.

243

ally possible to deduce the number of hydroxyl groups that were esterified and whether these were primary, secondary, or tertiary alcohols.

Intermolecular hydrogen bonding can alter the environment of a hydroxyl proton and produce a change in the chemical shift. The resonance frequency of the proton of an alcohol, phenol, enol, or a carboxylic acid therefore is sensitive to the concentration and the nature of the solvent as well as the temperature. Often the hydroxyl peak is obscured by methyl and methylene signals.

A convenient method for locating hydroxyl signals is to add deuterated water to the solvent, shake, and record the spectrum again. Deuterium exchange reduces the size of the hydroxyl peaks and thus reveals their position and number.

The hydroxylic proton of a primary or secondary alcohol is coupled with the vicinal protons and should give rise to a triplet or a doublet. However, since the hydroxyl proton is capable of exchanging at a rapid rate, this coupling may not be observable and the signal may appear as a broad singlet instead of a doublet or triplet.

Hydrogen exchange is catalyzed by acids. Hence, a spectrum that shows splitting of a hydroxyl proton can be simplified by bubbling hydrochloric acid gas through the solution or by adding a trace of trifluoroacetic acid (see Figure 24A and B) and thus in effect decoupling the hydroxyl proton and its vicinal neighbors. In deuterated chloroform or carbon tetrachloride, the hydroxyl peaks usually appear as broad singlets even though vicinal protons may be present. This is caused by the traces of acid that are generally found in these solvents.

When the spectrum of a secondary or a primary alcohol is recorded in dimethyl sulfoxide solution, the strong hydrogen bonding of the solvent prevents the hydroxyl peak from appearing at a higher field than 6τ and thus makes it easily discernible. In addition, the rate of proton exchange is so reduced that the effect of vicinal coupling becomes observable. The hydroxyl proton signal of methanol appears as a quartet at 5.92τ (Figure 25A).[81] The corresponding signals in primary, secondary, and tertiary alcohols are clearly resolved triplets, doublets, and singlets, respectively in the 4.5 to 6.0τ region. Hemiacetal

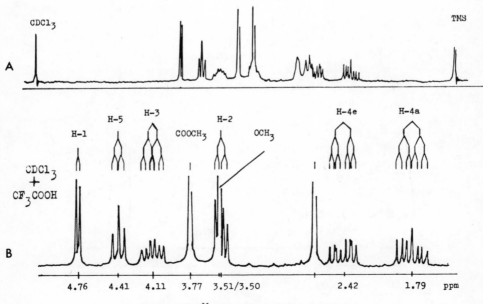

FIGURE 24.[35] (Chemical shift in δ units).

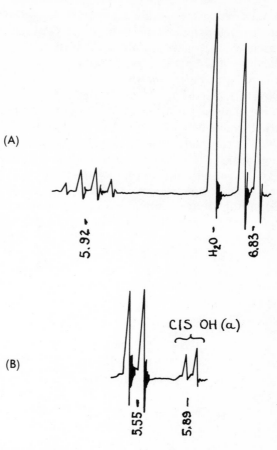

(A)

FIGURE 25.[81] A. NMR spectrum of methanol and water in dimethyl sulfoxide. B. Hydroxyl proton resonances of a mixture of trans-4-t-butylcyclohexyl alcohol (77%) and cis-4-t-butylcyclohexyl alcohol (23%) in dimethyl sulfoxide.

5.92

H_2O

6.83

(B)

CIS OH (a)

5.55

5.89

and hemiketal hydroxyl protons produce doublets and singlets, respectively in the 3.5–5.0 range. In the case of isomeric cyclohexanols, the signal due to an axial hydroxyl group group appears at a higher field than the corresponding equatorial group (see Figure 25B). A quantitative estimation of the isomers can therefore be carried out conveniently from a study of the NMR spectra in solution.*

Dimethyl sulfoxide is a good solvent for sugars; at the same time, unlike the usual solvent D_2O, it does not lead to mutarotation in most cases. A recent study[83] has found that the O_1—H proton in glucose and other sugars with the same configuration at C_1 and C_2, show a distinctive pattern—in α-anomers (O_1—H axial) a doublet appears at 3.70 τ, in the corresponding β-anomer (O_1—H equatorial) this doublet is further downfield by about 0.3 ppm. A further characteristic is that the J for the axial O_1—H is 4.0 to 4.5 cps but the J for the equatorial O_1—H is 6.0 to 7.0 cps. The other hydroxyl protons appear in the 4.9 to 6.0 τ range without obscuring the O_1—H protons. Mannose, arabinose and other sugars differing from glucose at C_2 do not fit this pattern.

For a mixture of anomers, the O_1—H resonance in dimethyl sulfoxide provides a quantitative estimate of the components. The spectra of polysaccharides also provide much information about the types of linkages involved.

3.8. Aromatic Systems. The characteristic feature of an aromatic system is the marked deshielding of the ring protons. For benzene derivatives these protons resonate in the 2 to 4 τ range, that is, at lower field than olefins and conjugated dienes. For nonbenzenoid

*For exceptions, see J. G. Traynham and G. A. Knesel, *J. Amer. Chem. Soc.*, **87**, 4220 (1965).

aromatic systems too, one can expect such low field chemical shifts. Thus, the observation that the cyclononatetraenyl anion[23] (XXIV) and the cyclooctatetraenyl dianion[24] (XXV) give single sharp peaks at about 3.0 and 3.16 τ, respectively, has been interpreted as an indication of aromaticity for these ions.

In trying to determine the aromaticity of annulenes (see for example, [18]-annulene, (XXVI)), Jackman[25] *et al.*, have used the criterion that a cyclic π-electron system should be able to sustain a magnetically induced ring current (see Section 6) and thus produce marked deshielding of the protons outside the annulene ring but shielding for the protons inside the ring. Using this test [18]-annulene has been deduced to be aromatic because it shows peaks at 1.1 τ (outer protons, relative area: ≈ 2) and 11.8 τ (inner proton, relative area: 1). On the other hand, [24]-annulene (XXVII), which displays a single resonance at 3.16 τ must be nonaromatic.

Monosubstituted benzenes may show a single peak (see Figure 15) or a complex pattern (see Figure 6). The coupling between ring protons varies in a regular fashion: J_{ortho}: 7 to

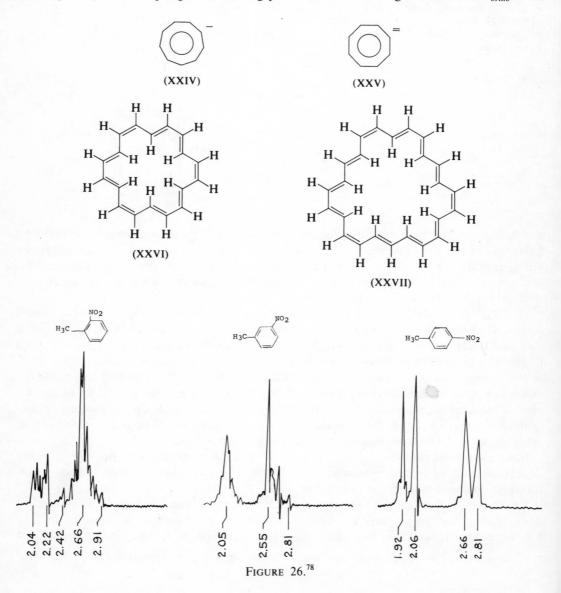

(XXIV)

(XXV)

(XXVI)

(XXVII)

FIGURE 26.[78]

10 cps; J_{meta}: 2 to 3 cps; J_{para}: 1 cps. *p*-Disubstituted benzene derivatives (see Figure 2) are easy to recognize because of their nearly symmetrical A_2B_2 pattern; the corresponding *o*- and *m*- derivatives give unsymmetrical spectra (see Figure 26).

3.9. Heterocyclic Systems. NMR spectroscopy has become an indispensible tool for studies on heterocyclic systems, whether in natural products or in synthetic molecules. A study of the chemical shift of ring protons and coupling constants often provides an easy access to information concerning the location of a substituent on a heterocyclic ring.[26] In the case of heterocycles with various possible tautomeric structures, NMR spectra are often the most reliable evidence for the tautomeric forms and equilibria.

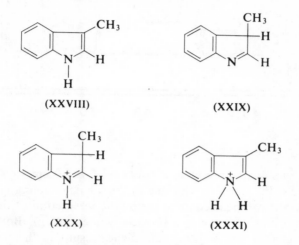

(XXVIII)   (XXIX)

(XXX)   (XXXI)

A specific example[27] is provided by a study of the spectra of 3-methyl indole (XXVIII) in neutral and in strongly acid solutions. On the basis of the low field position of the methyl resonance, the tautomeric form (XXIX) of this indole can be ruled out. In 12*M* sulfuric acid, the 3-methyl peak is moved upfield and split into a doublet (J = 7.5 cps); also a quartet corresponding to one proton appears. This spectral change supports the protonated structure XXX rather than XXXI.

4. Long-Range Coupling

4.1. Allylic Coupling. All the examples of coupling discussed so far have involved geminal or vicinal protons. Of a smaller magnitude, yet significant, is "long-range" coupling arising from an interaction between protons separated by four or more bonds.

Allylic coupling occurs in the system H_a—C_1=C_2—C_3—H_b and the coupling constant J_{ab} is dependent on the angle that the C_2—C_3 bond makes with the plane of the C_1=C_2 double bond. The value of the coupling constant, which is modified by solvents, is small—usually 0 to 3 cps. In some cases the smallness of the coupling leads only to a broadening of the signal. It has been reported[28] that in cyclohexyl systems allylic protons show stronger coupling when they are axial rather than equatorial.

4.2. Homoallylic Coupling. Homoallylic coupling has been defined as the interaction between protons H_a and H_b in the system H_a—C—C = C—C—H_b. The value of J_{ab} is quite small and occurs in the range of 0 to 1.6 cps. The NMR spectrum of 1,3-dihydro-1,3,5,7-tetramethyl-2H-azepin-2-one[29] (XXXII) (see Figure 27) demonstrates the effect of long-range coupling. Of the four methyl groups in the molecule, the N—CH_3 group stands apart because of its downfield position (6.88 τ). The doublet (J = 7.0 cps) centered at 8.64 τ must correspond to the methyl group at C_3 coupled with the vicinal proton on C_3. The

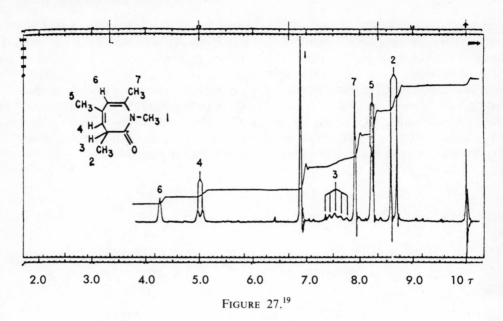

FIGURE 27.[19]

remaining two methyl signals appear as a doublet (J = 1.0 cps) at 7.99 τ and a triplet (J = 1.5 cps) at 8.22 τ; the former arises due to the allylic coupling between the 7-methyl and the H-6. The triplet can be accounted for by the interaction of the 5-methyl with the H-4 (allylic coupling) and with the H-3 (homoallylic coupling). Both types of coupling lead to the same value (1.5 cps) and this equivalence results in the 5-methyl signal being split into a triplet according to the n + 1 rule.

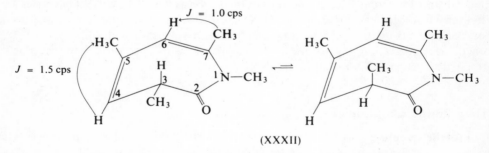

(XXXII)

4.3. Other Special Couplings. Spin information can also be transmitted through acety-lenic and allenic bonds.[30] Thus, the terminal protons in 1,3-pentadiyne (XXXIII) show coupling of 1.27 cps magnitude. In the allenic compound 1-chloro-1,2-butadiene (XXXIV), the protons form an ABX_3 system; the coupling between H-1 and H-3 amounts to 4.8 cps.

$$H_3C-C\equiv C-C\equiv C-H \qquad\qquad H_3C-CH=C=CHCl$$

(XXXIII)   (XXXIV)

The signal of the methyl group adjacent to the carbonyl in ethyl methyl ketone appears as a triplet[31] (J = 0.48 cps). This type of long-range coupling through the carbonyl group usually leads to only a broadening of the signal because of the very small value of the coupling constant.

There have been suggestions that spin information can be transmitted through space between two protons separated by several bonds in a favorable spatial relationship to each other. In any case, coupling between protons separated by four single bonds has been observed in many instances. Such coupling is sometimes pronounced ($J = 7$ cps in one case) in bridged bicyclic compounds. The NMR spectrum of such a system is considered later in some detail (see Section 4.4).*

Several authors have reported that the steric requirement for optimal spin-spin coupling between protons separated by 4σ bonds appears to be that these 4σ bonds form an "M" arrangement (XXXV). Thus, in certain 2-keto steroids, the C_{19}-methyl group is found to have a small coupling ($J = 1$ cps) with the axial proton at C_1.[32] Similar coupling has been observed for the C_{18}-methyl group and the axial 12-α-proton in some 11-ketosteroids.

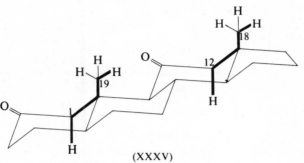

(XXXV)

4.4. Virtual Coupling. The signal for a proton in certain systems is more complicated than is warranted by the empirical considerations outlined before. Musher and Corey[33] have pointed out that if a group of protons are strongly coupled to one another, that is, for two coupled protons the coupling constant is much greater than the difference in chemical shift, they can interact with other protons as a group rather than as individual protons. As a result, a proton may be influenced by protons to which it has a zero coupling constant. This special type of spin interaction has been named "virtual coupling."

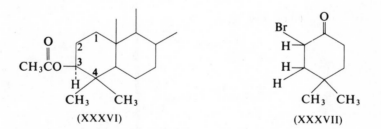

(XXXVI)   (XXXVII)

A striking illustration of virtual coupling is provided by H-3 in a triterpene acetate (XXXVI). This signal is a very broad peak without any discernible pattern whereas the 2-proton in 2-bromo-4,4-dimethylcyclohexanone, XXXVII, shows a clear quartet predicted by first order analysis. The complexity of the former signal has been ascribed to coupling with the C_2-methylene and virtual coupling with the C_1-methylene.

The spectrum of a substituted norbornene XXXVIII (see Figure 28) furnishes another example of virtual coupling. The two equivalent bridge-head protons H_c and H_f produce for their signal an irregular septet at 6.8 τ. This multiplicity has been explained on the basis of coupling and virtual coupling of each bridge-head proton with every other proton in the molecule except the other bridge-head proton. The coupling constants are shown

*C. W. Jefford, J. Gunsher and K. C. Ramey (*J. Amer. Chem. Soc.*, **87**, 4384(1965)) have reported *five* distinct long range couplings in the same molecule!

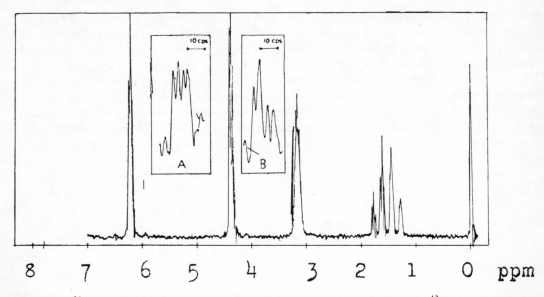

FIGURE 28.[34] NMR spectrum of XXXVIII in CCl_4 (bottom trace). Box A, ^{13}C pattern relative to the olefinic protons; Box B, ^{13}C pattern relative to the methine protons on chlorine-bearing carbons. (Chemical shift in δ units).

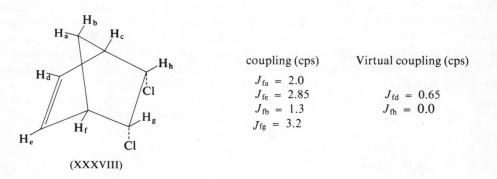

coupling (cps)	Virtual coupling (cps)
$J_{fa} = 2.0$	
$J_{fe} = 2.85$	$J_{fd} = 0.65$
$J_{fb} = 1.3$	$J_{fh} = 0.0$
$J_{fg} = 3.2$	

(XXXVIII)

here but their determination is discussed in Section 7.2. It should be noted that these multiple couplings call for a much higher multiplicity of the signal than observed. This is a feature of virtual coupling–it leads to an integration of the various separate spin interactions and produces what has been aptly described as a "deceptively simple" spectrum.

5. Stereochemical Information from NMR Spectra

5.1. Working Rules. In the early days of NMR spectrometry, most organic chemists used the new tool for deducing or confirming the gross structure of molecules. However, with the accumulation of spectral data and the development of several generalizations, it has now become possible to derive valuable stereochemical information about many types of molecules on the basis of chemical shifts, coupling constants, and long-range coupling. As a matter of fact, some of this information is not easily available from any other measurement.

The field of conformational analysis has specially benefited from NMR spectroscopy. The generalizations that are of value in this connection are (1) an axial proton appears at a higher field than the corresponding equatorial proton (an important exception to this has been reported);[84] (2) the coupling J_{aa} (8 to 14 cps) between two axial protons is larger than the coupling J_{ae} (≈ 1 to 5 cps) between an axial and an equatorial proton and the coupling J_{ee} (≈ 1 to 5 cps) between two equatorial protons; (3) the methyl signal of the acetyl group of a cyclohexyl acetate lies at a lower field when the acetoxy group is axial rather than equatorial. A similar relationship appears to exist for the methyl signals of acetamido groups derived from cyclohexylamines, although the change in upfield chemical shift going from the axial to the equatorial conformation is quite small. Cyclohexanol methyl ethers do not provide reliable information about the conformation of the hydroxyl group.

5.2. Configuration of Carbohydrates. The remarkable insight into the detailed stereochemistry of a carbohydrate derivative provided by the NMR spectrum is illustrated by a recent study.[35] Of the two possible products (**XXXIX, XL**) obtained from the hydrogenation of **XLI**, one was isolated as crystalline material. The spectrum of this compound obtained in deuterated chloroform solution was much impoved in resolution on the addition of a trace of trifluoric acid to suppress spin coupling between hydroxyl groups and neighboring protons (see Figure 24).

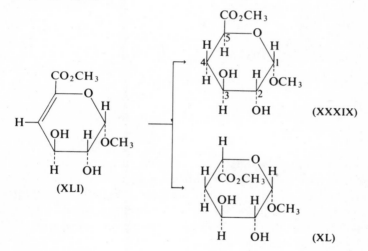

The most heavily deshielded proton is H-1 because of the two α-ether linkages. This proton must therefore correspond to the lowest field signal, viz., a doublet ($J = 3.0$ cps) at 5.24 τ. The triplet ($J = 5.0$ cps) at 5.59 τ should be due to H-5—the proton that is deshielded by an ether oxygen and an ester group. The multiplets at 5.89 and 6.50 τ were modified on the addition of trifluoroacetic acid: these must therefore correspond to H-2 and H-3, each of which is adjacent to a hydroxyl group. The three proton signals at 6.23 and 6.49 τ arise from the methyl resonance of the carbomethoxy and methoxy groups, respectively. The two remaining multiplets at 7.58 and 8.21 τ are to be assigned to the H-4 protons; the latter should correspond to the axial hydrogen on C_4 because it is at higher field.

Since the H-5 signal is a symmetrical triplet, the two vicinal protons (H-4) must be symmetrically situated with respect to H-5. This situation will obtain only if H-5 is in the equatorial position. The size of the coupling constant also (5.0 cps) makes it unlikely that H-5 is in the axial position since J_{aa} is usually of the order of 6 to 10 cps.

With only two neighboring protons, the signal for H-2 should be a quartet. Such a pattern is observed at 6.50 τ. The second line of the quartet is masked by the methyl resonance at 6.49 τ, but from the positions of the remaining three lines, the J values are easily determined to be 3.0 and 7.2 cps. Since $J_{1,2}$ has been found to be 3.0 cps from the doublet for H-1, one concludes that $J_{2,3}$ is 7.2 cps and H-2 and H-3 are therefore axial.

The H-3 signal is a sextet, therefore, of the three protons with which H-3 is spin coupled, two must be equivalent (to a first approximation) to each other. Since the coupling constants can be calculated to be 4.0 and 7.5 cps (for the equivalent protons), the following assignments can be made; $J_{3,4a} = 7.5$ cps; $J_{3,4e} = 4.0$ cps. The axial proton at C_4 is subject to the following couplings: $J_{4,5} = 5.0$ cps, J_{gem} and $J_{3,4} = 7.5$ cps. An octet is therefore expected; actually a septet with one of the lines with double the usual intensity is observed. J_{gem} can now be deduced to be 13.3 cps. By similar reasoning, an octet is also expected for the equatorial proton at C_4 with the following coupling constants: 5.0, 13.3 and 4.0 cps. Such is indeed the case for the signal at 7.58 τ.

It is now possible to deduce the conformation XLA and hence the configuration XL for the uronic acid since the coupling constants have indicated that H-3 and H-2 are axial and H-5 is equatorial.

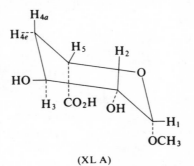

(XL A)

5.3. Configuration of Cyclohexanols. In complex spectra, difficulty is often experienced in making assignments for the different protons. One problem is to determine which signals are due to coupled protons, the other problem is to find which protons are coupled with which other protons. Some recent work[36] on cyclitols will now be described to illustrate the powerful methods that have become available for deciphering NMR spectra and for determining details of stereochemistry.

In the course of their study on some derivatives of inositol, McCasland and co-workers obtained an unexpected product which was a cyclohexanetetrol corresponding to one of the three structures XLIIA, LXIIB and XLIII. Neither the positions nor the relative configuration of the hydroxyl groups was apparent from the known chemistry of this compound.

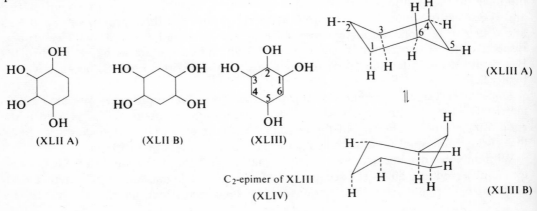

(XLII A)   (XLII B)   (XLIII)   (XLIII A)

C$_2$-epimer of XLIII
(XLIV)   (XLIII B)

The NMR spectrum (Figure 22A, p. 243) of the tetrol at 100 Mc showed a quartet at 22.2 δ and a complex pattern at 4.43 and 4.67 δ. The quartet obviously corresponds to the four methylene protons. Since the methylene quartet was virtually unchanged at 60 Mc, these signals must arise from spin coupling.

Further information was obtained by decoupling experiments. By appropriately irradiating O—C—H resonances while observing the methylene protons (Figure 22B) spin interaction between these two types of protons was nullified. Under these conditions the methylene quartet collapsed into a singlet showing that spectroscopically all the four methylene protons were equivalent.

In the next decoupling experiment the methylene protons were irradiated at the appropriate frequency while O—C—H signals were observed (Figure 22C). The lower field pattern now collapsed into a singlet at 4.67 δ corresponding to one proton and another signal at 4.43 δ corresponding to three protons.

The NMR spectrum (Figures 23A and B, p. 243) of the tetra-acetate of the tetrol was also studied at 60 and 100 Mc. Of the four acetate methyl groups, two were found to be equivalent. The methylene proton signals were obscured by the methyl proton signal; the remaining four protons produced a triplet (1H) at 5.58 δ and a multiplet (3H) at a somewhat higher field. Again recourse was taken to decoupling to gain further information (Figure 23C). Irradiations of the methylene protons changed the lower field pattern into a triplet (1H, J = 2.3 cps) at 5.58 δ, a singlet (1H) at 5.33 δ and a doublet (2H, J = 2.3 cps) at 5.13 δ. It was evident that the triplet and the doublet are produced by a proton with two equivalent vicinal protons. Furthermore, since the triplet at 5.58 δ was unaffected by the decoupling experiment, the corresponding protons must not be vicinal to either of the two methylene groups. The doublet pattern was different in the original spectrum, hence, the corresponding two equivalent protons must be vicinal to the methylene groups.

Going back to the NMR spectra of the tetrol, it is observed that the one proton signal at 4.67 δ is a quintuplet which collapses to a singlet on irradiating the methylene groups which consist of four equivalent protons. This proton, therefore, is not vicinal to the remaining three O—C—H type protons but is equally coupled with the four methylene protons. These requirements are satisfied by H-5 of structure XLIII.

The NMR spectrum of the tetra-acetate can be completely accounted for on the basis of structure XLIII. The multiplet (quintuplet?) at 5.33 δ must correspond to H-5 and the triplet at 5.58 δ to H-2. The smallness of the coupling constant (2.3 cps) rules out the possibility that the protons at C_2 and C_1 (and C_3) are diaxial.

The two equivalent acetoxy groups in the tetra-acetate must be those located on C_1 and C_3. In the tetrol the chemical shift for H-1, H-2 and H-3 are accidentally equal: the acetate spectra show that H-1 and H-3 are the truly equivalent protons.

The equivalence of the four methylene protons has important stereo-chemical connotations. If the cyclohexane ring is in the ideal chair conformation, these four protons cannot be equivalent. It is known that at room temperature conformational inversion from one chair form to another (for example, XLIIIA and B) is too rapid for NMR spectral differentiation. The spectrum that is actually recorded corresponds to an averaging of the different conformers. It is reasonable to assume that the time-average disposition of the protons approximates the stereochemistry implied by a planar cyclohexane ring; each proton now assumes a conformation that is intermediate between the axial and equatorial positions and two protons would be magnetically equivalent to a first approximation if each one "sees" the same type of environment. In the tetrol, the chemical shift of a proton must be particularly sensitive to the proximity of the hydroxyl groups. The observation that the methylene protons on C_4 (or C_6) are equal to each other requires that the hydroxyl groups at C_3 (or C_1) and C_5 be *trans* to each other. If these hydroxyl groups were *cis* instead, then the proton that was *cis* to two such groups would be at much lower field than the proton that was *trans* to both of these hydroxyls.

Two alternative structures XLIII and XLIV differing at C_2 can now be written for the tetrol. A choice between them is possible because the decoupled spectrum shows that H-1, H-2, and H-3 are magnetically equal in the tetrol, at least to a first approximation. Such equality is ruled out in the structure XLIV because H-2 sees two hydroxy groups in the immediate vicinity whereas H-1(and H-3) see only two protons on the α-carbon atoms C_2 and C_6(C_2 and C_4). In structure XLIII, however, the immediate neighbors of each of H-1, H-2 and H-3 are two protons and to a first approximation these three protons might appear equivalent to one another.

It was noted that in the tetra-acetate of the tetrol, H-2 is no longer equivalent to H-1 and H-3. This is not inconsistent with the structure XLIII because the acetyl group has free rotation around each single bond and the diamagnetic anisotropy in the vicinity of the π-electrons of the carbonyl is sensitive to the steric disposition of the proton *vis à vis*

the plane defined by the grouping $\underset{C}{\overset{O}{\underset{\Vert}{C}}}\diagdown_C$ (see Section 6).

5.4. The Karplus Equation.

Coupling constants between vicinal protons have assumed great significance for stereochemical studies. Karplus[37] has deduced from theoretical considerations a quantitative relationship (Eqs. 5-1 and 5-2)

$$J = 8.5 \cos^2\Phi - 0.28, \quad 0° \le \Phi \le 90° \tag{5-1}$$

$$J = 9.5 \cos^2\Phi - 0.28, \quad 90° \le \Phi \le 180° \tag{5-2}$$

between the coupling constant J of a $-\overset{|}{C}H-\overset{|}{C}H-$ fragment and the dihedral angle Φ between the two vicinal protons (see XLV and XLVI). Extensive work during the last few years has revealed that these equations are modified by the nature of the substituents in the vicinity of the protons. Thus, it appears necessary to derive a new set of equations to suit a given family of compounds. For 2-acetoxy-3-ketosteroids XLVIIA, Williamson and Johnson[38] have proposed the following modified version (Eqs. 5-3 and 5-4) of the Karplus equation:

$$J = 10 \cos^2\Phi, \quad 0° \le \Phi \le 90° \tag{5-3}$$

$$J = 16 \cos^2\Phi, \quad 90° \le \Phi \le 180° \tag{5-4}$$

For 2-bromo-3-ketosteroids XLVIIB, Abraham and Holker[39] have suggested the Eqs 5-5 and 5-6:

$$J_1 = 12.4 \cos^2\Phi \tag{5-5}$$

$$J_2 = 14.3 \cos^2 (120° \pm \Phi) \tag{5-6}$$

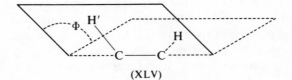

(XLV)

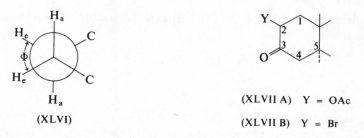

(XLVI)

(XLVII A) Y = OAc

(XLVII B) Y = Br

In spite of the uncertainty about the exact statement, the Karplus equation is often invoked for at least a qualitative evaluation of steric relationships in different types of molecules. In the chair form of a cyclohexane ring, the coupling J_{aa} between two adjacent axial protons can be expected to be large because Φ is almost 180°; for the diequatorial coupling J_{ee} and the axial-equatorial coupling J_{ae}, smaller values can be predicted because Φ is nearly 60°. Experimentally determined values (J_{aa} = 8-14, J_{ae} and J_{ee} 1-7 cps) are found to be in agreement with these expectations. From a knowledge of the appropriate coupling constant, therefore, it is possible to distinguish between *cis-* and *trans-* 1,2-disubstituted cyclohexane derivatives. The application of this principle is illustrated in a few problems. If, instead of a cyclohexane system, one considers a four-membered ring, the dihedral angle between *cis* substituents approaches 180° and that between *trans* substituents, about 110°. As a result, J_{trans} is now smaller than J_{cis}. Thus, the more stable, *trans* β-lactam **XLVIIIA** shows $J_{3,4}$ = 3.3 cps whereas the less stable, *cis* form **XLVIIIB** shows $J_{3,4}$ = 6.3 cps.

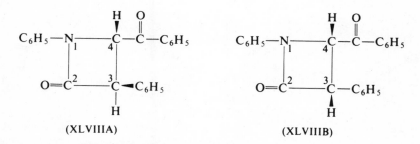

(XLVIIIA)

(XLVIIIB)

The application of the Karplus equation to a problem calls for a precise determination of the appropriate coupling constants. Sometimes that presents a difficulty. Thus, in the course of a study on the conformation of 1,4,4-trideuterocyclohexane dihalides (**XLIX**), Lemieux and Lown[40] found that a direct ABX analysis of the protons at C_2 and C_3 was not possible because of extensive overlap with C_6 protons. They could, however, determine the ABX parameters by spin decoupling experiments. By this means, the chemical shifts of the *a*- and *b*-protons were deduced as well as J_{ax}, J_{bx} and J_{ab} and the relative signs of these coupling constants.

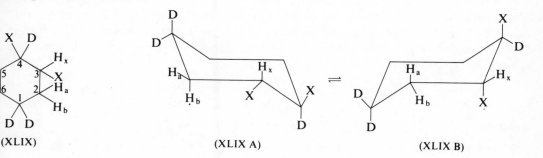

(XLIX)

(XLIX A)

(XLIX B)

From a consideration of the equilibrium between the conformational isomers **XLIXA** and **XLIXB**, it can be shown that

$$n J_{aa} + (1 - n) J_{ee} = J_{bx} \tag{5-7}$$

$$n J_{ae} + (1 - n) J_{ea} = J_{ax}$$

where n is the mole-fraction of **XLIXA**.

Dipole moment studies of Bender, Flowers, and Goering[41] had indicated a value of $n = 0.75$ and 0.43 for the diequatorial conformer (**XLIXA**) when $X = Cl$ and when $X = Br$, respectively. Using these values of n and Eqs. 5.7 and 5.8, the following coupling constants were obtained:

$$J_{aa} = 10.2, \ J_{ee} = 2.04, \ J_{ae} = 3.74 \text{ and } J_{ea} = 3.66 \text{ cps.}$$

The excellent agreement of these values with those in the literature[42] indicate the validity of this approach to the determination of conformation.

5.5. Conformational Equilibrium. Increasing use is being made of NMR spectroscopy for the determination of parameters related to the equilibrium between conformers. A recent publication will be discussed here to illustrate the methodology and the principles involved. Uebel and Martin[43] have studied the diazirine derivative L. This cyclohexane derivative may be represented as an equilibrium mixture of the two chair forms, LA and LB.

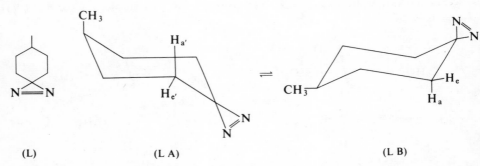

(L) (L A) (L B)

A parameter of importance in the equilibrium of an axially and an equatorially substituted cyclohexane derivative is the free energy difference A. If at equilibrium the mole-fraction of LA is Ne and of LB is Na and K is the equilibrium constant:

$$A = -\Delta F = RT \ln \text{Na/Ne} \tag{5-9}$$

and

$$K = \frac{\text{Na}}{\text{Ne}} \tag{5-10}$$

Assume now that the chemical shift of a ring proton is δe and δa in the equatorial and axial conformation, respectively. At normal temperature the rate of inversion of an individual molecule from one conformation to another is too rapid to permit the observation of δe and δa; what is actually observed is a single signal that is an average of these two values. This relationship is expressed in Eqs. 5.11 and 5.12.

$$\delta' \text{ obs} = \text{Na} \, \delta' a + \text{Ne} \, \delta' e \tag{5.11}$$

and

$$\delta'' \text{ obs} = \text{Na} \, \delta'' e + \text{Ne} \, \delta'' a \tag{5.12}$$

therefore,

$$(\delta'' - \delta'') \text{obs} = \Delta \text{obs} = \text{Na}\Delta' - \text{Ne}\Delta'' \tag{5.13}$$

where

$$\Delta' = \delta' a - \delta' e \text{ and } \Delta'' = \delta'' a = \delta'' e$$

The proximity of the three-membered diazirine ring system which possesses diagmagnetic anisotropy (see Section 1.5) leads to shielding of the equatorial proton. As a result, there is a large difference (1.32 ppm at $-50°$) in the chemical shift of the two protons at C-2. This difference $\delta' - \delta'' = \Delta$obs can be determined from an analysis of the spectrum resulting in assignments for the various lines using spin-decoupling techniques. Alternatively, $\delta' - \delta''$ can be obtained directly from the decoupling experiment without the precise determination of δ' and δ'' individually.

Uebel and Martin recorded the NMR spectrum of L at five different temperatures over the range of $-50°$ to $75°$ and thus had five values of Δobs. If the spectrum could have been measured at very low temperature there would have been no rapid equilibration and it would have been possible to make an actual measurement on the more stable conformer and thus obtain the value of Δ'.

Since Na + Ne = 1, Eq. (5.31) can we rewritten as

$$Na = (\Delta'' + \Delta obs) / (\Delta' + \Delta'') \tag{5.14}$$

$$Ne = (\Delta' - \Delta obs) / (\Delta' + \Delta'') \tag{5.15}$$

Therefore, Eq. (5.10) now becomes

$$K = Na/Ne = \frac{\Delta'' + \Delta obs}{\Delta' - \Delta obs} = \frac{\Delta''/\Delta' + \Delta obs/\Delta'}{1 - \Delta obs/\Delta'} \tag{5.16}$$

It is a reasonable assumption that Δ''/Δ' is nearly 1. Hence,

$$K \cong \frac{1 + \Delta obs/\Delta'}{1 - \Delta obs/\Delta'} \tag{5.17}$$

Uebel and Martin made another reasonable assumption, namely that ΔH for the interconversion of the conformers is temperature independent: ln K and $1/T$ then became linearly related. Using a computer program, a value of Δ' was sought that would minimize the standard deviation for this correlation as a function of the trial values of Δ'. In this manner Δ' was found to be 84.2 cps and it was calculated that $\Delta F_{30°} = -1.78$ kcal/mole, $\Delta H = -1.71$ kcal/mole and $\Delta S = -0.42$ esu. The A value for the methyl group was thus deduced to be 1.78 kcal/mole which is comparable to the values determined by other methods on other methyl cyclohexane derivatives.

5.6. Rotamer Population. Several studies have been made of the NMR spectra of 1,2-disubstituted ethanes for the determination of stereochemical details. One of the recent contributions in this area will be used here as an illustration.

Jung and Bothner-By[44] recorded the NMR spectra of *meso*-2,5-diphenylhexanediol-2,5 in pyridine at different temperatures. The A_2B_2 spectra were first analyzed by established methods.[45] An iterative computer program was then used to refine the values of coupling constants and the following were some of the figures obtained:

$$J_{AA'} = 11.86, J_{AB} = 13.36 \text{ at } 35°; J_{AA'} = 11.40,$$

$$J_{AB'} = 4.96, J_{AB} = 13.71 \text{ at } 81°.$$

For a typical disubstituted ethane derivative, the three rotamers LIA, LIB and LIC can be written. The populations of these three conformers are related: $P_2 = P_3 = \dfrac{1 - P_1}{2}$. It can be derived that

$$P_1 = \frac{(J_{AA'} - J_g)}{J_t - J_g} = \frac{J_t + J_g - 2J_{AB'}}{J_t - J_g} \tag{5-18}$$

and

$$J_{AA'} + 2J_{AB'} = 2J_g + J_t \qquad (5\text{-}19)$$

where J_t and J_g refer to the coupling between *trans* and *gauche* oriented protons.

From a consideration of a number of other compounds Bothner-By has calculated $J_g = 4.10$ and $J_t = 13.20$. This pair satisfies the Eq. 5-19. Substitution of these values in Eq. 5-18 shows that $P_1 = 0.85$ at 35° and 0.81 at 91°. As the temperature is raised, one can indeed expect the barrier between the different rotamers to become easier to surmount. The *trans* form of meso-2,5-diphenylhexanediol-2,5 is found to be about 1.1 kcal lower in enthalpy than the gauche forms.

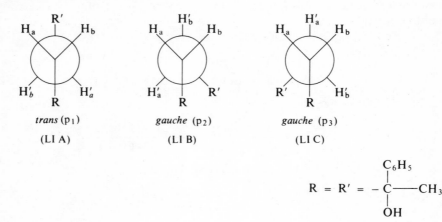

trans (p₁)   gauche (p₂)   gauche (p₃)

(LI A)   (LI B)   (LI C)

$$R = R' = -\underset{\underset{\text{OH}}{|}}{\overset{\overset{C_6H_5}{|}}{C}}-CH_3$$

5.7. The Quinolizidine Ring System.

The conformation of the quinolizidine ring system has been determined in several cases from NMR spectral data. Katritzky and co-workers[46] observed that in a series of N-methylquinolizidinium cations, the resonance of the N-methyl protons in *trans*-fused compounds was at a higher field than in the corresponding *cis*-fused systems.

The lone pair of electrons on the nitrogen of quinolizidine derivatives appears to affect, in a stereo-specific manner, the chemical shift of the proton on the adjacent ring-junction.[47] It has been suggested that the anisotropy of the lone pair of electrons of the nitrogen is similar to that in acetylenic compounds: (see LII and LIII) shielding ⊕ occurs along the longitudinal axis and deshielding ⊖ in the transverse direction.

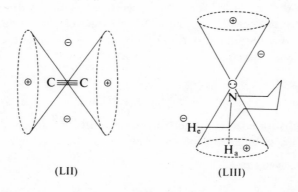

(LII)   (LIII)

If the ring-junction proton appears at a higher field than 6.2 τ, the quinolizidine system should be *trans*-fused; thus, the NMR spectrum of the *trans*-isomer LIVA reveals no single proton below 6.2 τ. In the spectra of the *cis*-fused compound LIVB and LV, however, one proton signals appear at 6.0 τ and 5.85 τ, respectively. For a *cis*-fused 6-member ring system, two different conformations are important; for the benzo-[a]-quinolizidine system these are represented by LIVB and LV.

A distinction between these alternatives is possible from an analysis of the spin-coupling of the ring-junction proton with the adjacent methylene protons. In LIVB, the coupling constants involved are J_{ae} and J_{ee} which are expected to be nearly equal. In LV, however, the two coupling constants J_{aa} and J_{ae} should be quite different from each other. This is precisely the case for LIVB and LV. The *cis*-isomer LIVB displays a triplet ($J_{ae} = J_{ee} = $ 5 cps) for the ring-junction proton and therefore corresponds to the conformation shown. The compound LV which is also *cis*-fused, depicts a quartet ($J_{aa} = $ 11 cps, $J_{ae} = $ 5 cps) instead of this triplet and is best represented by the conformation shown.

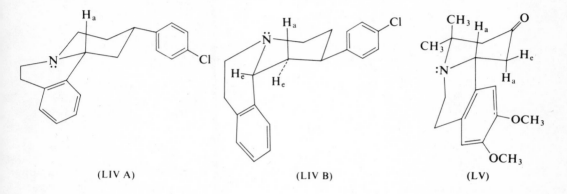

(LIV A)   (LIV B)   (LV)

6.   Long-Range Shielding by π-Electron Systems

6.1. Steric Requirements.   The chemical shift of a proton not only depends on the environment but also on the orientation of the neighboring groups. The π-electrons of the benzene ring and the carbonyl group show pronounced effect on the position of a proton signal which may be separated by several bonds. In general, if a proton is approximately in the plane of the aromatic ring or the plane containing the trigonal carbon and the double-bond oxygen, it is deshielded. If, however, the proton is positioned roughly above or under these functional groups and perpendicular to the planes mentioned above, there is shielding and the proton is shifted to an upfield position by as much as 1 ppm. Theoretical studies have shown that the long-range shielding effects of a carbonyl group or a benzene ring (shielding $\oplus$ or deshielding $\ominus$) can be approximately represented by the

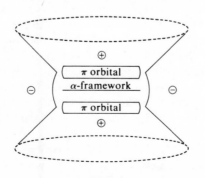

(LVI)

cone-shaped boundaries shown in LVI. Shielding in the appropriate direction has been observed for carbon-carbon double bonds, the cyclopropyl ring, and heteroaromatic rings.

This anisotropy (dependence on orientation) has provided a powerful tool for detailed stereochemical information not easily available otherwise. A few illustrative examples will be discussed here.

6.2. Anisotropy of Aromatic Systems. The reaction of benzal bromide with alkyllithium in presence of 1-butene[48] led to two epimeric cyclopropane derivatives, LVII and LVIII. The chemical shifts for the methyl protons in these isomers were found to be 9.13 and 8.98 τ, respectively. Taking into account the shielding effect of the aromatic ring, it could be deduced that LVII corresponds to the *cis* compound. The stereospecific synthesis of LVIII from *trans*-1-phenyl-1-butene by the Simmons-Smith reaction corroborated this finding.

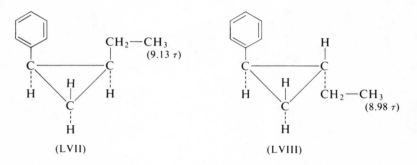

The anisotropy of the aromatic system has been shown to provide an easy distinction between *cis* C/D and *trans* C/D steroids in which the B-ring is aromatic.[49] From the partial molecular models of the isomeric anthrasteroids LIX and LX, it is evident that the C-18 methyl protons in the *trans* compound will be shielded by the B-ring. The C-18 methyl signals for LIX and LX were found to be located at 9.45 τ and 9.05 τ respectively indicating that LIX is the *trans* C/D compound, (Figure 29).

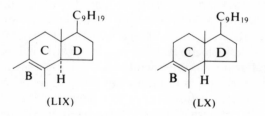

In some areas of stereochemistry NMR spectrometry can reveal information not available from other physical measurements. An example of this is afforded by a recent study on 1-phenylcyclohexenes.[50] The phenyl ring is capable of free rotation around the C-1-phenyl bond. The chemical shift of the olefinic proton will, of course, be influenced by the position of the benzene ring because of its anisotropy. Using appropriate theoretical considerations and making certain assumptions, curves were constructed for predicting the τ-value of the olefinic proton for different values of Φ, the dihedral angle between the olefinic proton and the plane of the phenyl ring (see LXI, LXIA and LXIB). It was argued that for 1-phenyl cyclohexene itself the phenyl ring was approximately in the plane of the ethylene bond. The chemical shift for the olefinic proton in this compound, 4.0 τ, was used as the reference for other 1-phenyl cyclohexenes with substituents in the *o*-position of the benzene ring or the 6,6-positions of the cyclohexene. The chemical shift of the

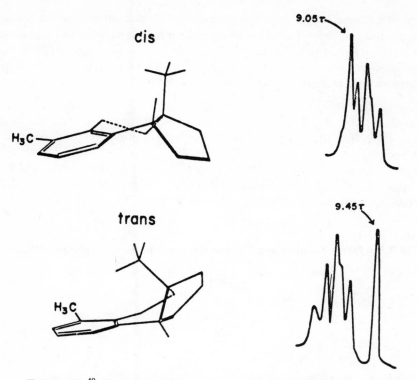

FIGURE 29.[49] Partial Dreiding models and partial NMR spectra of the isomeric anthrasteroids LIX (**trans**) and LX (**cis**).

olefinic protons, after certain corrections, were translated into the dihedral angle using the theoretical curves. Self-consistent values were obtained on the whole. Only a few of the findings will be cited here. It was concluded that the phenyl ring was nearly planar in the 6-methyl compound but in the 6,6-dimethyl and in o,o'-dimethyl compounds the dihedral angle was about 90°. The 6-phenyl compound appeared to have the phenyl group in the axial conformation at C-6 while the 1-phenyl ring was roughly planar. The UV

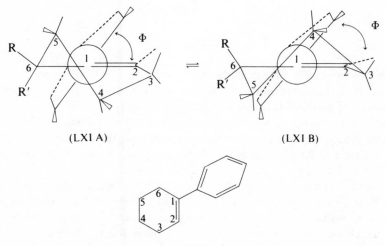

spectra supported these conclusions in a general way by indicating whether there was rotation of the phenyl ring from the plane of conjugation. No quantitative estimation of this rotation is possible from the UV spectra.

7. Spin Interaction of Protons With Other Nuclei

According to the theory of NMR spectroscopy any two nuclei with non-zero spins can show spin-spin interaction. The coupling of protons with many nuclei such as deuterium, fluorine, ^{13}C, ^{15}N, ^{17}O, ^{31}P, ^{199}Hg, etc., have received attention. We shall consider here only three such nuclei.

7.1. F-H Interaction. Many studies have been reported on the proton NMR spectra of fluoro compounds. The couplings between fluorine and protons are much stronger than the couplings between two analogously situated protons. A list of coupling constants is given in Table 3.

TABLE 3.[61] **Proton Fluorine and Fluorine-fluorine Spin-spin Coupling Constants (cps)**

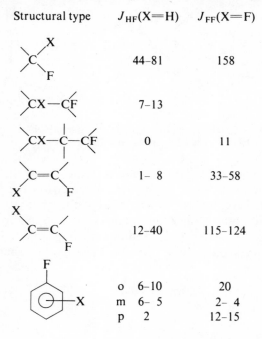

Structural type	$J_{HF}(X{=}H)$	$J_{FF}(X{=}F)$
	44–81	158
	7–13	
	0	11
	1– 8	33–58
	12–40	115–124
o	6–10	20
m	6– 5	2– 4
p	2	12–15

Taking advantage of the fact that chemical shifts in ^{19}F NMR spectra are ten to fifty times greater than the corresponding proton spectra, Roberts[85] has studied conformational equilibria of geminal-substituted fluoro compounds. This approach has provided useful information concerning several higher cycloalkanes. For example, the ^{19}F spectrum of 1,1,2,2-tetrafluorocyclooctane shows a complex temperature dependence which can be best explained on the basis of interconversions involving twist-boat and/or saddle conformations for cyclooctane.

Long-range H-F coupling has attracted considerable interest. In some cases such couplings involve nuclei separated by more than five bonds. It has been suggested that the spin interaction might take place through space rather than through the mediation of bonds. Although this point is unsettled, it has been firmly established that long-range coupling between proton and fluorine becomes observable only when they are in a particular stereochemical disposition with respect to each other. An empirical rule called the "converging vector rule" has been developed by Cross and Landis[51] for defining the steric requirements.

7.2. ^{13}C-H Interaction. Considerable theoretical interest attaches to the spin interaction between ^{13}C and protons. It is generally accepted that a linear correlation exists between the per cent of s-character of carbon orbitals and ^{13}C-H coupling constants. Some ^{13}C-H J values are reported in Table 4. It may be noted that they are much larger than analogous H-H coupling constants.

It is fortunate for NMR spectroscopists that the natural abundance of ^{13}C is only 1 per cent. Proton NMR spectra recorded in solution do not show the satellites due to ^{13}C-H

TABLE 4. ^{13}**C—H Coupling Constants (cps)**

Structural Type	$J_{13_{CH}}$	$J_{13_{C-CH}}$	$J_{13_{CCCH}}$	$J_{13_{COCH}}$	$J_{13_{CNH}}$	$J_{13_{CNCH}}$	Ref.
benzene	158						62
pyridine	179						62
cyclohexane	123						63
$Cl_3C\,^{13}CHO$	207.2						62
$(CH_3CH_2)_2\,^{13}CDOH$		4	5.3				64
$CH_3-\overset{\alpha}{CH_2}\,^{13}C(OH)\overset{\beta}{(CH_3)_2}$		4 (α) 4.1(β)	4.0				64
$\overset{\alpha CH_3}{\underset{\overset{\mid}{^{13}CH_3-C(Cl)CH_2CH_3}}{}}\,\beta$	132		4.2 (α) 3.2 (β)				64
$CH_3-\,^{13}COOCH_2CH_3$		6.0		3.1			64
$CH_3CH_2\,^{13}CO_2CH_3$		6.5	5.3	4.0			64
$C_6H_5-C\equiv\,^{13}C-H$	251						63
$^{13}CH_3C\equiv CH$	131.4		3.6				65
$CH_3C\equiv\,^{13}CH$	247.6		4.8				65
$\overset{\alpha}{CH_3}-\,^{13}C\equiv\overset{\beta}{CH}$		10.6(α) 50(β)					65
$\underset{H-\overset{13}{\triangle}-H}{H_3C\diagdown\diagup CH_3}$	220						66
$C_6H_5NH-CS-NH-\,^{13}CH_3$	140				2.7		53
$C_6H_5CH=N-\,^{13}CH_3$	134.2					13.2	53

interaction. When a liquid sample is used without a solvent, additional signals due to ^{13}C-H couplings may make their appearance. These signals carry valuable information about the H-H couplings too and are useful for an accurate determination of the J values in a complex pattern of proton resonance lines. A recent study[34] on norbornenes will be cited here as an illustration (also see Section 4.4).

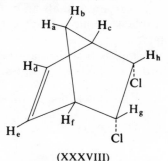

(XXXVIII)

The spectrum of the norbornene XXXVIII (Figure 28) is complicated by long-range couplings and virtual coupling. Thus, the protons H_g and H_h produce a tight triplet at 4.4 τ. Theoretical considerations show that since these protons are magnetically equivalent their mutual coupling constant cannot be evaluated from this spectrum alone. The satellites of this triplet due to ^{13}C-H interaction is not observable in the ordinary spectrum. By using a time averaging computer device (Mnemotron CAT digital computer), the spectrum was scanned a large number of times to improve the signal to noise ratio. During this operation, the noise increases as $N^{1/2}$, but the signal increases as N (where N is the number of scans). The resulting spectrum showed that the satellite bands consisted of four lines. A simple analysis of this pattern gave the following coupling constants:

$$J_{^{13}CH_b} = 155 \pm 1 \text{ cps, } J_{gh} = 7.5 \pm 0.1 \text{ cps}$$
$$J_{fg} = 3.2 \pm 0.1 \text{ cps, } J_{cg} \cong 0$$

By a study of the ^{13}C-H satellite of the olefinic proton resonances, the following coupling constants were determined:

$$J_{de} = 5.5 \pm 0.1 \text{ cps, } J_{cd} = 2.85 \pm 0.1 \text{ cps}$$
$$J_{ce} \cong 0.65 \text{ cps}$$

A knowledge of these coupling constants permitted a complete interpretation of a very complex spectrum (see Section 4.4 for further discussion).

An elegant use has been made by Karabatsos *et al.*[52] of the ^{13}C-H interaction in a study of the mechanism of rearrangement of neopentyl compounds. The spectrum of neopentyl-1-^{13}C tosylate is shown in Figure 30: this is a composite of the spectra of TsOCH$_2$C(CH$_3$)$_3$, and TsO^{13}CH$_2$C(CH$_3$)$_2$, (LXIIA). In LXIIA the methylene signals is split by ^{13}C-H coupling and it appears as a doublet that is placed symmetrically around the methylene signal in the unlabelled compound. All other protons in both give coincident signals. By a comparison of the area under the methylene signals for the isomers it could be calculated that the ^{13}C content was 55.8 per cent.

The spectrum of the *t*-amyl alcohol LXIIB obtained by the solvoysis of this tosylate is shown in Figure 31. Satellite peaks for the methylene quartet (≈ 8.5 τ) can be easily observed (at 7.45 and 9.55 τ). Integration established the ^{13}C content at the methylene carbon to be substantially unchanged from that for the tosylate. The absence of satellites for the signals of the methyl groups indicate the lack of ^{13}C incorporation at C-1 or C-4.

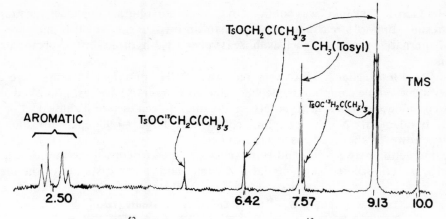

FIGURE 30.[52] NMR spectrum of neopentyl-1-^{13}C tosylate.

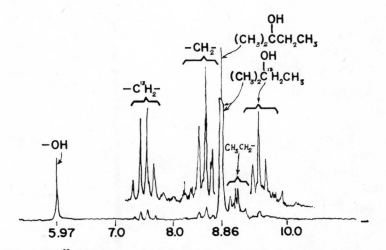

FIGURE 31.[52] NMR spectrum of t-amyl alcohol obtained from solvolysis of LXIII.

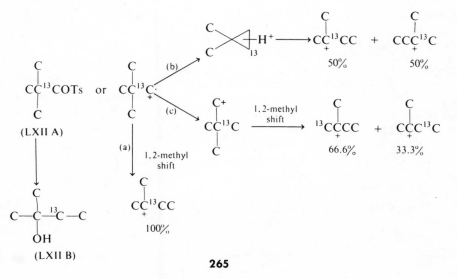

The inference that the label was confined to C-3 was corroborated by mass spectral studies. These results support a rearrangement mechanism involving 1,2-methyl shift and rule out several alternative pathways, such as those involving 1,3-hydride shift or protonated cyclopropanes.

7.3. ^{15}N-H Interaction. Until very recently, ^{15}N-H coupling constants were available for only a few simple compounds. Roberts and co-workers[53] have just published a study of ^{15}N-H coupling constants in a variety of organic molecules (see Table 5). For protons directly bonded to ^{15}N, the coupling constant is large (≈ 90 cps), for longer range coupling, however, the J value is less than 5 cps.

The interaction between ^{15}N and H makes NMR spectroscopy a method of great potential for biogenetic studies using ^{15}N-labeled compounds and for studies of the mechanism

TABLE 5. ^{15}N—H Coupling Constants (cps)

Structural Type	$J_{^{15}N-H}$	$J_{^{15}NCH}$	$J_{^{15}NCCH}$	$J_{^{15}N-N=CH}$	Ref.
CH_3—$^{15}NH_3Cl$	75.6	0.8			53
$(C_6H_5)_2C=NH$	51				53
H_2—^{15}N—CO—NH_2	89				53
C_6H_5NH—CO—^{15}NH—C_6H_5	89.7				54
CH_3—CO—$C(=N$—^{15}NH—$C_6H_5)$—$COOCH_2CH_3$	96.2				54
$CH_3CO\,^{15}NH_2$	89		1.3		53
C_6H_5—$CH_3^{\alpha}=^{15}N$—CH_3^{β}		3.9(α) 0.6(β)			53
C_6H_5—$CH=^{15}N$—C_6H_5		3.8			54
H—$C(=^{15}N$—$C_6H_5)$—$N(CH_3)_2$		2.5			54
C_6H_5—$CH=N$—$^{15}NHC_6H_5$	92.7			6.6	54
CH_3—$^{15}N=C=S$		3.3			53
CH_3—$C\equiv^{15}N$			1.7		53
H—$C(=O)$—$^{15}N(CH_3^{\alpha})(CH_3^{\beta})$ (γ)		15.6(γ) 1.2(α) 1.1(β)			53
H—$C(=N$—$C_6H_5)$—$^{15}N(CH_3^{\alpha})(CH_3)$ (β)		$\approx 0(\alpha)$ 8.4(β)			54
cyclohexane-fused ^{15}N—CH_3 imide (dioxo)		1.4			53

of certain reactions. As an illustration can be cited an examination of the possibility that the phenyldiazonium ion undergoes "tumbling."

$$[C_6H_5—^{15}N≡N]^+ \rightleftharpoons [^{15}N≡N—C_6H_5]^+$$

The sequence of reactions shown in Chart 4 was carried out with ^{15}N-labeled aniline (isotopic purity ≈ 95 per cent).[54] Had there been any phenyl migration, the products LXIII and LXIV would have been admixed with the labeled species LXIIIA and LXIVA, respectively. The NMR spectra of LXIII and LXIV, however, showed no noticeable peak for ^{14}N-H; instead, doublets (J = 92.7 and 96.2 cps, respectively) corresponding to ^{15}N-H were observed. The conclusion, therefore, is that no appreciable aryl migration occurs in arylidiazonium compounds under the reaction conditions studied.

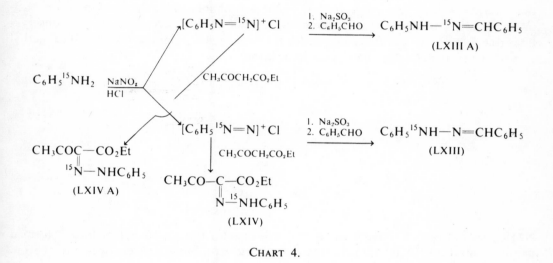

CHART 4.

8. Newer Trends

NMR spectroscopy has become an integral part of organic chemistry. Its value for structure determination will be considerably enhanced in the future with the availability of spectrometers using oscillator frequencies of 200 Mc or even 300 Mc. Studies on conformation and other subtler aspects of stereochemistry will continue to rely heavily on NMR data. Increased use of this tool can also be predicted for studies on reaction mechanism and kinetics. A brief illustration of this aspect of NMR spectroscopy will be provided here from some recent literature.

The sensitivity of the proton signal to a change in the magnetic environment has provided the physical organic chemist with an unusually valuable probe for studies on reaction mechanism. Increasing use is being made of NMR spectroscopy for detecting reaction intermediates such as the carbonium ion. The spectrum (see Table 6) of allyl fluoride in liquid sulfur dioxide solution is consistent with the covalent structure LXVA but a solution of LXVA in a mixture of antimony pentafluoride and liquid sulfur dioxide gives a simplified spectrum which has been construed as evidence for the mesomeric allyl car-

TABLE 6.[55]   **N.M.R. Shifts (in ppm. from External TMS) of the Allyl and Methallyl Cations as Hexafluoroantimonate Complexes in SO_2—SbF_5 Sol. at $-60°$**

	$=CH_2$		$-CH-$	$-CH_2F$	$-CH_3$
$CH_2{=}CH{-}CH_2{-}F$ (in SO_2)	-5.14 *(trans)*	-5.01 *(cis)*	-5.52	-4.56 ($J_{HF} = 47.5$)	
$[CH_2{\cdots}CH{\cdots}CH_2]^+SbF_6^-$			-8.97	-9.64	
$CH_2{=}C(CH_3){-}CH_2{-}F$ (in SO_2)	-4.81		-4.69	-4.32 ($J_{HF} = 46$)	-1.47
$[CH_2{\cdots}C(CH_3){\cdots}CH_2]^+\ SbF_6^-$			-8.95		-3.85

bonium ion (LXVB).[55] The broad doublet peak (4H) at 1.03 τ and the unresolved broad singlet (1H) at 0.36 τ are in accord with the structure LXVB. The stikingly low value of the chemical shift for the single proton signal is probably indicative of appreciable 1,3-interaction leading to a partial charge on the middle carbon (LXVIA). Similar observations (see Table 6) have also been made for the next higher homolog LXVIB. The methyl group is strongly deshielded here in the ionic form.

$$H_2C{=}CH{-}CH_2F + SbF_5 \longrightarrow H_2C{=}CH{-}\overset{+}{C}H_2 + [SbF_6]^-$$

(LXV A) $\updownarrow$

$$H_2\overset{+}{C}{-}CH{=}CH_2$$

(LXV B)

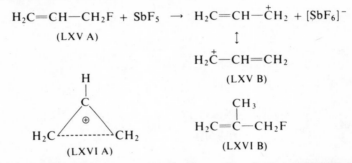

(LXVI A)   (LXVI B)

NMR spectra (Table 7) have been cited as evidence for the ion LXVIIB which is formed on dissolving LXVIIA in chlorosulfonic or sulfuric acid, but which changes into the ion LXVIIIB in 5% SO_3-95% H_2SO_4.[56] The latter ion is also obtained by dissolving mesitoic acid chloride (LXVIIIA) in chlorosulfonic or sulfuric acid.

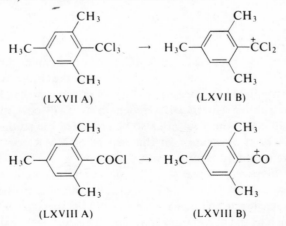

(LXVII A)   (LXVII B)

(LXVIII A)   (LXVIII B)

Convincing evidence for the existence of benzenonium ions can be obtained from NMR studies. An equimolar mixture of HF + SbF_5 serves to protonate aromatic hydrocarbons.[57] The use of the aprotic solvent liquid sulfur dioxide prevented an alteration of the NMR spectrum due to proton exchange with the medium. The spectrum at low tem-

TABLE 7.[56a] N.M.R. Spectra of Solutions of Mesitoyl Chloride and Trichloromethylmesitylene in $HCISO_3$ and H_2SO_4: Values in ppm; Relative Areas in Parenthesis

	$HCISO_3$			H_2SO_4		
	τ_1	τ_2	τ_3	τ_1	τ_2	τ_3
$RCOCl$	2.64(2)	7.36(6)	7.50(3)	2.63(2)	7.33(6)	7.48(3)
$RCCl_3$	2.56(2)	7.13(2)	7.48(3)	2.56(2)	7.12(6)	7.46(3)

perature (Figure 32) was fully consistent with the benzenonium ion LXIX expected from 1,2,4-trimethylbenzene.

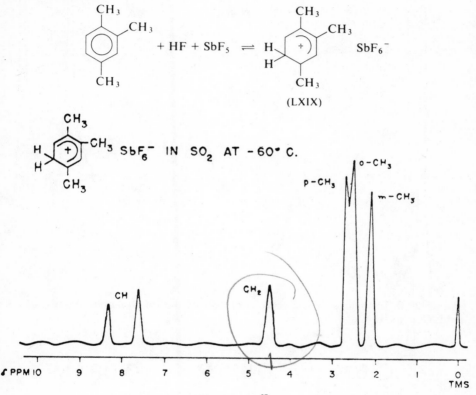

(LXIX)

SbF$_6^-$ IN SO$_2$ AT −60° C.

FIGURE 32.[57]

The halide exchange between covalent trityl halides and trityl cations may occur according to two alternative mechanisms (8.1) and (8.2).[58]

$$Ar_3CCl + Ar_3C^+Y^- \rightleftharpoons Ar_3C^+Y^- + Ar_3CCl \qquad (8.1)$$
$$(LXXA) \qquad (LXXB)$$

or

$$Ar_3CCl \rightleftharpoons Ar_3C^+Cl^-$$
$$Ar_3C^+Cl^- + Ar_3C^+Y^- \rightleftharpoons Ar_3C^+Y^- + Ar_3C^+Cl^- \qquad (8.2)$$

The bimolecular mechanism (Eq. 8.1) requires second-order kinetics whereas the $S_N 1$ type process (Eq. 8.2) calls for first-order kinetics.

The methyl signal in the NMR spectrum of a methylene chloride solution of LXXA appears as a sharp peak at 7.68 τ; the corresponding peak in LXXB occurs at 7.30 τ. For an equimolar mixture of LXXA and LXXB at 37°, a sharp peak is observed at 7.50τ—precisely the chemical shift expected for exchange averaging the methyl protons; $\frac{1}{2}(7.60 + 7.30) = 7.49\ \tau$. At lower temperature the line broadens and finally the singlet gives place to a doublet (Figure 33). The shape of this doublet is dependent on the concentration of LXX A and B (see Figure 34).

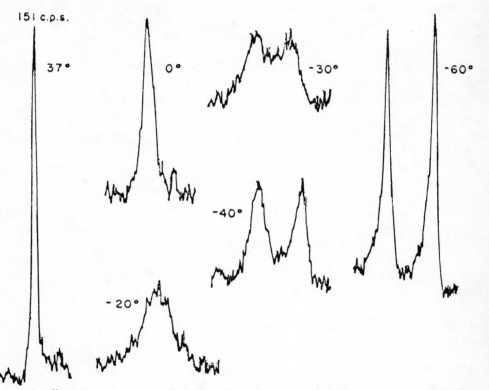

FIGURE 33.[58] Temperature dependence of methyl protons for equimolar mixture of LXXA and LXXB in CH_2Cl_2.

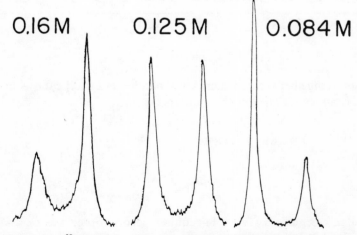

FIGURE 34.[58] Concentration (LXXB/LXXA) dependence of line broadening of methyl protons of LXXA and LXXB in CH_2Cl_2 at $-56°$.

Theoretical considerations indicate a correlation between the line half-widths and the lifetimes of both species. It was found that the line-broadening data was in agreement with the S_N1 mechanism and not the bimolecular mechanism. It was also possible to utilize the temperature dependence on the spectra to construct an Arrhenius plot and determine that $E_a = 7.5$ kcal/mole.

In spite of the versatility of NMR spectroscopy, there are certain structural problems that are better approached with the help of other spectral methods. The precise information on carbonyl functions available from infrared spectra is not easy to obtain from NMR spectra.* Ultraviolet spectra, too, can outdo NMR spectra in some cases in furnishing details concerning conjugated systems. The fragmentation pattern of some complex molecules in mass spectroscopy, such as indole alkaloids, may afford a large amount of structural data not always available from NMR spectra.

The sample size required for infrared, ultraviolet, or mass spectra (1 mg or less) is much smaller than for NMR spectra (5 to 50 mg). Time averaging computer devices, however, can reduce the sample size to the order of a few milligrams or even a fraction of a milligram if a micro-cell is used. These devices, however, are expensive and their use is time-consuming.

Limitations of space have restricted the number and variety of spectra examined in this chapter. The selection of topics discussed has, of course, been influenced by the personal preference of the author. To minimize the documentation, most of the references have been chosen from recent publications which in turn cite earlier literature. A set of problems has been provided for the reader to gauge his progress in spectral interpretation. There already are many subtleties and special techniques that can be mastered only through close familiarity with a large number of spectra. Such is the pace of progress in NMR spectroscopy that further sophistication in techniques and interpretation will continue to come for a long time.

PROBLEMS

1. Deduce the possible structures for the compound $C_{10}H_{19}Cl$, from its NMR spectrum (CDCl$_3$, 60 Mc., Figure 35, p. 272).

2. The bromination of menthone led to a dibromo compound which gave the NMR spectrum (CCl$_4$, 60 Mc) shown in Figure 36 (p. 272). Deduce the structure, configuration and conformation of this bromo derivative.

Menthone

3. Figures 37 and 38 (p. 273) correspond to two of the three isomeric compounds (LXXIA, B and C). Make spectral assignments and determine which structures are represented by the two spectra.

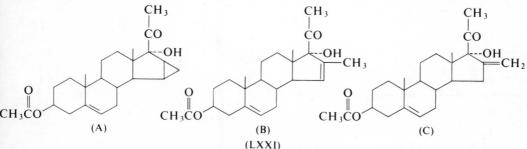

(A)   (B)   (C)

(LXXI)

*According to H. M. Fales and T. Luukkainen (*Anal. Chem.*, **37**, 955 (1965)) the carbonyl groups in a compound can be counted by integrating the 6.2 τ peak (CH$_3$—O—) in the NMR spectrum of the easily prepared O-methyloxime derivative ($>$C$=$O $\rightarrow$ $>$C$=$N—OCH$_3$) of the compound.

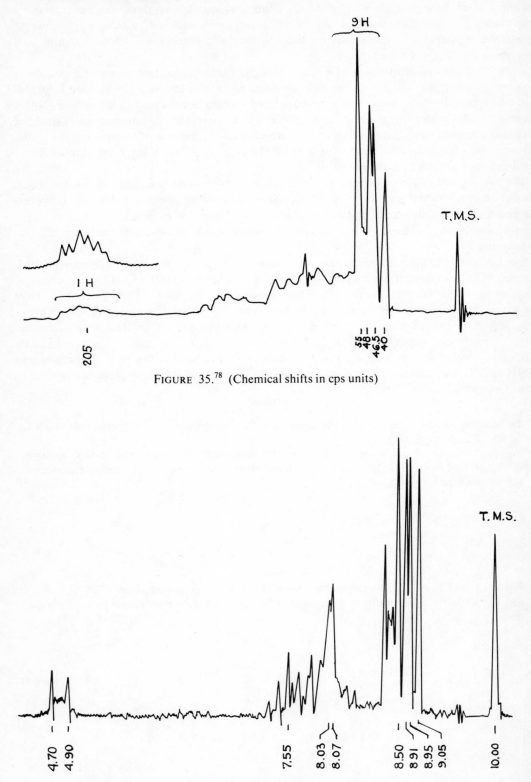

FIGURE 35.[78] (Chemical shifts in cps units)

FIGURE 36.[78]

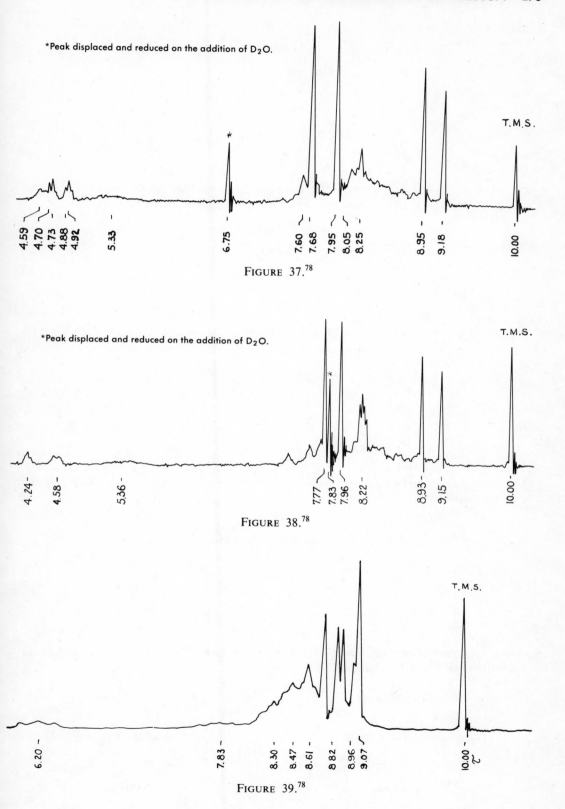

*Peak displaced and reduced on the addition of D₂O.

FIGURE 37.[78]

*Peak displaced and reduced on the addition of D₂O.

FIGURE 38.[78]

FIGURE 39.[78]

4. Make as many assignments as possible in the NMR spectrum (CDCl$_3$, 60 Mc, Figure 39, p. 273) of santanolide A.

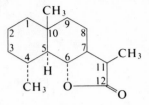

Santanolide A

5. The NMR spectra (CDCl$_3$, 60 Mc) of the three possible isomers of LXXII are shown in Figures 40, 41, and 42. Correlate the spectra with the conformation of the isomers.

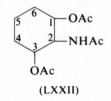

(LXXII)

6. Does either the structure LXXIII or LXXIV correspond to the spectrum in Figure 43 (p. 276)?

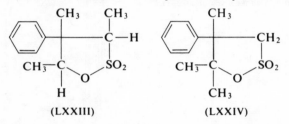

(LXXIII)   (LXXIV)

7. Make complete spectral assignments (Figure 44, p. 276) for the γ-lactam LXXV. Calculate the coupling constants.

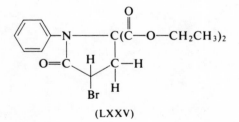

(LXXV)

8. Account for the difference between the NMR spectra (Figures 5, p. 224 and 45, p. 276) of the isomeric compounds LXXVI and LXXVII.

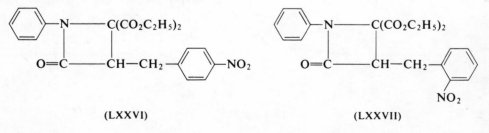

(LXXVI)   (LXXVII)

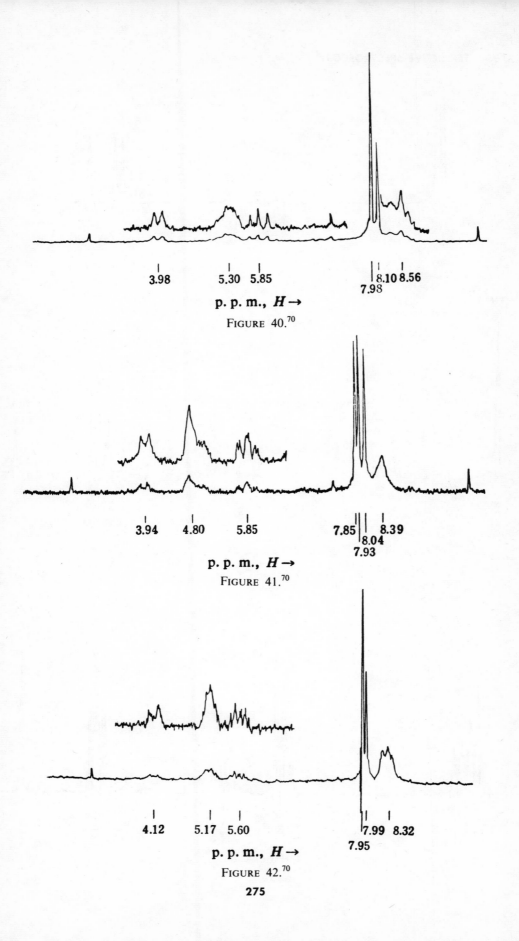

3.98   5.30 5.85 | 8.10 8.56
                              7.98

p. p. m., *H* →

FIGURE 40.[70]

3.94   4.80   5.85   7.85 | 8.39
                              8.04
                            7.93

p. p. m., *H* →

FIGURE 41.[70]

4.12   5.17 5.60   7.99 8.32
                          7.95

p. p. m., *H* →

FIGURE 42.[70]

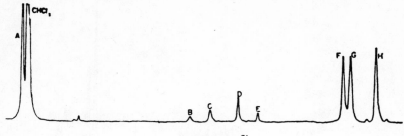

FIGURE 43.[71]

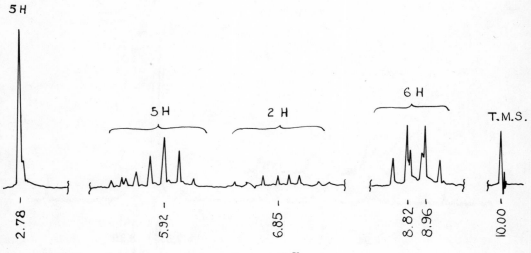

FIGURE 44.[78]

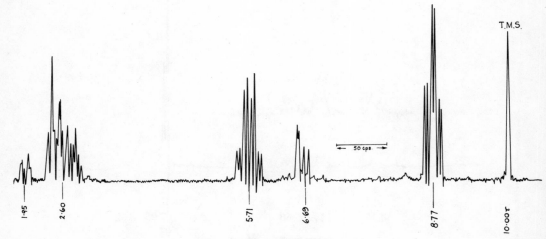

FIGURE 45.[78]

9. Which of the following structures (LXXVIII A, B, C and D) are consistent with the NMR spectrum (Figure 46, p. 278) of α-elemene?

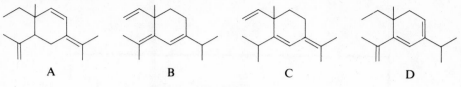

A   B   C   D

(LXXVIII)

10. A study of the NMR spectrum of the tetraacetate of a pentopyranose (LXXIX) has led to the following coupling constants: $J_{12} = 6$, $J_{45} = 3.2$, and 8 cps. The other coupling constants could not be derived because of the overlap of signals. The $8\ \tau$ region of the spectrum shows two sharp methyl peaks: $8.09\ \tau$ (3H), $8.23\ \tau$ (9H). Deduce the stereochemistry of LXXIX.

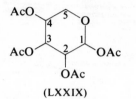

(LXXIX)

11. The NMR spectra (60 Mc, $CDCl_3$) of the three isomeric bicyclooctane derivatives LXXX, LXXXI and LXXXII are shown in Figures 47, 48 and 49 (p. 279). Assign the structures to these spectra.

(LXXX)

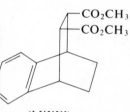

(LXXXI)

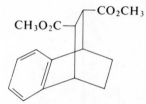

(LXXXII)

12. The reaction of methyl isocyanate with salicylaldehyde leads to a 1:1 addition product for which structures LXXXIII and LXXXIV are probable. The NMR spectrum of this compound in dimethyl sulfoxide solution recorded on a 60 Mc spectrometer is shown in Figure 50 (p. 280). Does this spectrum agree with either of these structures?

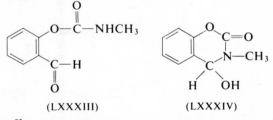

(LXXXIII)   (LXXXIV)

13. McCasland and Horswill[82] had proposed the structure LXXXV for a cyclohexane tetrol. Determine whether the spectra in Figure 8 support this assignment.

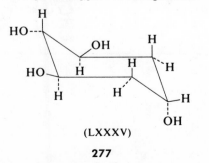

(LXXXV)

277

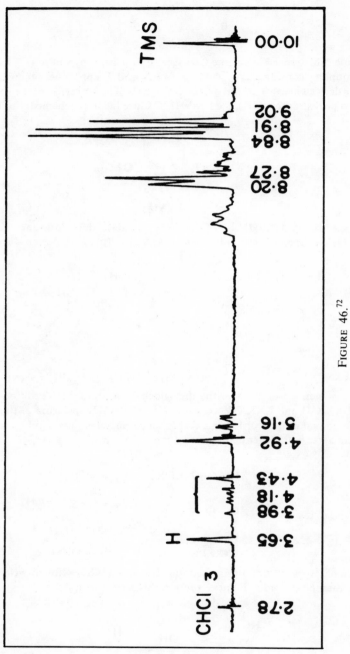

FIGURE 46.[72]

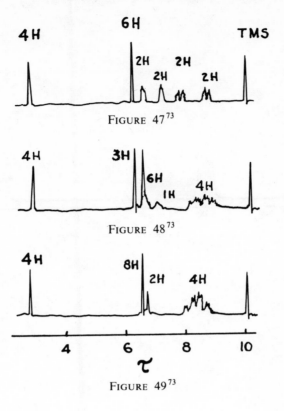

FIGURE 47[73]

FIGURE 48[73]

FIGURE 49[73]

14. During the polymerization of 4-vinylpyridine, a crystalline trimer was obtained. Its NMR spectrum (100 Mc, CDCl₃, Figure 51, p. 280) showed five multiplets with chemical shift of 8.55, 7.20, 3.00, 2.25, and 1.80 δ and relative intensities of 2:2:1:1:1, respectively. The chemical shifts refer to the center of the bands. Show that this spectrum is in agreement with the conformation LXXXVI. Make complete assignments to the resonance lines.

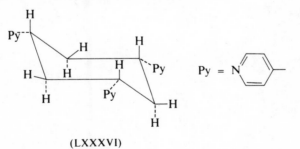

(LXXXVI)

15. The alkaloid vincaminine is closely related to vincine, LXXXVII. From a study of the NMR spectra (Figures 52 and 53, pp. 280–81) of these two compounds deduce structural features of vincaminine.

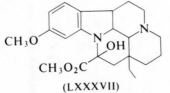

(LXXXVII)

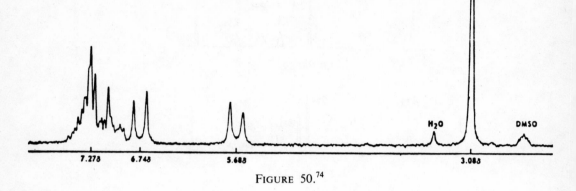

FIGURE 50.[74]

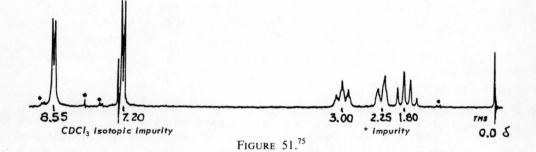

FIGURE 51.[75]

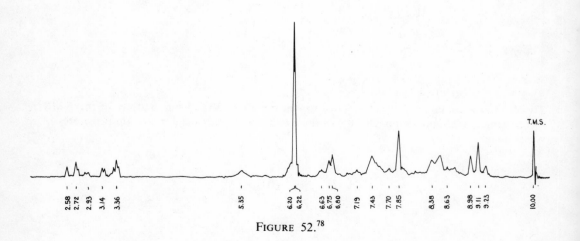

FIGURE 52.[78]

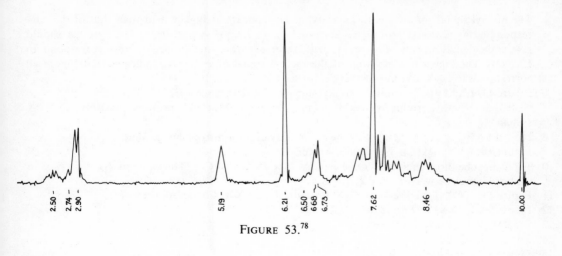

FIGURE 53.[78]

ANSWERS

1. No ethyl side chain or olefinic proton present. It must be a ring compound with three secondary methyl groups or one secondary methyl and one isopropyl group. The chlorine atom must be on the ring to account for only one strongly deshielded proton.
2. The doublet at 4.80 τ indicates one proton on a carbon carrying bromine. The other bromine therefore is at C-4. The large value of the coupling constant for the doublet (12 cps) corresponds to J_{aa}. Hence the conformation of the dibromo compound is LXXXIX. Note the uncertainty about the stereochemistry at C-4.

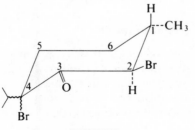

(LXXXIX)

3. Figure 37: LXX; note the AB spectrum of the exo-methylene group centered at 4.80 τ. Figure 38: LXIX; note the long range splitting of the methyl signal at 8.23 τ.
4. The multiplet at 6.20 τ must be due to H-6. The tall peak at 9.07 τ corresponds to the unsplit angular methyl group. The two doublets centered at 8.96 τ and 8.82 τ ($J = 5.4$ and 6.3 cps) are the signals of the secondary methyl groups at C-4 and C-11 respectively. The small deshielding of the methyl at C-4 is due to the proximity of the lactone group.
5. The three possible iosmers in their lowest energy conformations are LXXII A, B anc C.

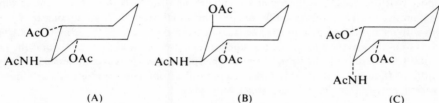

(A)   (B)   (C)

(LXXII)

The methyl signals of an equatorial acetyl group appears at higher field than that of the corresponding axial acetyl group (see Section 5.1). In LXXII A and C the OAc groups should give coincidental signals. Figure 41, with three separate methyl peaks must correspond to LXXIIB. The higher field position of the methyl signal of —N—Ac indicates that Figure 40 corresponds to LXXIIA. For further details see Ref. 70.

6. Figure 43: LXXIVB; note unsplit methyl signals. For details see Ref. 71.

7. Note that the ethyl groups are slightly nonequivalent and the ring protons constitute an ABX system.

8. Note the ABC system generated by the asymmetry of the *o*-nitrophenyl group.

9. Figure 4B: LXXVIII (C). For details see Ref. 72.

10. There must be three equatorial OAc groups—one of them at C-4. The value of J_{12} = 6 cps is in the border area between J_{aa} and J_{ae} (or J_{ee}).

11. Figure 47: LXXXI; Figure 48: LXXXII; Figure 49: LXXX. For details see Ref. 73.

12. Figure 50: LXXXIV. For details see Ref. 74.

13. See Ref. 36 for a detailed discussion.

14. For details see Ref. 75.

15. Figure 53. For details see Ref. 76.

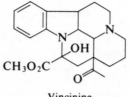

Vincinine

APPENDIX

Nuclear Magnetic Resonance Phenomenon

One of the fundamental parameters of a nucleus is its spin number I. Unless this number is zero, the nucleus behaves as a small magnet when placed in a magnetic field (I = ½ for H, ^{13}C, F, and ^{15}N). The magnetic axis of the nucleus can assume 2I + 1 orientations with respect to the external magnetic field, each such orientation corresponds to a quantized energy level. Transitions between these levels are governed by the relationships expressed by Eq. A.1 and A.2.

$$\text{Energy of transition, } \Delta E = \frac{\mu H_0}{I} \tag{A.1}$$

where

$$\mu = \text{magnetic dipole of the nucleus, } H_0 = \text{magnetic field,}$$
$$I = \text{spin number (½, 1, 1½, etc.)}$$

$$\Delta E = h\nu \tag{A.2}$$

where ν is the frequency of the electromagnetic radiation absorbed or radiated during the transition.

Now, suppose that the nucleus is placed in a magnetic field H_0 such that the magnetic dipole is in one of the quantized orientations (see Figure 54). The situation then is analogous to a top that is given a spin with its axis at an angle to the vertical (i.e., the direction of the gravitational field of the earth): as is well-known, the axis of the top undergoes a precessional motion around the vertical —the crown of the top describes a horizontal circle. The spinning nucleus also undertakes this type of gyroscopic motion. If, now, the nucleus is subjected to an electromagnetic radiation the frequency, ν, of which is varied, energy transfer will take place only when

$$h\nu = \frac{\mu H_0}{I} \qquad \text{or} \qquad \nu = \frac{\mu H_0}{hI}$$

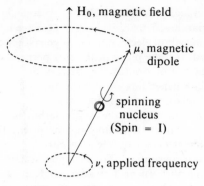

H_0, magnetic field

μ, magnetic dipole

spinning nucleus (Spin = I)

ν, applied frequency

FIGURE 54.

This is called the resonance frequency and the effect of the radiation of this frequency will be to force the nucleus to the quantized orientation corresponding to the next higher energy level. For protons, $I = \frac{1}{2}$, $\mu = 1.42 \times 10^{-23}$ erg/G. The resonance frequency for protons in a magnetic field $H_0 = 14{,}090$ G will be given by Eq. A.3.

$$\nu = \frac{(1.42 \times 10^{-23}\,\text{erg/G})\,(14{,}090\,\text{G})}{(6.6235 \times 10^{-27}\,\text{erg sec})\,(\frac{1}{2})} \tag{A.3}$$

$$= 60.0\,\text{Mc/sec}$$

For a 200 Mc NMR spectrometer for protons, the stable magnetic field H_0 must be

$$\frac{(200\,\text{Mc/sec.})\,(6.6235 \times 10^{-27}\,\text{erg sec.})\,(\frac{1}{2})}{(1.42 \times 10^{-23}\,\text{erg/G})} = 46{,}645\,\text{G}$$

It will not only be necessary to generate this strong field but also keep its variations lower than 1 in 10^8 or 10^9. This extremely homogenous field need be achieved over only a small volume—enough to encompass the sample for recording NMR spectra.

NMR spectroscopy would have been of little value to organic chemists if all the protons in a molecule resonated at the same frequency, ν, when placed in a given magnetic field H_0. Fortunately, the effective magnetic field, H_{eff}, for any particular proton is slightly different from the applied field H_0: these two can be related by Eq. A.4.

$$H_{eff} = H_0 - \delta H_0 = H_0(1 - \delta) \tag{A.4}$$

where δ = shielding constant (see below).

The magnetic field δH_0 induced at a particular proton is a measure of the "shielding" produced at that proton by its total environment. This shielding may be caused by several factors that are discussed below.

The applied magnetic field induces the electron associated with a nucleus to circulate in a specific manner. The motion of electrons generates a magnetic field opposing the applied magnetic field. This phenomenon is referred to as local "diamagnetic shielding."

The electron distribution around a nucleus is influenced by the neighboring atoms. For example, a proton bonded to a carbon atom has a higher electron density than a proton bonded to an oxygen atom. The local diamagnetic shielding will be greater for the C-H proton and it will appear at a higher field than the O-H proton. In case of an enol or a carboxyl group, the proton is almost devoid of its electrons, such protons are therefore subject to very little shielding and appear at very low field (as low as $-7\,\tau$ in some cases).

Under certain circumstances the applied magnetic field could induce an electron circulation leading to a secondary magnetic field that *enhances* the applied field, H_0; this is called paramagnetic shielding. Thus, in case of acetylene if the applied magnetic field is along the molecular axis, no paramagnetic currents are generated. If, however, the molecule is so oriented that the applied field is perpendicular to the molecular axis, the acetylene protons experience an induced magnetic field that adds to the applied field and produces shielding. Acetylenic protons therefore appear at a high field (7.12 τ). Similar paramagnetic shielding is produced by other π-electron systems such as C≡C, C=O or by the lone pair of electrons on nitrogen (see Section 5.7).

When an aromatic ring is placed with the plane of the ring perpendicular to the applied magnetic field, a ring current is induced by the motion of the π-electrons. This ring current produces diamagnetic or paramagnetic shielding depending on the location of a given proton in the molecule *vis à vis* the ring (see LVI and Section 6).

Even when the aromatic ring is not a part of the molecule but is present in the solvent, it may affect the effective shielding at a proton. Depending on the orientation, different protons in the molecule will be shielded to different extent by the ring current (see Section 2.4) in the solvate aromatic ring (such as benzene and pyridine). For an approximate calculation of the shielding effect of benzene on the protons of a norbornene derivative, see Ref. 34.

Another contributing factor to the shielding of a proton arises from the long-range effect of a group of electrons not directly associated with the proton. Such an effect is significant only when the field induced by the diamagnetic circulation of these electrons is not spherically symmetrical. The absence of this symmetry is referred to as "diamagnetic anisotropy." It causes shielding at a distant proton even after the field has been averaged over all orientations with respect to the direction of the applied field. McConnell[77] has derived an approximate Eq. (A-5) for the shielding σ of a proton by an axially symmetrical group of electrons

$$\sigma = \frac{(3\cos^2\theta - 1)(\chi_L - \chi_T)}{3r^3} \qquad \text{(A.5)}$$

where r is the distance between the proton and the electrical center of gravity of the electrons, θ is the acute angle which r extends at the symmetry axis (see Figure 55), and $(\chi_L - \chi_T)$ is a measure of the diamagnetic anisotropy of the electrons.

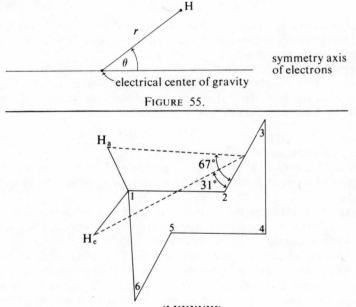

FIGURE 55.

(LXXXVIII)

Even the qualitative application of Eq. A-5 to cyclohexane yields some interesting results. Consider the axial and equatorial protons at C-1 in LXXXVIII. These protons are symmetrically situated with respect to the bonds C_1—C_2 and C_1—C_6. The electrical center of gravity of bond C_2—C_3 may be assumed to be the mid-point of the bond. The angle θ (see Eq. A.5) for the axial and the equatorial proton is 67° and 31°, respectively. The value of $(3\cos^2\theta - 1)$ is negative for $\theta = 67°$ and positive for $\theta = 31°$. The axial proton therefore will be shielded more than the equatorial proton by bonds C_2—C_3 and C_5—C_6. By comparison the effect of the more distant bonds C_3—C_4 and C_4—C_5 may be neglected (note that $\sigma \alpha \ 1/r^3$). The net result will be that the axial proton should appear at a higher field than the equatorial proton. This is in agreement with experimental observations.

In correlating shielding with chemical shift it should be noted that it is customary to record NMR spectra as a plot of the intensity of energy absorption *versus* increasing magnetic field (see Figure 1). Hence, smaller the shielding (i.e., smaller the value of σ), smaller is the magnetic field at which the proton resonance line will appear in the spectrum. On the τ scale this corresponds to a smaller τ value.

Much higher accuracy can be obtained in measuring the small difference between two large numbers rather than the numbers themselves. In determining the chemical shift of a particular proton, what is measured is in effect the difference in the magnetic field H_1 and H_2 corresponding to the resonance of the proton and the standard instead of measuring H_1 and H_2. In the present day commercial instruments, the same purpose is served by holding the magnetic field constant and varying the frequency of the electromagnetic field which lies in the radio frequency range.

REFERENCES

1. Bhacca, N. S., Johnson, L. F., and Shoolery, J. N., "NMR Spectra Catalog," Vol. 1, 1962; Bhacca, N. S., Hollis, D. P., Johnson, L. F., and Pier, E. A., Vol. 2, Palo Alto California, Varian Associates, 1963; Neudert, W., and Röpke, H., "Atlas of Steroid Spectra," Springer Verlag, New York, 1965.
2. Tiers, G. V. D., Tables of τ-values, Central Research Department, Minnesota Mining and Manufacturing Company, St. Paul, Minnesota.
3. Prepared by Professor W. von Phillipsborn of the University of Zürich and circulated privately.
4. Wiberg, K. B., and Nist, B. J., *J. Am. Chem. Soc.*, **83**, 1226 (1961).
5. Leonard, N. J., Paukstelis, J. V., and Brady, L. E., *J. Org. Chem.*, **29**, 3383 (1964).
6. Bernstein, H. J., Pople, J. A., and Schneider, W. G., *Can. J. Chem.*, **35**, 65 (1957).
7. Pople, J. A., Schneider, W. G., and Bernstein, H. J., "High Resolution Nuclear Magnetic Resonance," New York, McGraw-Hill Publishing Co., Inc., 1959.
8. Jackman, L. M., "Applications of Nuclear Magnetic Resonance Spectroscopy in Organic Chemistry," New York, Pergamon Press, 1959.
9. Roberts, J. D., "Nuclear Magnetic Resonance Applications to Organic Chemistry," New York, McGraw-Hill Publishing Co., Inc., 1959.
10. Wiberg, K. B., and Nist, B. J., "The Interpretation of NMR Spectra, New York, W. A. Benjamin, Inc., 1962.
11. Zürcher, R. F., *Helv. Chim. Acta*, **44**, 1380 (1961); *ibid.*, **46**, 2054 (1963).
12. Cohen, A. I., and Rock, S. R., *Steroids*, **3**, 243 (1964).
13. Tori, K., and Aono, K., *Ann. Report of Shionogi Res. Lab.*, **14**, 136 (1964).
14. Malinowski, E. R., Manhas, M. S., Müller, G. H., and Bose, A. K., *Tetrahedron Letters*, 1161 (1963).
15. Tori, K., and Kondo, E., *Steroids*, **4**, 713 (1964).
16. Rosen, W. E., Ziegler, J. B., Shabica, A. C., and Shoolery, J. N., *J. Amer. Chem. Soc.*, **81**, 1687 (1959).
17. Kutney, J. P., *Steroids*, **2**, 225 (1963).
18. Shafer, P. R., Davis, D. R., Vogel, M., Nagarajan, K., and Roberts, J. D., *Proc. Natl. Acad. Sci., U.S.*, **47**, 49 (1961); Whitesides, G. M., Grocki, J. J., Holtz, D., Steinberg, H., and Roberts, J. D., *J. Am. Chem. Soc.*, **87**, 1058 (1965).
19. Moriarty, R. M., *J. Org. Chem.*, **30**, 600 (1965), and references therein.
20. Gutowsky, H. S., Karplus, M., and Grant, D. M., *J. Chem. Phys.*, **31**, 1278 (1959).
21. Whitesides, G. M., Holtz, D., and Roberts, J. D., *J. Amer. Chem. Soc.*, **86**, 2628 (1964).
22. Hall, L. D., and Johnson, L. F., *Tetrahedron*, **20**, 883 (1964).
23. Katz, T. J., and Garratt, P. J., *J. Am. Chem. Soc.*, **85**, 2852 (1963); LaLancette, E. A., Benson, R. E., *ibid.*, **85**, 2853 (1963).
24. Katz, T. J., *J. Am. Chem. Soc.*, **82**, 3785 (1960).

25. Jackman, L. M., Sondheimer, F., Amiel, Y., Ben-Efraim, D. A., Gaoni, Y., Wolovsky, R., and Bothner-By, A. A., *J. Am. Chem. Soc.*, **84,** 4307 (1962).

26. Katritzky, A. R., (Ed.), "Physical Methods in Heterocyclic Chemistry," Vol. II, Chap. 9, New York, Academic Press, Inc., 1963.

27. Hinman, R. L., and Lang, J., *Tetrahedron Letters*, **21,** 12 (1960).

28. Collins, D. J., Hobbs, J. J., and Sternhell, S., *Tetrahedron Letters,* 197 (1963); Wittstruck, T. A., Malhotra, S. K., and Ringold, H. J., *J. Am. Chem. Soc.*, **85,** 1699 (1963).

29. Paquette, L. A., *J. Am. Chem. Soc.*, **86,** 4096 (1964).

30. Snyder, E. I., and Roberts, J. D., *J. Am. Chem. Soc.*, **84,** 1582 (1962).

31. Takahashi, K., *Bull. Chem. Soc.*, Japan, **35,** 1046 (1962).

32. Bhacca, N. S., Gurst, J. E., and Williams, D. H., *J. Amer. Chem. Soc.*, **87,** 302 (1965).

33. Musher, J. I., and Corey, E. J., *Tetrahedron*, **18,** 791 (1962).

34. Laszlo, P., and von Ragué Schleyer, P., *J. Amer. Chem. Soc.*, **86,** 1171 (1964).

35. Schmidt, H. W. H., and Neukom, H., *Tetrahedron Letters*, 2063 (1964).

36. McCasland, G. E., Furuta, S., Johnson, L. F., and Shoolery, J. N., *J. Org. Chem.*, **29,** 2354 (1964).

37. Karplus, M., *J. Chem. Phys.*, **30,** 11 (1959).

38. Williamson, K. L., and Johnson, W. S., *J. Amer. Chem. Soc.*, **83,** 4623 (1961).

39. Abraham, R. J., and Holker, J. S. E., *J. Chem. Soc.*, 806 (1963).

40. Lemieux, R. U., and Lown, J. W., *Canad. J. Chem.*, **42,** 893 (1964).

41. Bender, P., Flowers, D. L., and Goering, H. L., *J. Amer. Chem. Soc.*, **77,** 3463 (1955).

42. Anet, F. A. L., *J. Amer. Chem. Soc.*, **84,** 1053 (1962).

43. Uebel, J. J., and Martin, J. C., *J. Amer. Chem. Soc.*, **86,** 4618 (1964) and references cited therein.

44. Jung, D., and Bothner-By, A. A., *J. Amer. Chem. Soc.*, **86,** 4025 (1964).

45. Ref. 7, p. 142.

46. Katritzky, A. R., *Record Chem. Progr.*, **23,** 223 (1962).

47. Uskoković, M., Bruderer, H., von Planta, C., Williams, T., and Brossi, A., *J. Amer. Chem. Soc.*, **86,** 3364 (1964) and references therein.

48. Closs, G. L., and Moss, R. A., *J. Amer. Chem. Soc.*, **86,** 4042 (1964).

49. Steele, J. A., Cohen, L. A., and Mosettig, E., *J. Amer. Chem. Soc.*, **85,** 1134 (1963).

50. Garbisch, E. W., *J. Amer. Chem. Soc.*, **85,** 927 (1963).

51. Cross, A. D., and Landis, P. W., *J. Amer. Chem. Soc.*, **86,** 4005 (1964) and earlier references cited therein.

52. Karabatsos, G. J., Orzech, C. E., and Meyerson, S., *J. Amer. Chem. Soc.*, **86,** 1994 (1964).

53. Binsch, G., Lambert, J. B., Roberts, B. W., and Roberts, J. D., *J. Am. Chem. Soc.*, **86,** 5546 (1964).

54. Bose, A. K., and Kugajevsky, Irene, Unpublished work.

55. Olah, G. A., and Comsarow, M. B., *J. Am. Chem. Soc.*, **86,** 5682 (1964).

56. Robinson, E. A., and Ciruna, J. A., *J. Am. Chem. Soc.,* **86,** 5677 (1964); Deno, N. C., Friedman, N., and Mockus, J., *ibid.*, **86,** 5677 (1964); Gillespie, R. J., and Robinson, E. A., *ibid.*, **86,** 5676 (1964).

57. Olah, G. A., *J. Am. Chem. Soc.*, **87,** 1103 (1965).

58. Freedman, H. H., Young, A. E., and Sandel, V. R., *J. Am. Chem. Soc.*, **86,** 4722 (1964).

59. A modified version of Prof. W. von Phillipsborn's rearrangement of Tiers Tables.[2]

60. Reprinted by permission from ref. 9, p. 85.

61. Reprinted by permission from ref. 9, p. 86.

62. Malinowski, E. R., Pollara, L. Z., and Larmann, J. P., *J. Am. Chem. Soc.*, **84,** 2649 (1962).

63. Muller, N., and Pritchard, D. E., *J. Chem. Phys.*, **31,** 768 (1959).

64. Karabatsos, G. J., Graham, J. D., and Vane, F. M., *J. Am. Chem. Soc.*, **84,** 37 (1962).

65. Shoolery, J. N., Johnson, L. F., and Anderson, W. A., *J. Mol. Spec.*, **5,** 110 (1960).

66. Closs, G. L., *Proc. Chem. Soc.*, 152 (1962).

67. Dietrich, M. W., and Keller, R. F., *Anal. Chem.*, **36,** 258 (1964).

68. Mohacsi, E., *J. Chem. Educ.*, **41,** 38 (1964).

69. Abrahams, A., Wiberley, S. E., and Nachod, F. C., *Applied Spectroscopy*, **18,** 13 (1964).
70. Suami, T., and Ogawa, S., *Bull. Chem. Soc.*, Japan **37,** 194 (1964).
71. Ohline, R. W., Allred, A. L., and Bordwell, F. G., *J. Am. Chem. Soc., **86,** 4641 (1964).
72. Pakniker, S. K., and Bhattacharyya, S. C., *Tetrahedron*, **18,** 1509 (1962).
73. Tori, K., Takano, Y., and Kitahonoki, K., *Ber.*, **97,** 2798 (1964).
74. Strube, R. E., and Mackellar, S. A., *Recueil*, **83,** 1191 (1964).
75. Segre, A., *Tetrahedron Letters*, 1001 (1964).
76. Holubek, J., Strouf, O. Trojánek, J., Bose, A. K., and Malinowski, E. R., *Tetrahedron Letters*, 897 (1963).
77. McConnell, H. M., *J. Chem. Phys.*, **27,** 226 (1957).
78. Recorded on a Varian DP-60 NMR spectrometer in the NMR laboratory of Stevens Institute of Technology.
79. Kalsi, P. S., Chakravarti, K. K., and Bhattacharyya, S. C., *Tetrahedron*, **19,** 1073 (1963).
80. Wenkert, E., and Beak, P., *J. Am. Chem. Soc.*, **83,** 998 (1961).
81. Chapman, O. L., and King, R. W., *J. Am. Chem. Soc.*, **86,** 1256 (1964).
82. McCasland, G. E., and Horswill, E. C., *J. Am. Chem. Soc.*, **76,** 2373 (1954).
83. Casu, B., Reggiani, M., Gallo, G. and Vigevani, A., *Tetrahedron Letters*, 2839 (1964).
84. Nickon, A., Castle, M. A., Harada, R., Birkoff, C. E., and Williams, R. O., *J. Am. Chem. Soc.,* **85,** 2185 (1963); Wellman, K. M. and Bordwell, F. G., *Tetrahedron Letters*, 170 (1963).
85. Roberts, J. D., Abs. 19th National Org. Chem. Symposium, Amer. Chem. Soc., June, 1965, p. 77.

GENERAL REFERENCES

A. *Books*

1. Pople, J. A., Schneider, W. G., and Bernstein, H. J., "High Resolution Nuclear Magnetic Resonance," New York, McGraw-Hill Publishing Co., Inc., 1959.
2. Jackman, L. M., "Applications of Nuclear Magnetic Resonance Spectroscopy in Organic Chemistry," New York, Pergamon Press, 1959.
3. Roberts, J. D., "Nuclear Magnetic Resonance," New York, McGraw-Hill Publishing Co., Inc., 1959.
4. Roberts, J. D., "An Introduction to Spin-Spin Splitting in High Resolution NMR Spectra." New York, W. A. Benjamin, Inc., 1961.
5. Wiberg, K. B., and Nist, B. J., "The Interpretation of NMR Spectra," New York, W. A. Benjamin, Inc., 1962.
6. Bhacca, N. S., and Williams, D. H., "Applications of NMR Spectroscopy in Organic Chemistry (illustration from the steroid field)," San Francisco, Holden-Day, Inc., 1964.
7. Bible, R. H., "Interpretation of NMR Spectra," New York, Plenum Press, 1965.

B. *Brief Surveys*

1. Gutowsky, H. S., "Nuclear Magnetic Resonance" in "Technique of Organic Chemistry," (A. Weissberger, Ed.), Vol. I, Part IV, 3rd ed., New York, Interscience Publishers, Inc., 1960.
2. Conroy, H., "Nuclear Magnetic Resonance in "Organic Structural Elucidation," in "Advances in Organic Chemistry," Raphael, R. A., Taylor, E. C., and Wynberg, H., Eds.), Vol. II, New York, Interscience Publishers, Inc., 1960.
3. Corio, P. L., *Chem. Rev.*, **60,** 363 (1960); Baldeschweiler, J. D., and Randall, E. W., *Chem. Rev.*, **63,** 81 (1963).
4. Phillips, W. D., "High Resolution H^1 and F^{19} Magnetic Resonance Spectra of Organic Molecules," in Determination of Organic Structures by Physical Methods, Nachod, F. C., and Phillips, W. D., Eds.) Vol. 2, Chap. 6, New York, Academic Press, Inc., 1962.
5. "Part II: High Resolution NMR spectroscopy," in "NMR and EPR Spectroscopy," (The NMR EPR Staff of Varian Associates), New York, Pergamon Press, 1960.
6. Stothers, J. B., "Applications of Nuclear Magnetic Resonance Spectroscopy," in "Techniques

of Organic Chemistry" Weissberger, A., Ed., Vol. XI, Chap. IV, New York, Interscience Publishers, Inc., 1963.

7. White, R. F. M., "Nuclear Magnetic Resonance Spectra," in "Physical Methods in Heterocyclic Chemistry (A. R. Katritzky, ed.), Vol. II, Chap. 9, New York, Academic Press, Inc., 1963.

8. Silverstein, R. M., and Bassler, G. C., "Nuclear Magnetic Resonance Spectroscopy" in "Spectrometric Identification of Organic Compounds," New York, John Wiley & Sons, Inc., 1963.

9. Dyer, J. R., "Nuclear Magnetic Resonance Spectroscopy" in "Applications of Absorption Spectroscopy of Organic Compounds," Englewood Cliffs, New Jersey, Prentice-Hall, Inc., 1965.

COMPOUND INDEX

SUBJECT INDEX